THE WARBLERS
OF AMERICA

THE WARBLERS
OF AMERICA

*A Popular Account of The Wood Warblers as
they occur in the Western Hemisphere*

By LUDLOW GRISCOM, ALEXANDER SPRUNT, Jr.
and other ornithologists of note

Illustrated by JOHN HENRY DICK

THE DEVIN-ADAIR COMPANY · NEW YORK
1957

TO CAROL ROESLER

Printed in the United States of America.

Color illustrations printed in Holland

by Smeets Lithographers.

Library of Congress Catalog Card Number 57–8861

Designed by Lewis F. White.

FIRST PRINTING

CONTENTS

CONTENTS

PUBLISHER'S PREFACE

THIS BOOK IS INTENDED for the general reader interested in birds, as well as for the more advanced student wishing to have at hand a brief but comprehensive account of the entire family of wood warblers.

It grew out of an original determination by the artist, John Henry Dick, to paint those species which breed regularly north of the Mexican border—to paint them in typical habitat during the breeding season. A series of field trips began, involving the Western mountains, Southern swamps and Canadian woods. That he was ultimately able to study at first hand such rarities as Bachman's, Swainson's, Kirtland's and the Colima Warbler and to sketch them all in the field, is a tribute to Mr. Dick's determination to do a thorough job. But in the course of time, a desire for perfection caused one after another of the early paintings to be discarded as failing to reach the high standard the artist set for himself, until only the Black-throated Blue and the common Redstart remained from the original set. The result, we believe, is a happy one, made the more so by the excellent six-color offset reproductions which were printed in Holland under the direction of Mr. Paul Steiner. In almost all cases these are entirely faithful to the originals.

Meanwhile, it was thought fitting to have a brief write-up accompany each plate; the assistance of the artist's friend and neighbor, Alexander Sprunt, Jr. was sought. Right then and there, the question had to be faced as to whether another bird picture book—however excellent the artist's work—was to be issued, or whether a serious contribution to ornithology should be attempted, one that might exceed in coverage and perhaps in value both Chapman's pioneering *"Warblers of North America,"* long out of print and out of date and having inferior plates, and the late Arthur Cleveland Bent's valuable *"Life Histories of North American Wood Warblers,"* also out of print and in any event lacking any color plates, and, being a Government publication, hard to come by for the average birder.

Ludlow Griscom was consulted, and in part because of the excellence of the artist's work and in part because warblers had been his pet hobby for some fifty years, he took over with enthusiasm the editorial direction of the expanded and long-needed book. The first thing Mr. Griscom suggested was that the term "North American" be re-defined in more realistic terms to include the whole continent, from the Arctic tree line to the Panama Canal. "For is it not true that in this day of air travel, those who pursue the hobby find it increasingly easy to reach both northern breeding ground and winter habitat? And is it not preferable in any new book to consider this highly migratory family on those extremes of range as well as, for the most part, simply as spring and autumn visitors?"

And so, as the book grew, Alexander F. Skutch, James Bond, Emmet Reid Blake and Eugene Eisenmann were invited to do their chapters on the resident warblers south of the Border and on the behavior of our migrating species as they winter in Mexico, Central America, the West Indies and Panama. Three new color plates were added depicting 31 of the more tropical species. These were of necessity done from skins rather than from field observation. It is the first time that these species have been shown in color in a book. For the sake of completeness, Emmet Blake was then asked to contribute a short summary of the South American species, about which relatively little is known. They also are described here for the first time and two additional color plates show them for the first time in color.

At this point and despite the fact that jacket covers had already been printed, it became necessary to drop the word "North" from our title.

The behavior of the family in northern latitudes was assigned to Frederick C. Lincoln, J. A. Munro, W. Earl Godfrey, W. W. H. Gunn and Roland C. Clement, all of whom cooperated magnificently in describing the summer breeding habits of the warblers in Alaska, and in Canada from Coast to Coast. In addition, Dr. Gunn, whose tape recordings of warbler songs are outstanding, has, with the assistance of Dr. Donald J. Borror of Ohio State University, rendered the songs of 39 species into phonetic interpretations with a view to making them easier to remember and for the sake of comparison.

The individual write-ups of the species which breed in the United States and Canada were taken on by Alexander Sprunt, Jr., who has done 31 of them himself and assigned the rest to others who have made special studies of particular birds. The space allotted to each of these birds naturally varies; but particular emphasis has been given to the lesser known species. This is typically evident in the case of the Colima vs. the Myrtle and Swainson's vs. the Black-and-White, with much more space allotted to the former birds. Bent's *Life Histories* contains ample information on the well-known species and should be consulted when further data are required; our biggest task has been to keep the number of pages down to reasonable length. The ranges of these birds as recorded reflect the new 1957 A.O.U. Check-list. It was decided not to include accidental records, with the exception of a few casuals reported from the Old World.

The range maps show approximate breeding areas as of publication; they will be altered as new areas are found or as habitats change. In the case of the Yellow Warbler, which is to be found almost everywhere no map was included for obvious reasons. Migration routes and winter ranges were not attempted because our knowledge of them is still far from complete.

A word about the black and white drawings. These were done primarily as decorations and space fillers and should be judged in that light. They are not to scale, some being life size and others much less so, depending upon the amount of space available on the pages.

The new Check-list has also been followed throughout for nomenclature, spelling and classification of species. We are indebted to Dr. Alexander Wetmore and the late Professor Josselyn Van Tyne for their willingness to make this list available prior to publication.

Following an earlier A.O.U. decision, subspecies are treated as equally important races of the one bird rather than as subordinates. Thus, there are now, scientifically speaking, no Eastern, Rocky Mountain,

Lutescent or Dusky Orange-crowned Warblers—there is one Orange-crown, *Vermivora celata,* with four races designated by scientific names only. For the sake of those who prefer the old nomenclature, common names have been listed as "local names" when two or more races are recognized by the A.O.U. Except for these, subspecies have been generally suppressed; but an indication of the total number described, throughout the family, will be found in Appendix A.

In this connection too, it was thought wise to drop the old A.O.U. numbers, which seemed to accord special status to nominate races and no longer to serve any valid function. Authorities have been omitted in the case of the tropical warblers as have most egg measurements. Both seemed unnecessary for the purposes of this book. Bibliographical references have been inserted only where necessary due to limitation of space.

We are very greatly indebted to those contributors who went out of their way to make the book a worthy one by volunteering their services in checking, coordinating and editing the various chapters; especially Messrs. Blake, Bond, Broun, Clement, Eisenmann, Gunn and Walkinshaw. Ludlow Griscom, Roger Peterson and James Bond deserve special thanks for their careful criticism of the artist's drawings and color work prior to reproduction and for their helpful suggestions. A special word of thanks to Alexander F. Skutch and the Cooper Ornithological Society for allowing us to use his fine warbler summary from the first volume of his *Life Histories of Central American Birds,* and to J. Fred

Denton, Maurice Brooks, Irston R. Barnes, Leslie Tuck, Paul Harrington, George H. Lowery, Jr. and Henry M. Stevenson for their own valuable contributions.

The following individuals and institutions not previously thanked have contributed generously of their time and facilities, especially in making warbler skins available to the artist: Dean Amadon, Charles O'Brien and the American Museum of Natural History, New York; James Bond and the Academy of Natural Sciences, Philadelphia; E. M. Burton, E. Burnham Chamberlain and the Charleston Museum; George M. Sutton, Josselyn Van Tyne and the University of Michigan; Kenneth C. Parkes and the Carnegie Museum, Pittsburgh.

Thanks are also due to Lester L. Snyder, and James L. Baillie of the Department of Ornithology, Royal Ontario Museum, for providing access to distribution maps, and to J. D. B. Harrison, Department of Northern Affairs and National Resources, Ottawa, for providing maps of the Canadian Forest Regions.

In presenting *The Warblers of America* to the public at this time, the artist, the publisher and all the contributors hope that it will fill a gap in the ornithological literature of the day and that it will make that most colorful and in many ways little known family of strictly Western Hemisphere birds, the *Parulidae* or Wood Warblers, more familiar to the average person.

DEVIN A. GARRITY

THE WARBLERS
OF AMERICA

Hooded Warbler

Pink-headed Warbler

CHAPTER 1

AN INTRODUCTION TO THE WARBLER FAMILY

THE WOOD WARBLERS are a compact family of small birds containing about 116 species.* They are essentially confined to the New World, and many migratory species nest in temperate North America. In the tropics their headquarters is in the mountainous regions. The plumage is extremely varied, with intricate color patterns in the genus *Dendroica* and somewhat simpler patterns but larger areas of bright color in *Myioborus* and *Basileuterus*. Yellow is the prevailing bright color; but orange, blue, red and chestnut are present in many species. In the highlands of Mexico and Guatemala there is a genus (*Ergaticus*) in which the plumage is almost wholly bright red. Those warblers which breed beyond the tropics and which are for the most part highly migratory usually show pronounced sexual differences in plumage; and when this is true, marked seasonal changes in the coloration of the males may occur. But among the non-migratory warblers of the tropics, the sexes are on the whole alike in plumage, and even the most brilliant of them wear the same bright hues throughout the year.

The food of the warblers consists almost wholly of insects, which these active birds capture while they flit and hop ceaselessly through the foliage of trees and bushes, or for which they dart out on the wing. Some members of the family (*Geothlypis, Chamaethlypis*) forage in grassland; not a few hunt over the ground, or along the banks of

* Arriving at the total number of species is difficult since there are taxonomic areas in which no two authorities seem to agree. See following chapter and Appendix A, which lists 113 species, following Zimmer (*Amer. Mus. Novit.*, 1949, No. 1428, pp. 53–57), Blake and Bond concurring.

3

streams, some (*Seiurus*) walking, others (*Basileuterus fulvicauda*) hopping along. The Black-and-White Warbler creeps over the trunks and limbs of trees, seeking the small creatures that lurk in crevices of the bark. Fruit does not enter largely into the diet of the wood warblers; but the hardy Myrtle and Audubon's warblers eat many small berries during the fall and winter; and Tennessee Warblers are fond of grapes and bananas.

Voice is well developed in this family. The voices of most are not strong nor are their phrases especially varied, but the songs are so persistently repeated that they make up in quantity what they lack in brilliance. Some, however, have rich, strong voices all out of proportion to their size. Among the best musicians that I have heard in this family are the Painted Redstart, Collared Redstart, and Ground-chat (Gray-crowned Yellowthroat). The Yellow-breasted Chat is something of a mimic, but of the call notes rather than the songs of other birds; his repertoire is amazing but contains far more harsh notes than sweet. Flight songs have been recorded for the Yellow-breasted Chat, Ovenbird, Louisiana Waterthrush, Worm-eating Warbler, Common Yellowthroat, and MacGillivray's (Tolmie's) Warbler. In their winter homes, the migratory species do not often sing, but many, perhaps all, species deliver a few songs before their departure in the spring. In this family, song is largely restricted to the male; but the female Buff-rumped Warbler delivers a beautiful, rich warble, very different from the ringing crescendo of her mate, to which it responds.

Nuptial feeding is recorded by Lack (*Auk,* 1940:177) for five species of wood warblers: Yellow, Bay-breasted, Black-throated Blue, Pine, and Prothonotary. Schrantz (*Auk,* 1943:376) gives additional instances of feeding of the female by the male Yellow Warbler; and Sturm (*Auk,* 1945:197) saw male American Redstarts bring food repeatedly to their incubating mates. From Sturm's description of the behavior of his Redstarts, I suspect that the male brought food in anticipation of the nestlings rather than as an intended offering to his incubating partner. The male Pink-headed Warbler who repeatedly brought food to the nest in my presence seemed to desire to feed the still unhatched nestlings rather than his mate, who at times incidentally received the food. When a male Crescent-chested (Hartlaub's) Warbler brought a morsel to the nest where his mate incubated, she would not accept it. The male Buff-rumped Warbler occasionally feeds his mate in the period of incubation, both on and off the nest. Some males of this species seem afraid to approach the nest while the female incubates.

Polygamy rarely occurs in the family; but in the Ovenbird, Hann (*Wilson Bulletin,* 1937:155) found two instances of males with two mates, and later (*Wilson Bull.* 1940:69) a case of polyandry.

The nest may be placed in trees at a good height, in bushes, on the ground, or in niches in banks and ledges of rock. Rarely, as in the Prothonotary Warbler, it is built in a cavity in a tree or stump or in a cranny in a man-made edifice. Usually the wood warbler's nest is a simple, cup-shaped structure, but in *Myioborus, Basileuterus, Ergaticus* and *Seiurus aurocapillus* it is a roofed, oven-shaped construction with a round doorway in the side, placed in a niche in a bank or cliff, on a steep slope, or, in the last-mentioned species, on level ground. The Parula Warblers place their nests amid swinging tufts of beard-lichen (*Usnea*) or Spanish "moss" (*Tillandsia*), or in bunches of green moss on trees.

The nest is built by the female, usually without help from her mate. But the male Buff-rumped Warbler seems regularly to take a large share in the work of building; and one Slate-throated Redstart helped his mate regularly, although in several other pairs of this species that I watched the male failed to bring anything to the nest. In the Black-throated Green Warbler the male apparently helps to build only on the first day, if at all (Pitelka, *Wilson Bull.,* 1940:5). Nest building by males has also been observed in the Prothonotary Warbler by Walkinshaw (*Wilson Bull.,* 1941:4) and in the Black-throated Blue Warbler by Harding (*Auk,* 1931:513, 516). Yet in most species which have been watched while building, the female worked unaided.

The eggs of wood warblers are usually white or cream or are lightly tinted with green, blue or pink, rarely with deeper green, and in nearly all species they are more or less heavily spotted or blotched with shades of brown, chestnut, lilac or black, the markings as a rule heaviest on the large end, where they form a cap or "wreath." Very rarely warblers lay unmarked eggs, among them the Swainson's, Bachman's, and Crescent-chested. The eggs of the last, although usually immaculate white, are at times faintly speckled.

In Costa Rica the Buff-rumped (River)

Warbler appears regularly to lay two eggs; but even within the tropics the sets of most species of warblers average larger. The Golden-crowned Warbler lays three or four eggs in Trinidad (Belcher and Smooker, *Ibis,* 1937:522). Species of *Myioborus* in Central America lay two or three, more commonly the larger number; the Pink-headed Warbler of the Guatemalan highlands lays from two to four. Northern warblers lay larger sets; three, four or five are recorded for most species, and rarely six or seven or even nine. Four is perhaps the most usual number for the species breeding in the United States and Canada.

Incubation is performed only by the female, so far as our information goes. The rhythm of coming and going varies considerably with the species and even within the species. In some the average session on the eggs was found to be less than half an hour; among these are the American Redstart (Sturm, *Auk,* 1945:196; Kendeigh, *Wilson Bull.,* 1945:162, Baker, *Wilson Bull.,* 1944:86), the Black-throated Blue, Chestnut-sided, and Blackburnian Warblers (Kendeigh, *loc.cit.*), Crescent-chested Warbler, Pink-headed Warbler, and Collared Redstart. Average sessions of from half an hour to an hour were recorded for the Black-throated Green Warbler (Nice and Nice, *Bird-Banding,* 1932:95), Slate-throated Redstart, and one Buff-rumped Warbler. Another Buff-rumped Warbler took sessions which averaged 85 minutes in six hours of observation. The absences from the nest of some incubating warblers are surprisingly short. In many hours of watching at a nest of the American Redstart, Sturm found that the female took recesses from her eggs ranging from 1 to 11 minutes and averaging 3.3 minutes. Baker and Kendeigh recorded only slightly longer absences for this species. Average recesses of under ten minutes were found for the Black-throated Blue Warbler and Chestnut-sided Warbler by Kendeigh and for the Pink-headed Warbler and Collared Redstart by me. The Buff-rumped Warblers which sat for long periods also took long recesses which averaged half an hour or more. Most of the warblers of which we have studies covered their eggs between 60 and 80 per cent of the daylight hours; but a few were far more constant in incubation, the Redstart studied by Sturm sitting on some days as much as 93 per cent of the time. The Ovenbirds studied by Hann (*loc.cit.*) incubated at times for 90 per cent or a little more of the hours of daylight.

Incubation periods ranging from 11 to 12 or, exceptionally, 14 days have been recorded by various authors for several North American species of *Dendroica, Geothlypis, Oporornis, Setophaga, Seiurus,* and *Protonotaria.* Kendeigh (*Wilson Bull.* 1945:163) considers 12 days the normal incubation period for a number of warblers which he studied in the state of New York. Central American Warblers have distinctly longer incubation periods that range from 13 (rarely) or 14 to 16 days for species of *Myioborus, Ergaticus* and *Basileuterus,* and not infrequently 17 days is required in the last. Possibly the longer period of incubation for this group of warblers is associated with the fact that all build oven-shaped nests, whereas the more northern warblers, with the exception of *Seiurus* and *Protonotaria.* use open nests. (Among the tanagers, the species which build closed nests have longer incubation periods.) Possibly also, the shorter incubation periods of the northern species are associated with a general acceleration of their reproductive processes correlated with the shorter breeding season.

The nestlings when newly hatched are blind, bear sparse natal down, and have the interior of the mouth yellow. They are, in all species for which we have information, fed by both parents, which carry the food in their bills; but the young are brooded by the female alone. Although some male warblers may be slow in beginning to bring food (see Nice and Nice, *loc. cit.*) usually they begin to attend the nestlings very soon after they hatch. The parents of many species, both tree- and ground-nesting, feign injury in a spectacular manner when their eggs or young appear to be in danger; but I have failed to witness such displays at numerous nests of the Buff-rumped Warbler.

The nestling period for North American species is usually between 8 and 10 days, and rarely 11 days. Even the hole-nesting Prothonotary Warbler remains in the nest no longer than this. The Central American warblers studied by me had distinctly longer nestling periods, just as they had longer incubation periods. Pink-headed Warbler nestlings that had been handled left when 11 days old. Undisturbed nestlings of two species of *Myioborus* departed at ages varying from 12 to 14 days. The nestling period of the Buff-rumped Warbler ranges from 12 to 15 days.

Helpers at the nest are rarely found among the wood warblers. Both the Central

American and the North American representatives of the family, with rare exceptions, rear only a single brood each year, and long before the following breeding season the families break up. Hence opportunities for the young of an early brood to feed a subsequent brood rarely occur. At times adult warblers give food to young of other species. Kendeigh (*loc. cit.*) saw a pair of Black-and-White Warblers feed a fledgling Ovenbird. Rea and his companions (*Wilson Bull.* 1945:262) watched a Black-and-White Warbler take food to a nestful of Worm-eating Warblers in the face of strong opposition from the parents. De Garis (*Auk,* 1936:423) found a nest of the Kentucky Warbler to which a second male, apparently an abnormal individual, brought food for the incubating female, although occasionally he was chased by another male who sang better and appeared to be her mate.

The acquisition of the adult plumage is strikingly different in the migratory and non-migratory members of this family. Young males of the migratory species go south in the immature plumage, pass the winter in that plumage, and then take on the bright nuptial attire before returning to their breeding grounds in the north. In the non-migratory Central American species of *Myioborus, Basileuterus* and *Ergaticus,* the sexes of which are alike, the young of both sexes acquire a plumage essentially like that of the adult soon after leaving the nest.*

ALEXANDER F. SKUTCH

* Note: This chapter first appeared in "*Life Histories of Central American Birds*"; Pacific Coast Avifauna no. 31. Cooper Ornithological Society, Berkeley, Calif., 1954. It is reprinted with their kind permission.

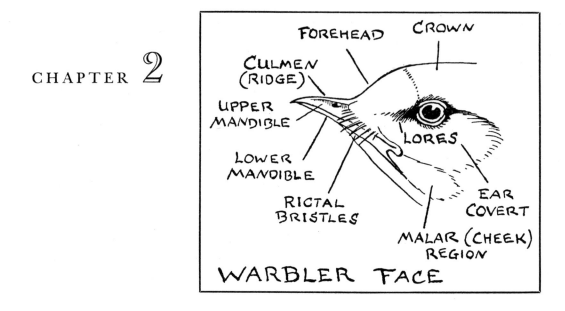

CHAPTER 2

WARBLER FACE

(diagram labels: FOREHEAD, CROWN, CULMEN (RIDGE), UPPER MANDIBLE, LOWER MANDIBLE, RICTAL BRISTLES, LORES, EAR COVERT, MALAR (CHEEK) REGION)

THE CLASSIFICATION OF WARBLERS

I. HISTORY OF CLASSIFICATION

THE great Swede Linnaeus (*Systema Naturae,* 1758), in his attempt to devise a system of classification based on natural relationships for the mounting welter of living plants and animals—a product of the age of exploration—started an impulse which persists to this day. Most naturalists were Europeans at that time, and randomly collected specimens of North American birds were being sent to Europe for description. Recalling that there was no concept of a New World family of "Wood Warblers" at that time, it is not surprising to see what wild guesses were made about the identity of such warblers as happened to reach the cabinets of these gentlemen. Readers should be interested to learn that 19 were named *Motacilla* (Wagtails), one was called *Parus* (Titmouse), three were referred to as *Turdus* (Thrushes) and five as *Muscicapa* (Flycatchers). Wilson and Audubon began calling them Warblers and 14 new species discovered prior to 1835 were called *Sylvia* (Old World Warblers). By 1839 it became clear that our Warblers were not the same as the Old World Warblers, so *Sylvia* became *Sylvicola* and the family became *Sylvicolidae,* or American Wood Warblers, and were called that as late as 1874 by Baird, Brewer and Ridgway. Actually, this was an inadvertence as Baird had already shown that the name *Sylvicola* was pre-empted and that the genus should be called *Dendroica.* Then the family name became Mniotiltidae (on erroneous grounds). It is now called *Parulidae* for more technically correct reasons.

Even in 1885 the great British ornithologist R. Bowdler Sharpe (*Cat. of Birds of the British Mus.,* vol. 10, p. 225) accepted

8

this family with great reluctance, complaining that it contained too many forms not closely allied, and he foretold a drastic readjustment of the family. He "guessed" that *Vermivora* and the brown warblers would prove to be Wrens, that *Icteria* (the Chat) was an aberrant Vireo, and that the Redstart and other "flycatching" warblers were in fact Flycatchers (just as Audubon thought), and that tropical forms were Tanagers.

For decades the welter of Song Birds (Oscine Passeres) have defied any logical or natural classification, and people have been forced, for "convenience" sake, to select pretty arbitrary characteristics. Thus the Oscine Passeres were divided into nine- or ten-primaried birds, at which Sharpe protested, and this has already broken down in the case of the Vireos and two Old World families. Efforts are now being made to find some definite anatomical characters which may prove of assistance.

The New World is full of nine-primaried Oscine Passeres: The Finches, of which one subfamily (*Richmondeninae*) is wholly American; the Icterids (Blackbirds and Orioles) wholly American; the Tanagers, wholly American; the Honey Creepers, wholly American; and the Wood Warblers, all with a welter of genera and species in the tropics. On the basis of skins only, it is impossible to decide to which family to refer many obscure tropical genera and species. It has been suggested that they are all one great "family," and that the so-called families just listed should be reduced to subfamily rank. This scheme is predicated on the assumption that all nine-primaried Oscines are of common ancestry,

an unlikely proposition incapable of proof, as Sharpe remarked many years ago.

It is perhaps natural for field students to look for and want obvious, readily apparent "family" characters of size, shape, color, behavior, etc., but this is rarely possible. Gadow, years ago, remarked that if the Oscine Passeres were treated consistently with "older" family groups, the Oscines would be reduced to three families only: the Swallows, the Larks, and all others (more than 5000 species, or three quarters of the birds on earth!).

Anatomy is the basis of sound family differences. This requires dissection in mammals, birds, fish and even wild flowers, and the family characters are often of hair-splitting technicality. Perhaps the best illustration for modern bird students is that of the Finches (*Fringillidae*), or "thick-billed" seed-eaters, the old order *Conirostres*. If we rely on the anatomy of the palate and the jaw muscles, which are externally invisible, the Fringillids appear to be a wholly unnatural assemblage, and should be divided into at least three families and many subfamilies. Moreover, it appears probable that all the thinner-billed nine-primaried Oscines in the New World are descended from a primitive Emberizine or Bunting stock, as Wetmore, Glenny and Tordoff believe, thus accounting for the hopeless inosculation of various alleged New World families. Thus, in the remarkable "Finches" of the Galapagos Islands, famous for the varied shapes and sizes of the bill, we have a slender-billed insect-eating *Certhidea* (a supposed Warbler), a nectar-feeding *Geospiza scandens* and a fruit-eating *G. crassirostris*, and an insect-eating

Camarhynchus, all obviously developed from the same stock by what is now called "adaptive radiation." The chief trouble is that too many tropical genera remain undissected. (*See chapter 15, Introduction.*)

We may now pass to a revised diagnosis of the Wood Warbler family as:

1. Slender-billed or flat-billed nine-primaried Oscines with ridged tarsus.
2. The tongue not deeply cleft or fringed at the tip (to eliminate the Honey Creepers).
3. Bill with no distinct subterminal tomial notch (to exclude the nine-primaried Vireos).
4. Jaw muscle pattern similar to the Pepper Shrikes (*Cyclarhis*), but less massive and with the *pterygoideus dorsalis* muscle farther advanced.
5. Ectethmoid foramen double or constricted; lachrymal bone fused.
6. Palate with conspicuous posterior ridge, lateral ridges disappearing posteriorly.
7. Palato-maxillary bones always present except in adult *Icteria.*

"Wood Warblers," says Beecher (*Auk,* 1953, p. 307), "are the most slender-billed Oscines with fully pinnate adductors. The efficiency of the pinnate adductors has permitted the reduction in mass of both muscle and bone in the head region, and this, I think, is responsible for their adaptive success."

Further than this it is not necessary to go, as we become involved in uncertain speculation. As already stated, one group of students believe that the Wood Warblers are descended from the Emberizine Finches, but Beecher reduces these finches to a subfamily of the *Parulidae.* The Honey Creepers (*Coerebidae*) are broken up into two subfamilies, more or less as Ridgway suggested, one part joining the Warblers, the brush-tongued remainder the Tanagers. Mayr and Amadon reduce the Warblers to a subfamily of the Tanagers; Tordoff maintains the family, but reduces the Tanagers to a subfamily of the Finches. Many rare but important genera still remain undissected, and it is impossible to do anything with aberrant genera such as *Leucopeza* and *Rhodinocichla,* sometimes called "Warblers." They will not be treated further here.

In the meantime field students need not worry. All North American Warblers are clearly warblers in size, color (never brilliant or glossy), insect-eating habits (rarely fruit-eating), and behavior. They are readily distinguishable from Vireos and other small Oscines. Even the aberrant Yellow-breasted Chat (*Icteria*) proves to be a Warbler. The only apparent exception is the Bahama Honey Creeper or Bananaquit, a rare vagrant to Florida, which in life would *appear* to be a warbler—and which Beecher considers a warbler.[*]

* *References*

1. Ridgway, R. *Birds of North and Middle America,* Vol. 1, 1901, pp. 13–18. Vol. II, 1902, pp. 425–773, deals with the Warblers. The two volumes cover the American Nine-primaried Oscines.
2. Mayr, E. and Amadon, D. *A Classification of Recent Birds.* Amer. Mus. Novit. no. 1946, 1951, 42 pp.
3. Wetmore, A. *A revised classification of the birds of the World.* Smithsonian Misc. Coll., 117, no. 4, pp. 1–22.
4. Beecher, W. J. *Convergence in the Coerebidae.* Wilson Bull., Vol. 63, 1951, pp. 274–287.
5. Beecher, W. J. *Phylogeny of the Oscines.* Auk, 1953, pp. 270–333.
6. Glenny, F. H. *A systematic study of the main arteries in the region of the heart-Aves. The Fringillidae.* Part I. Ohio Journ. Sci., 42, no. 2, 1942, pp. 84–90.
7. Tordoff, H. B. *A systematic study of the avian family Fringillidae based on the structure of the skull.* Misc. Publ. Mus. Zool. Univ. Mich., no. 81, 63 pp.
8. Tordoff, H. B. *Relationships in the New World nine-primaried Oscines.* Auk, 1954, pp. 273–284.

II. VARIATIONS IN STRUCTURE, GENERIC CHARACTERS

The chief defect of this rather arbitrary and not clearly defined family is that it has become the victim of "warbler specialists".* No Oscine families today have so high a percentage of monotypic genera (nearly one-half), and something relatively radical should clearly be done. It should be noted that Ridgway's 1902 classification of genera (which in essence is that followed by the A.O.U.) is based on Baird's *Review of American Birds*, 1865, in which all subgenera were raised to full generic rank! A review of the generic characters currently used is in order:

1. *Bill shape and size.* The study of adaptive radiation has taught us that differences in bill shape and structure are very poor taxonomic characters, and we now recognize that we have been grossly deceived for years by purely fortuitous similarities in the stout bills of the finch and sparrow type. In Wood Warblers bill structure has been worked to death and some have almost used a hand lens to find such differences as the presence or absence of a minute subterminal notch on the maxillary tomium.

Certain types should be obvious to the observer: the relatively long slender bill of the Black-and-White, both brown species, and the Prothonotary Warbler; the short, acutely pointed bills of *Vermivora;* the shorter stouter bills of *Dendroica;* the clearly curved culmen of *Granatellus,* *Chamaethlypis* and *Icteria;* and the broad, relatively flat or depressed bills of the flycatching warblers.

2. *Rictal bristles.* These are closely associated with the bill characters. In Warblers, bristles progress from "obsolete" or inconspicuous to very conspicuous. It is clearly a fine point as to where to draw the line in using them as generic characters.

3. *Length of tarsus.* Most Warblers have the tarsus about ⅓ the length of the wing, but it is variable in *Oporornis, Wilsonia,* and *Dendroica.* It is ¼ the length of the wing in *Mniotilta, Cardellina, Setophaga,* and some species of *Dendroica.* It is more than ¼ the wing length in *Limnothlypis, Helmitheros, Protonotaria.* It is almost half as long as the wing in *Chamaethlypis.* In view of these variations, this character should clearly be used with caution.

4. *Cohesion of toes.* Warblers are perhaps peculiar in that the basal phalanges of the toes are united in varying degrees. Unhappily, this proves to be a matter of specific variation in *Vermivora* and *Dendroica,* and is of doubtful generic value.

5. *Primary or wing-tip structure.* In most Warblers the outermost (or ninth) primary is longer than the fifth, exceptionally shorter (as in *Catharopeza*), or, much more rarely, shorter than the first (*Teretistris*). In *Icteria* the ninth is longer than the third. The wing-tip demonstrates the degree to which the longest primaries project beyond the secondaries. As a general rule in birds, northern or migratory species tend to have a longer wing-tip than tropical or sedentary birds. This is beautifully illustrated in the genus *Dendroica,* where the resident West Indian species

---

* Carried to the extreme by C. J. Maynard who split the North American *Dendroica* into 14 genera!

have a shorter wing-tip—in other words, the ninth is shorter than the fifth. Similarly, the migratory flycatching warblers have a longer wing-tip than the resident tropical genera such as *Myioborus, Euthlypis, Basileuterus*. The wing-tip is remarkably long in *Limnothlypis, Peucedramus*, and notably short or rounded in *Geothlypis, Chamaethlypis, Teretistris, Microligea*, and *Granatellus*.

6. *Tail length and shape*. It is obvious to students that the tail can be 1) shorter than the wing (as in *Vermivora* and *Dendroica*), 2) about as long as the wing (as in *Chamaethlypis, Icteria, Wilsonia canadensis*, most *Geothlypis, Myioborus, Euthlypis*, and *Ergaticus*), or 3) longer than the wing (as in *Geothlypis nelsoni*, the Hooded and Wilson's Warblers, and *Basileuterus rufifrons*). Clearly, no reliable generic characters exist here. In shape the tail may be rounded as in most Warblers, graduated (as in *Chamaethlypis* and *Microligea*), or more rarely emarginate (as in *Seiurus*). Unfortunately, too many genera have species approximating at least two types; the variations are specific rather than generic.

7. *Tail pattern*. Field students are accustomed to the fact that most Warblers show flashes of white in the tail. They know that every species of *Dendroica* shows this trait except the Yellow, where white is replaced by yellow. They rarely stop to think that these patches are lacking in the "brown" warblers; in the genus *Vermivora* only three species possess them. They are present in *Catharopeza*, lacking in *Leucopeza, Oporornis, Geothlypis, Teretistris, Chamaethlypis*, and *Basileuterus*. Only one species each of *Microligea* and *Wilsonia*

possess them; while *Setophaga* has yellow in the Redstart, white in the Painted Redstart, and none in the Red-faced. It seems clear that there are no real generic characters here.

8. *Color*. It is clearly impossible to define any color characters for Warblers as a whole. They are beautiful rather than brilliant, though a few are dull and sombre. Thus, the genera *Vermivora* and *Dendroica* clearly lack any general type of coloration, and Ridgway's key makes far too much use of color, in default of structural characters. An example is seen in a series of related genera: the Black-and-White (*Mniotilta*), the brown Swainson's (*Limnothlypis*) and Worm-eating (*Helmitheros*), and the brilliant yellow Prothonotary (*Protonotaria*). Obviously the question fairly arises, have we here four monotypic genera? Actually, brilliant yellow is common in Warblers, brown reappears in certain tropical species of *Basileuterus*, and *Dendroica pharetra* of Jamaica is streaked black and white.

9. *Song*. I am a great believer (within limits) that the character of the song can be used as a clue to indicate relationships. Warblers are poor singers as a whole, the majority having high, wiry, buzzy or trilling songs. There are, however, certain marked exceptions, and we must remember that there are surprising exceptions even within the genus. Thus *Seiurus, Oporornis* and *Geothlypis* have loud ringing songs of notable carrying power. The Chat has a bizarre medley of ventriloquial caws, toots and whistles. Swainson's Warbler has a loud rich song, a cross between that of the Louisiana Waterthrush and the Hooded War-

bler. *Catharopeza bishopi* has a very fine song, superior to that of any species of *Dendroica*. Many readers will already know that in the genus *Wilsonia*, the Hooded Warbler has a loud ringing song greatly superior to the feeble rattle of the Wilson's Warbler; and that the songs of the *Dendroica* are of very uneven esthetic merit. Even more remarkable are cases of undoubted convergence. Thus, *Oreothlypis superciliosa* (now *Vermivora*) has a coloration and song recalling *Parula*. In tropical America the widely ranging *Basileuterus fulvicauda*, of generally brownish coloration, lives along rocky brooks and streams, and teeters and sings just like a Louisiana Waterthrush. On the other hand, the songs of many other species of *Basileuterus* are just as poor as those of most Warblers.

III. THE PROBLEM OF HYBRIDS

The constant hybridization between Golden-winged and Blue-winged Warblers (producing Brewster's and the rare recessive Lawrence's) is now well-known; the important point is that these hybrids are fertile. Further instances have multiplied in recent decades. We have now found Blackpoll x Bay-breasted, Audubon's x Myrtle (several records), and Hermit x Townsend's. It has been suggested that the mysterious and lost Carbonated Warbler of Audubon was a hybrid, Cape May x Blackpoll. The implication of all this is that birds we think of as distinct species on the basis of striking and easily observable color differences are genetically more closely allied. Even worse are three cases of intergeneric hybrids. I have examined both

specimens of the recently discovered Sutton's Warbler (*Dendroica potomac* Haller) and agree with others that they are both Parula x Yellow-throated Warbler hybrids. Many years ago (1880) Langdon described *Helminthophaga cincinnatiensis* from Madison, Ohio, which Ridgway (1880) immediately suggested was a hybrid Blue-winged x Kentucky Warbler. Even more remarkable, a second specimen has recently been obtained in Michigan (McCamey, 1950, *Jack-Pine Warbler*, 28:67–72, 1 plate). Moreover, Burleigh (*Auk*, 1944, 61:291–293) has described another such hybrid, Parula Warbler x Redstart. It should be clear that the occurrence of such intergeneric hybrids seriously impugns the validity of the genera involved, but it would be absurd to reduce the family to one genus on that account. Such cases are routine in the ducks, grouse and hummingbirds.

Hellmayr's *Catalogue of Birds of the Americas*, Part VIII, 1935 (pp. 331–526), recognized 25 genera and at least 114 species, plus many subspecies and hybrids. Of these genera Hellmayr found serious fault with at least two. Ridgway (1902) recognized 26 North and Middle American genera and guessed that there might be over 200 species. We now need a somewhat drastic revision of the genera of the *Parulidae* based on badly needed anatomical studies and dissections. For the purposes of this volume, however, the classification and names of the new A.O.U. Check-list are followed throughout.*

LUDLOW GRISCOM

* In the Appendix B will be found Mr. Griscom's suggestions for reducing the warbler family to 16 genera. See also The Topography of a Warbler facing page 288.

CHAPTER 3

THE TECHNIQUES OF WARBLER STUDY

WARBLERS are at once the delight and despair of field observers, and the "sport of bird-study" is first reached for most people through these abundant and often colorful birds. To the ignorant and uninitiated their existence is unknown, but finally, book learning and search leads to an astonishing awareness that twice annually our woods are thronged with brightly colored birds. The "deserted" woods of the days of our ignorance prove to be alive with animated forms; our ears finally become attuned to a series of faint voices, high buzzing songs, or lisping *tseeps* or *chucks,* and before we know it we are embarked on an almost never-ending adventure. Who can tell how many species the next flock will contain? When will our delighted eyes finally come to rest on some rare or uncommon species wandering in

from the far south or the even further west? How many years will it take before the recorded faunal literature has become approximated in our own personal experience?

Depending upon the amount of time and energy available for field work, it takes a minimum of five to twenty years to become an expert in every season, and it is completely beyond the natural capacity of most individuals. As we shall see below, it calls for great physical energy, exceptional hearing ability, a ready and retentive memory for detailed facts instantly available, and a fund of enormous patience. These talents are quite beyond the capacity of the average individual, one very good reason why warbler study is a true sport, and why warbler virtuosos command a modicum of respect and attention. Moreover, it is a true sport in that bountiful nature provides an almost limitless amount of variety. It happens that no two migrations are exactly alike; some are "good," others notably poor, and the time schedule varies remarkably. The variety and number of individuals of the several species is never the same in any one year. Even in the breeding season you cannot find the same number of nesting pairs in your pet region. Finally, if you happen to possess an inquiring mind, the causes back of this extreme variation lead to a perpetual study terminated only by old age, loss of energy and the necessary physical equipment. I can truly say that my active field work on warblers in the spring and fall of 1957, my 50th consecutive year of study, was just as enjoyable as my first in 1907. Actually much more so, as knowledge and experience yield more enjoyment than the thrill of novelty does to the completely inexperienced. It made no difference that no species were left to add to my life-list, that I had personally experienced the very earliest, the very latest or the very best warbler migrations ever recorded in the Northeast; the *chance* remained that 1955 might offer something a little bit different from usual, as it did! This feeling or reaction is almost impossible to explain to those not possessing it.

I list below the various stages by which expertness in warbler study may be attained:

I. Clearly the first step is to acquire an awareness of warblers. It is the elementary test of untrained powers of observation.

II. First attempts. For obvious reasons most people start in spring when bright colors and songs are at a maximum and the confusing and more difficult immature and winter plumages are absent. There are still many "spring specialists" in the East, people who go regularly to Central Park, New York City, or Mt. Auburn Cemetery, Cambridge, Mass., year after year, but are never seen afield at other seasons. The mastery of the fall migrations and the inclusion of the entire range of variation of the species calls for a memory completely outside their capacity and they never try. I have known people thrilled at seeing a relatively uncommon species, sincerely unable to recall that they had seen it previously on several occasions. They were in the happy state of perpetually adding to their unkept life-list! This lack of factual memory seems to be the principal weakness of many women birders.

III. After the spring migration has been mastered, those with the necessary enthusiasm or natural aptitude have two choices. They can tackle the problems of breeding or nesting species, or plunge at once into the more difficult study of the winter or immature plumages of the *fall* migration. Many students have a real complex on fall plumages, confess they know nothing about them, and give up because they are unable to identify the various species with the ease they do in spring. For those with a really fine pair of ears, the absence of song is indeed a handicap. In many cases adult males and females have plumages different from those worn in spring; the immatures may again be quite different, and, more rarely, the two sexes are distinguishable.

The fall migration begins in late July during the "dog days" of summer; but in the Northeast it is not until the first cool nights in late August that finding migrating warblers in any numbers becomes a relatively simple proposition. It admittedly takes considerable enthusiasm to go daily during August to Central Park, in the hope of digging out the first transient. The number of new facts to be memorized, and the new time schedules, are all difficult. Moreover, the flocks of migrating warblers often move so rapidly through the woods that one cannot run fast enough to keep up with them, and they are frequently completely lost. This is a routine event in spring also, but then all one has to do is to stop and listen for a new outbreak of song.

Such difficulties reach an extreme in fall in coastal seashore thickets in the Northeast. Granted a big wave of warblers in a high, cold northwest wind, and the thickets will be bursting with birds. These all hug the thickets closely and have to be trampled out. Then they dart to the nearest thicket and disappear, permitting only the briefest flash of size, shape and color. Even an experienced team of four must sadly admit that ninety per cent are not satisfactorily identified, and the inexperienced are hopelessly confused. In fact, this is an extreme way of testing young and enthusiastic observers. If they are unwilling to admit that most warblers were not identified, they are careless, superficial and overconfident, and need some discipline.

Actually the fall migration of warblers is by far the most fascinating, as well as the most difficult and most sporting proposition. For years people have complained to me, "I never see a Connecticut Warbler." The real answer in most cases proves to be that they have never tried often nor hard enough!

IV.   Summer involves at least local familiarity with the regular breeding population. It may, of course, be extended to include almost every nesting North American species. It involves special nest finding ability, the techniques of which have been markedly declining in my lifetime. It is no longer a matter of course as it was in the earlier days of William Brewster. The reasons are partly historical and partly sentimental. In Brewster's day it was still possible to describe the nests and eggs of various warblers for the first time, or the previously unknown nestling plumages of various species. This naturally provided the necessary stimulus for effort, an incentive lacking to later students, especially when we consider that the modern techniques of life history studies remained to be invented. Moreover, the rise of protection and the sentiment against collecting has laid the stress on identification in the field as a substitute for the further amassing of specimens. This has caused the abandonment of the routine youthful collecting of nest and eggs at just the ideal age when the necessary skills should have been acquired.

The net result is that I have known only four men in my life whose ability at finding warbler nests bordered on the spectacular, notably, William Brewster, Beecher S. Bowdish, P. B. Philipp and Henry Mouseley. Of these all but Brewster turned in poor performances in field identification in spring and fall migration, and they would not compare with the modern run of good warbler experts. The late W. de Witt Miller of Plainfield, N.J., always claimed that you had to specialize in one or the other, really to become a virtuoso. When he set out to discover the early and late nesting dates of his local breeding species, he abandoned active study of the spring and fall migration.

V.   Very few warblers winter regularly in the United States. In recent years, in a cycle of notably mild winters, a few individuals of several species have been found casually in extreme southern Florida and extreme southern Texas, but with little published evidence as yet that they have survived the entire season. It is clear that studying warblers on their normal winter quarters in tropical America is largely a question of favorable opportunity for most of us. I am convinced that this is the greatest remaining neglected opportunity for special study of our North American species. Having by extreme good fortune visited the West Indies and Central America a good deal, I have a certain number of observations to make.

Psychologically, all museum collectors in the tropics have been explorers. They hoped to find something new, some rare species of the little known tropical birds, and they regarded the flood of North American migrants and winter visitants as a nuisance. I well recall the annoyance of Dr. Frank M. Chapman when the Olalla brothers sent him a series of nearly fifty Canada Warblers from eastern Ecuador. On a limited budget he deeply resented having to pay them $1.00 per skin and find storage space for them in an already crowded collection. I was similarly annoyed when Underwood sent me over one hundred Black-throated Green Warblers and ninety-nine

Rose-breasted Grosbeaks from the mountains of central Honduras. The money spent did not advance the science of ornithology very much.

Incidentally, F. M. Chapman expressed a conclusion which has since been accepted uncritically. Interested in life zone distribution in his *Distribution of Bird Life in Colombia* (1917, pp. 183–185) he has a chapter on North American migrants, in which he attempts to show that winter visitants have no definite "zonal boundaries," and cites specimens collected to show that six species occurred variously from the tropical to the temperate zone, while five were of tropical and subtropical occurrence. Carriker, in his *Birds of Costa Rica*, found the distribution of migrants rather confusing and "unaccountable." My own impression in Central America is that Chapman's view is not true in the least, and that some of the specimens collected at lower altitudes or on the western rather than the eastern slope may represent migrants, not winter residents. Perhaps the best comment on this is to be found in the superb summaries of Alexander F. Skutch in Bent's *Life Histories of North American Wood Warblers*. Here for the first time is an excellent resident observer, and we are no longer dependent upon the data supplied by purely random collecting.

I now raise the following rhetorical question. Granting that birds migrate through the tropics, on what date is the migration over, and at what locality is a collected individual on its proved winter quarters? There is no sure answer to this question except by continuous observation in the field. I am convinced that the literature is replete with *phony* winter records, which if literally correct are at most utterly casual. Notable cases are Cozumel Island and the Yucatán Peninsula, known highways of migration, but as yet improperly worked at the height of the season by skilled and interested observers aware of the problem. Note the remarkable results recently obtained by Raymond A. Paynter, Jr., who happened to reach the islands on the Campeche Bank at just the right time of the year (*Auk,* 1953, pp. 338–349). Another neglected area is Corn Island off the east coast of Nicaragua, reported by J. L. Peters to be occasionally swarming with land bird transients, and the islands off Bocas del Toro, western Panama. It is clear that Bond obtained most interesting information on the islands in the Bay of Honduras.

There are still elements of mystery about the migration routes to winter quarters chosen by many North American warblers. It is most reasonable that many uncommon or rare species, like the Swainson's Warbler, should disappear in the tropics, so that we are as yet unable to say definitely what are its principal winter quarters. But it is not reasonable when we come to birds such as the Cerulean and Blackpoll Warblers, birds which are individually abundant, and have both been found commonly in proved winter quarters, to appear later in abundance on known breeding grounds in North America. By what route do the swarms of these birds travel between the extremes of their range? I submit that we have here a real mystery, and I trust that some of my readers may catch fire and do something about it. What is badly needed is trained observers who will visit possible or probable migration centers, who will look for North American transients at the proper dates and not waste time adding as many tropical birds to a life-list as possible. Chapman's guess (*loc. cit.*) may well prove to be the correct one, that the Isthmus of Panama is not the route used by many of these birds in entering South America in numbers; and it is just possible that many North American migrants (various warblers, Veery, Gray-cheeked Thrush) fly non-stop (except casually) over more ocean water than has been previously admitted. In this connection students should read the article by J. A. Allen (*Auk,* 1900, pp. 363–367) on the migrants at Santa Marta, Colombia.

It is my firm conviction that the study of transient warblers in North America has been greatly overdone. Following the migration of warblers is of the greatest importance to beginning students, but they merely discover for themselves what has long been known and recorded in local areas almost throughout North America. For those, therefore, really interested in the study of warblers, I feel convinced that a record of counts of individuals is really important and that there is no end to this field in sight.

I happen to have had the experience of moving to Cambridge, Massachusetts, from the New York City region after studying all the existing references to the birds of Massachusetts, and my first reaction was one of great disappointment because I found that nearly all those warblers which were called "common" on migration were no more so here than I had found them in New York. It took me five years to find out that due to marked ecological changes, the status of birds had been greatly altered; we had to discover all over again those few places in eastern Massachusetts where warblers really occurred in some numbers.

For another thing, as I read the various books about this fascinating family of birds, I learned that the Cape May Warbler, in my early years a bird considered rare in the East, was regarded as a common migrant in western Pennsylvania—but no counts of individuals were ever given to give significance to these designations. From my reading of books, also, I was convinced that Ohio was probably the best place for migrating warblers in eastern North America, and that on rare occasions, waves of warblers would be recorded around Washington, D.C., (notably in 1866) that put to shame anything that we could produce around New York City. A brief residence in Washington in 1917 confirmed this impression, and when I spent some years at Cornell University, in my early teens, I experienced there a greater rush of warblers than I have ever found in either New York or Cambridge.

I am consequently convinced that counting individuals year after year, and in many places, is the only way to bring out these facts and thus supply a fair series of contrasting data. Fortunately, this is now being done, and more and more books are being published that give these detailed facts. It was beautifully done by Allan D. Cruickshank in his 1942 book, *Birds Around New York City,* in which his standard of measurement was at least nine hours of vigorous birding. I used exactly the same unit of measure in my *Birds of Dutchess County, New York;* and precisely the same unit of measure in the more recent *Birds of Massachusetts,* with Miss Dorothy E. Snyder as my colleague. Milton Trautman did it splendidly in *The Birds of Buckeye Lake, Ohio;* and Charles T. Clark and Margaret M. Nice have given long series of counts for Lincoln Park, Chicago (*Spec. Publ. No. 8,* Chicago Acad. of Sc., 1950, based on the field work of William Dreuth). Among other things, these reports show that the fall migration of warblers in the Middle West is incomparably better than anything known in the East.

LUDLOW GRISCOM

CHAPTER 4

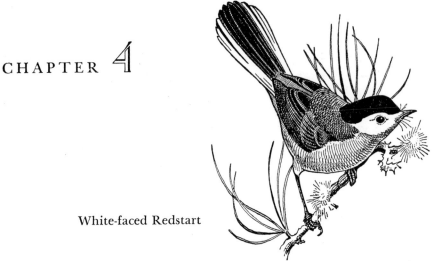

White-faced Redstart

THE SONGS OF WARBLERS

Just as there is no such thing as a typical style of coloration in wood warblers, so there is no such thing as a typical song. Those who maintain the contrary adopt the arbitrary view of calling a certain style of song "typical," and calling everything different an exception! Some few species have real vocal ability, but generally speaking, they rank low as songsters, while many have weak, rattling, trilling or hissing songs of no esthetic appeal whatever.

In eastern North America the numerous species furnish a supreme test of the hearing ability and musical memory of the student. In some the pitch is so high, up to 14,000 vibrations in the Blackpoll, that poor ears cannot hear them at all. The rarer species are heard so seldom on migration, that for most of us it is a real feat to remember the song for eleven months and spot it at once the following May. Many species, by no means closely related, have not only difficult but very similar songs. Finally individual variation is great, and aberrant songs are almost common. When it is recalled that all these songs vary in pitch, volume, and quality, it is not surprising that it is impossible to provide a written description which will enable a beginner to recognize one of the less striking ones at once the first time.

The annual song cycle deserves some general remarks, since it is a neglected field. In most species it is quite brief, as the breeding period is so rapid. Warblers are popularly thought of as singing freely on migration, but this idea arose because bird study began in the northern States. Actually the migrating hosts are almost silent in the tropics and largely so in the southern States. As a rough generalization most of the species have completed two-thirds to three-quarters of the journey to their breeding grounds before singing freely. The members of the genus *Oporornis* (Kentucky, Connecticut, Mourning and MacGillivray's) and the Chat are notable for very rarely singing on migration. The Pine Warbler sings freely all fall and winter on pleasant days. Many sing an occasional snatch during the fall migration, but these songs are usually weak and often atypical.

Because the subject is descriptively so difficult, and no two people can agree on the musical value or quality of similar songs, it has been thought best to give some analysis of all the northern species in this chapter, thus avoiding detailed and repetitious comparative descriptions under each species. The following rough classification of birds heard in the general vicinity of New York City and Cambridge, Massachusetts, for the most part, is presented, though I am keenly aware that a group of experts could debate the matter indefinitely. On their northern nesting grounds most species offer a more elaborate song pattern, as a comparison with Chapter 5 will reveal.

I. VERY HIGH, THIN, WIRY, OR HISSING SONGS; NON-MUSICAL.
    a. Of greater volume. BLACK-AND-WHITE, REDSTART (imm. male).
    b. Less volume. BAY-BREASTED, BLACKBURNIAN, CAPE MAY, BLACKPOLL, PRAIRIE.
    c. Particularly high pitch. BLACKPOLL, CAPE MAY, BLACKBURNIAN, PRAIRIE.
    d. Lower pitch. BLACK-AND-WHITE, BAY-BREASTED, REDSTART.

    e. Pronounced lisping or hissing quality. CAPE MAY, BLACKBURNIAN, BAY-BREASTED.
    f. Excessively high and thin. BLACKPOLL.
    g. More strident. BLACK-AND-WHITE, REDSTART. (see Group IV c)
    h. A buzzy quality. PRAIRIE. (See Group II a)
    i. A monotone; 3–7 leisurely syllables, varying to an indefinite number given rapidly. BLACKPOLL.
    j. Going evenly up the chromatic scale, usually 8 syllables. PRAIRIE. (*cf. Chap. 5*)
    k. Song in twos, the second note lower, repeated 3–7 times in relatively *leisurely* tempo. BLACK-AND-WHITE. (*cf. Chap. 5*)
    l. Song in twos, repeated three times, *very* rapid and hissing. BAY-BREASTED.
    m. Six syllables, a strong accent on the 5th and a drop on the 6th, which is sometimes omitted; tempo rapid. REDSTART (adult male).
    n. Nine syllables, the first 8 in twos; tempo very variable, sometimes as slow as No. 3, or as fast as No. 5, *never* as fast as No. 4. REDSTART (imm.).
    o. Number of syllables indefinite; song in two parts, a series of single or double notes, followed by an extremely high thin part, attaining the pitch of the Blackpoll, ending in a hiss or a rapid series of hisses. BLACKBURNIAN.
    p. Number of syllables indefinite; the most characterless song of the group; if the syllables are in twos, suggesting a feeble Black-and-White or long continued and slower Bay-breasted; best recognized when the preliminary notes are single, and the song trails off in a series of lisping hisses, which often suggest the call note of the Golden-crowned Kinglet, and without the sharp rise in pitch characteristic of the Blackburnian. CAPE MAY.

[*Comment:* These are the first songs to be lost by the elderly; they are inaudible to poor ears and audible at close range only by average ears. Only one person out of a hundred can ever hope to cut all of them out of a chorus at 200 yards or more, and be right with the first bird of the spring. All but the Prairie have non-typical or aberrant songs, which can be learned on the breeding grounds for the time being only.]

II.   SONGS WITH AN INSECT-LIKE BUZZING OR EVEN A HOARSE, "BURRY" QUALITY; NON-MUSICAL.
   a.   Pitch higher, more buzzy. WORM-EATING, GOLDEN-WING, BLUE-WING, PRAIRIE, CERULEAN (var.) The Parula might be put here by some. (see Group III c)
   b.   Pitch lower; hoarser or burry. BLACK-THROATED BLUE, BLACK-THROATED GREEN, CERULEAN (var.) See also Mourning Warbler. (VI e)
   c.   1.   Monotone, syllables indefinite. WORM-EATING.
      2.   Going evenly up the chromatic scale, usually eight syllables. PRAIRIE.
      3.   Syllables four, one buzz, followed by 3–4 in a lower pitch. GOLDEN-WINGED (typical).
      4.   Two syllables, one shorter (inhaled), the second much longer (exhaled). BLUE-WINGED. (cf. Chap. 5)
      5.   A rapid series of buzzes. GOLDEN-WINGED (second or "late summer" song).
      6.   With a rolling r. quality. CERULEAN (var.)
   d.   1.   Three, four or five syllables with leisurely intervals, the last at least rising in pitch. BLACK-THROATED BLUE.
      2.   Monotone, a more rapid series of hoarse notes. BLACK-THROATED BLUE (uncommon var.).
      3.   Five syllables, the 2nd heavily accented, and nos. 2 and 5 higher in pitch. BLACK-THROATED GREEN.
      4.   Seven more rapid syllables, the 6th lower in pitch than the others.

BLACK-THROATED GREEN (common var.).
      5.   A rapid roll, with a terminal high Redstart-like note. CERULEAN (var.).

III.   PITCH HIGH; OF A CHIPPING OR TRILLING TYPE; NON-MUSICAL.
   a.   Of lesser volume and more "chipping" quality. WORM-EATING, BACHMAN'S, ORANGE-CROWNED.
   b.   Of greater volume, but similar quality. TENNESSEE. (cf. Chap. 5)
   c.   Of greater volume and more "trilling" quality, clearer and louder. PARULA, CERULEAN, MYRTLE, YELLOW-THROATED (poor), PINE.
   d.   1.   Monotone; syllables indefinite and very rapid. WORM-EATING. (see Group IIa)
      2.   Similar, but with a rolling r. quality. BACHMAN'S.
      3.   Seven or nine syllables; 2–3 double tsips, followed by 3 very rapid singles; tsip-pee, tsip-pee, tsip-pee; ti-ti-ti. NASHVILLE.
      4.   Like the last in quality, but colorless and characterless, the first notes single, not in twos; very difficult. ORANGE-CROWNED.
   e.   1.   Beginning with Nashville-like tsips, the second part is longer with a strident chappering quality and strongly crescendo, the volume at the close often amazing. TENNESSEE.
   f.   1.   A long roll, going evenly up the chromatic scale. PARULA.
      2.   A long roll, preceded by 2–3 Redstart-like notes, or the last note suddenly high. CERULEAN (more common).
      3.   A loose, characterless junco-like trill, either rising in pitch or dropping at the end. MYRTLE.
      4.   Very similar, but song in two indefinite parts, the second more rapid and a lower pitch. YELLOW-THROATED (poor).

5. Monotone; a long, even trill, the intervals between syllables much greater than Worm-eating, and greater than Chipping Sparrow. PINE.

[Comment: Some people would not agree in calling the songs in subsection f 3–5 non-musical. Some people cannot distinguish a Worm-eating or Pine Warbler from a Chipping Sparrow, their ears not being sensitive to the minute differences in tempo and quality. Others cannot distinguish a good Myrtle from a poor Yellow-throated. The songs of Bachman's, Orange-crowned, and Cerulean properly rank as very difficult.]

IV. HIGH PITCHED, BUT LOUD AND STRIDENT.
a. A monotone *weet-weet-weet,* with a varying number of syllables. PROTHONOTARY.
b. In two parts; three loud slow notes followed by a more rapid series descending the scale; occasionally of definite musical quality. NORTHERN WATERTHRUSH.
c. Very high and wiry; six syllables in rapid tempo, a strong accent on the 5th and a drop on the 6th. REDSTART. (*cf.* II c 5)

[Comment: Students should note that in form and structure the song of the Redstart is almost exactly the same as the Yellow Warbler. They differ in tempo, pitch and quality.]

V. SONG OF SOME MUSICAL QUALITY, LOUDER, CLEARLY DIVIDED INTO A SERIES OF COUNTABLE SYLLABLES.
a. Very rapid, 4–7 syllables, a strong accent on the penultimate. MAGNOLIA.
b. Tempo more even, four single notes plus a couplet; *sweet-sweet-sweet-sweet; swéeter.* YELLOW.

c. Slightly more rapid than the last with an abrupt drop on the last syllable (6–8). CHESTNUT-SIDED.
d. Syllables in threes or fours. YELLOW-THROAT.
e. More rapid (9–10 syllables) with two abrupt changes of tempo in the middle; in syncopated time. CANADA.
f. In two or three parts, at first low, increasing in volume to loud and ringing with a terminal *roll.* KIRTLAND'S (poor).

VI. LOUD AND RINGING; OF MARKED MUSICAL QUALITY.
a. See V f KIRTLAND'S WARBLER (good).
b. See III f 4; a warbler trying to sing like an Indigo Bunting. YELLOW-THROATED (good).
c. Like a Carolina Wren, in twos. KENTUCKY.
d. Like an Ovenbird, in twos, without any emphasis or crescendo. CONNECTICUT.
e. Very rapid, with a burry or throaty quality; 8 syllables in twos. MOURNING.
f. Up to 8 syllables, the last but one strongly accented, a pronounced drop on the last; happily described as a long and glorified Magnolia. HOODED.
g. Very fine songster; 8 syllables, starting with three loud clear ringing notes and a rich descending warble. LOUISIANA WATERTHRUSH. (*cf. Chap.* 5)
h. Intermediate between the last two; very variable in quality and number of syllables (5–10); highly ventriloquial. SWAINSON'S. (*cf. Chap.* 5)

VII. WEAK, INDEFINITE AND CHARACTERLESS SONGS.
a. A short rapid series of thin, lisping notes. PALM.
b. A short series of chattering or rattling notes, descending the scale. WILSON'S.

c. A feeble and indefinite trill. MYRTLE (poor) (*cf*. III f ₃)

d. Louder and more musical in quality (as in V c) but characterless. CHESTNUT-SIDED WARBLER (the so-called second song).

[*Comment:* The second song of the Chestnut-sided is an ideal illustration of the difficulty of warbler songs and the reaction of the individual. Some people have no trouble in recognizing this song and regard it as routine and easy. Some others simply cannot learn it, and no expert can teach them how, even in the field, with the bird performing before them; the trick is lost in a week.]

VIII. AN EXTRAORDINARY CRESCENDO IN TWOS, ATTAINING A TRULY ASTONISHING VOLUME. OVENBIRD.

IX. AN EXTRAORDINARY MEDLEY of caws, toots, chucks, whistles and mews delivered in disconnected and variable order; highly ventriloquial. YELLOW-BREASTED CHAT.

X. FLIGHT SONGS; FINE AND IMPRESSIVE.
a. Based on the normal song, which is continued into a long rich warble. OVENBIRD, LOUISIANA WATERTHRUSH and YELLOWTHROAT.

b. Totally different from normal song; canary-like; very low and inaudible at any distance; rare and little known. PROTHONOTARY.

LUDLOW GRISCOM

[*Comment:* "Whisper songs" are also low, canary-like and inaudible at any distance. These are not necessarily uttered in flight; OVENBIRD, YELLOWTHROAT, ARROW-HEADED and presumably other warblers occasionally sing in this manner, also certain Tanagers (*e.g. Phaenicophilus*).

(JAMES BOND)]

John H. Dick
'55

PLATE 1
PROTHONOTARY WARBLER
Page 46

Adult Male

Fledgling

Adult Female

Fledgling

CHAPTER 5

INTERPRETATIONS OF SOME WARBLER SONGS

An Analysis of the Songs of 39 Species on Their Northern Nesting Grounds *

BLACK-AND-WHITE WARBLER

2–2¼″	(a) weezy weezy weezy weezy we*zee* we*zee* we*zee*
2″	(b) we*zee* we*zee* we*zee* zee-ah zee-ah zee-ah zee zee zee
2½″	(c) tseet tseet tseet tseet tseet tseet tseet tseet tseet tsee
1″	(d) seetsy seetsy seetsy see
2¾″	(e) see see see see see bee bee bee tzee-tzee(-tzee) see

The "bee" note in example (e) is at a lower pitch than the remainder of the song. It is frequently a component of the full song sung on the nesting territory.

PROTHONOTARY WARBLER

1¾–2″   sweet sweet sweet sweet sweet sweet sweet sweet sweet sweet

Songs of this species are quite uniform. The "sweet" phrase is repeated 7 to 12 times at a uniform pitch with a rhythmic swing; a loud, ringing song.

SWAINSON'S WARBLER

1¼″   (a) tee-o tee-o (tee) whit-sut-say bee-o

* *Note:* These songs were tape-recorded in nature by Dr. W. W. H. Gunn, who then analysed them by slowing down the playbacks. The numbers in the left-hand column indicate duration of song in seconds. The six additions by Dr. Borror are the result of playbacks at reduced speed followed by audiospectrographs of all the patterns he found. Both men have collaborated on the first all-warbler record, on which additional species are recorded.

1¼″ (b) tee-o tee toot-sut-say bee-u
1¼″ (c) whee-u whee whit-sut-say bee-o
1¼″ (d) whee whee whee toot-tut-say bee-o
1¼″ (e) tee-u tee-u whee-beet-sit-say see-o

(toot to rhyme with boot; sut and tut to rhyme with foot).

These interpretations represent songs heard from 7 or 8 Swainson's Warblers in the vicinity of Charleston, West Virginia. As the literature indicates, they have loud, ringing songs closely resembling those of Louisiana Waterthrushes both in tonal quality and phraseology. Certain characteristic differences are evident, however. First, songs of Swainson's Warblers are noticeably shorter in duration, being composed of fewer syllables. Then too, the slow opening notes comprising the first part of the song differ markedly in phrasing between the two species and, although there is a remarkable resemblance in the second portion of the song, the Louisiana Waterthrush then typically goes on to add a final phrase missing from songs of Swainson's Warblers.

WORM-EATING WARBLER

2–3″ (a) eeeeeeeeeeeeeeeeeeeeeeeeeeeeeeeeeeeee

The song is a buzzy trill, with the notes uttered at the rate of about 25 a second. It is a little like the songs of a chipping sparrow and pine warbler, but is faster than most of the songs of these species. (Borror)

GOLDEN-WINGED WARBLER

1¼–1¾″ (a) zee bzz bee; zee bzz bee; zee bzz zu bee
1″ (b) zzz zee-zee; zzz zee-zee-zee; zzz zee-zee

These represent successive songs in song sequences of two different birds.

BLUE-WINGED WARBLER

1–2″ zee bee; zee bee bee; zee bee tzi-tzi-tzi-tzi-tzi

Variations such as these appear in same song sequence.

BACHMAN'S WARBLER

1½–2″ (a) zee zee zee zee zee zee zee zee chew
1½–2″ (b) zee zee zee zee zee zee zee zee chwee

The song consists of 7–9 short buzzy notes, uttered at the rate of about five a second, and ends with a short, slurred note. The buzzy notes are higher in pitch than those in the songs of the black-throated green warbler, and are quite similar to the buzzes in some golden-winged warbler songs. [Borror]

TENNESSEE WARBLER

2½–3½″   (a) ticka ticka ticka ticka swit swit chew-chew-chew-chew-chew-chew
2½–3½″   (b) tenna tenna tenna tenna chip chip see-see-see-see-see

A loud, rhythmic song in three sections; each bird has his own syllabic interpretation and combination of the number of syllables per section of the song; the second section is nearly always the shortest. Example (b) departs somewhat from the literal in an attempt to incorporate the name of the bird.

ORANGE-CROWNED WARBLER

2″   si-si-si-si-si-si-si-si-si-si-si-si-si-si-si-si-si-si-si-si

The song consists of about 18–22 notes repeated rapidly. At about half-way, the pitch drops a small but noticeable amount, sometimes rising again just at the end. Amplitude falls off slightly near the end. When recorded and replayed at reduced speed, each note might be interpreted 'tew,' but this is not really recognizable as such at normal speed. Songs of different individuals seem fairly uniform.

NASHVILLE WARBLER

1¾–2¼″   (a) see-bit, see-bit, see-bit, see-bit, ti-ti-ti-ti
1¾–2¼″   (b) see-it see-it see-it see-it, ti-ti-ti
1¾–2¼″   (c) seet seet seet seet ti-ti-ti-ti-ti

The song is normally composed of two parts, the second part being sung more rapidly and at a lower pitch than the first. Individual birds vary the number of phrases in each part. The phrase repeated in the first part appears to be composed of one or two syllables, depending on the speed at which it is sung.

PARULA WARBLER

1¾″   (a) zzzzzzzzzzzzzzzzzzz-zip
1½–2″   (b) bz-bz-bz-bz-bz-zzzzzzzzzz-up
1¼–1½″   (c) bzz-bzz-bzz-zzzzzz-up
1¼–1½″   (d) zee zee zee zzzzzzz-zip
1½″   (e) twee twee twee zee-zee-zee-wip

The songs are of two general types, a steady buzzy trill that rises in pitch and ends in a sharp slurred note (a), and two series of buzzy notes, the first series slower and lower-pitched than the second, with a sharp slurred note at the end (b-e). Songs of the second type vary in the number and character of the notes; in some (b-d) the second series of buzzy notes is much like the buzzy trill in the first type of song (a), but in others (e) the buzzy notes in the second part are a little longer. [Borror]

YELLOW WARBLER

    1¼–1¾″   tzee tzee tzee tzee tsitta tsitta tsee

This is an interpretation of the commonest form of song. There are many variants, including some that resemble songs of Chestnut-sided, and Magnolia Warblers and American Redstarts.

MAGNOLIA WARBLER

    1–1¼″   (a) chew-chew-chew-chew wit-see
    1–1¼″   (b) tsee-a tsee-a tsee-a tsee-a witsy
    1–1¼″   (c) wit wit witty swit
    1–1¼″   (d) been been been-dichew
    1–1¼″   (e) swee swee swee wit-see
    1–1¼″   (f) weet weet wit-sweet
    1–1¼″   (g) chip chip witty-swee
    1–1¼″   (h) sue sue sue wit-see

Song is brief and rather weak. Syllabic content very variable, with 'chew', 'wit', and 'swee' or 'see' turning up most frequently. Phrases with 'chew' are low in pitch and those with 'see' are high.

CAPE MAY WARBLER

    1¼″   (a) seet seet seet seet (seet see)
    1¼″   (b) see see see see see
    1¼″   (c) tew-be tew-be tew-be tew-be tew-be tew-be tew-be tew-be see-see-see

Cape May songs are weak, high-pitched, and usually delivered from a tree-top. (a) and (b) are examples of the commoner song, which is rather deliberate; (c) is more complex and less frequently heard.

BLACK-THROATED BLUE WARBLER

    1″   (a) zee-oo zee-oo zee
    1¼″   (b) dzeurr dzeurr dzee

Very deliberate presentation; last phrase up-slurred.

MYRTLE WARBLER

    2″   (a) che-che-che-che-che-che-che-che chee-chee-chee-chee
    1¼″   (b) chew-chew-chew-chew chit-chit-chit
    1¾″   (c) chee chee chee chee che-che-che

In the first two examples, the second part is at a higher pitch; in the third example, it is lower. Presentation is not hurried.

BLACK-THROATED GREEN WARBLER

1¼″   (a) zee-zee-zee(-zee-zee) zoo zee
1½–1¾″   (b) zee, zee, zee-zoo zee

Black-throated Greens commonly follow two song patterns. Individual males commonly sing both types. The difference is chiefly one of tempo rather than phrasing. The pattern shown in example (a) is sung rapidly, the first three notes (sometimes four or five) being crowded together. The second pattern is sung more slowly, with a noticeable pause between the first three notes, but the fourth following closely on the third. The 'zoo' notes indicate a drop in pitch.

CERULEAN WARBLER

1–1¾″   (a) switty, switty, switty tsi-tsi-tsi-zee
1½″   (b) tzeed tzeed tzeed tzeed tzeed tsi-tsi-tsi zee
1″   (c) chee chee chee chee chee tzee

Last syllable drawn out and up-slurred.

BLACKBURNIAN WARBLER

1½″   (a) teetsa teetsa teetsa teetsa teetse e e e
1¼–1½″   (b) sleecha sleecha sleecha sleecha sleecha sleeee
1¾″   (c) sleecha sleecha sleecha sleecha sleecha sleecha
1½″   (d) seetcha seetcha seetcha seetcha seetcha
1½″   (e) tche-see tche-see tche-see tche-see tche-see tche
1¾″   (f) see-a see-a see-a tchew-tchew-tchew

Last syllable usually but not always up-slurred. Last example, typical in Sault Ste. Marie—Blind River—Chapleau area of Ontario, resembles song of Golden-crowned Kinglet.

YELLOW-THROATED WARBLER

1½–2″   (a) teedle teedle teedle . . . tew tew tee
1½″   (b) teedle teedle teedle . . . teedle

The songs consist of 6–12 notes or phrases uttered at the rate of four or five a second, with the last few being a little lower in pitch and uttered a little more rapidly. The pitch in each phrase is wavering but the trend is downward. The song sometimes (a) ends with a short up-slurred note. In songs with ten phrases or less (b) the phrases are usually similar. The songs of the eastern (yellow-throated) and mid-western (sycamore) races of this species are very similar, and have a quality somewhat similar to that of an indigo bunting's song. [Borror]

CHESTNUT-SIDED WARBLER

1½″	(a)	tsee see see see see swee-*beat*-you
1½″	(b)	chee chee chee chee swee-*beat*-you
1¾″	(c)	chew chew chew chew chitty chitty swee-beat-you
1¾″	(d)	chew chew chew chew chee chee chitchee witchee

Examples (a) and (b) are the common form, with the emphatic, down-dropping ending.

BAY-BREASTED WARBLER

1¼″	(a)	see-at*zee*-at*zee*-at*zee*-at*zee*
1½″	(b)	seetzy-seetzy-seetzy-seetzy-see

The song is short, has a ringing quality like the call-note of the Golden-crowned Kinglet.

BLACKPOLL WARBLER

2″	ti-ti-ti-ti-ti-ti-ti-ti-ti-ti-ti-ti-ti-ti-ti-ti-ti-ti-ti-ti-ti-ti-ti-ti-ti-ti-ti-ti-ti

One note repeated very rapidly as many as 30 times and at such a high pitch that it is almost a hiss; pitch remains constant but song becomes louder in second half, fading away again at the end. [*Comment:* The Blackpoll has a slower, more deliberate song with fewer notes, likewise crescendo—diminuendo, often heard on migration. (James Bond)]

PINE WARBLER

2¼″	chi-chi-chi-chi-chi-chi-chi-chi-chi-chi-chi-chi-chi-chi-chi-chi-chi-chi

One note repeated rapidly about 18–20 times; the pitch rises slightly near the middle and then falls again near the end; amplitude fairly constant.

[*Comment:* There is much more variation in the songs of this species, even in a single individual, than this description implies. The songs consist of trills that have a chirping sparrow or junco-like quality. Some songs consist of a series of similar notes uttered at rates of 10–25 a second, and others of 2-note phrases uttered at rates of 9–11 a second. (D. J. B.)]

KIRTLAND'S WARBLER

1½–2″	(a)	chip chip chip-chip-chip-teoo-teoo-weet-weet

The song is loud, clear, musical, and a little lower in pitch than most other warbler songs. The first two or three notes are separated by slightly longer intervals than the others, giving the effect of the bird taking a few notes to really get going. [Borror]

PRAIRIE WARBLER

1½–1¾″	(a)	te-te-te-te-te-te-te-te-te-te-te-te-te-te-te-te
1½–1¾″	(b)	tze-tze-tze-tze-tze-tze-tze-tze-tze-tze-tze-tze-tze-tze

PLATE 2
WORM-EATING WARBLER
Page 55

Worm-eating Adult

BLACK-AND-WHITE WARBLER
Page 43

Female

Male

John H. Dick
'55

One note repeated moderately rapidly 14–16 times, with amplitude fairly constant but pitch rising steadily in even steps.

[*Comment:* The songs in our recordings contain from 6 to 43 notes each, uttered at rates of 4–19 a second. Most songs are 2–3 seconds in length. (D. J. B.)]

PALM WARBLER

    1½″   she-she-she-she-she-she(-she)
      or   zee-zee-zee-zee-zee-zee(-zee)

A two-syllabled 'thew-wee,' sung so rapidly that it sounds like one syllable, repeated six or seven times at a moderately fast pace and fairly constant amplitude.

OVENBIRD

    2¼–4½″   (a) teacher teacher teacher teacher teacher teacher teacher
    2¼–4½″   (b) teach teach teach teach teach teach teach teach teach
    2¼–4½″   (c) chip chip chip chip chip chip chip chip chip chip

One phrase repeated 5–15 times with a more or less pronounced crescendo. Slow songs emphasize two syllables, faster ones reduce this to 'teach' (example b) and very fast ones sound something like example (c). Flight song, delivered more often at dusk or at night and more often in the latter part of the nesting season, is a pleasant-sounding but excited outpouring of notes, with 'teach, teach' occurring in one part of it.

NORTHERN WATERTHRUSH

    2″   (a) *sweet sweet sweet* swee-wee-wee chew-chew-chew-chew
    2″   (b) cheep cheep cheep we-we-we chew-chew-chew-chew-chew-chew

A loud, clear, three-parted song with the first part delivered slowly and with emphasis.

LOUISIANA WATERTHRUSH

    2″   (a) tsee-a tsee-a tsee-a chew chew tzwee chew-wee
    1¾–2″   (b) tseet tseet tseet tseet chew chew chew weet weet-wee
    1½″   (c) see-ut see-ut see-ut sit-say-twee bee-o tew-wee
    1½″   (d) tew-bee tew-bee tew tut-tut-say bee-o tew-wee

First part not as loud as in previous species; more variation in last part.

KENTUCKY WARBLER

    1½–2½″   (a) perta*lee* perta*lee* perta*lee* . . . perta*lee*
    1½–2″   (b) pa*teeah* pa*teeah* pa*teeah* . . . pa*teeah*
    2–2½″   (c) per*lee* per*lee* per*lee* . . . per*lee*

The songs consist of a series of 5–11 (usually 6–8) similar phrases, uttered at the rate of

2½–4 phrases a second. The phrases are loud, clear, and well separated, and usually appear to have a rising inflection. The songs of different birds differ slightly (a-c, above). [Borror]

CONNECTICUT WARBLER

1¾″	(a) chippy-chuppy chippy-chuppy chippy-chuppy chippy-chuppy chip
1¼″	(b) chip chup-ee, chip chup-ee, chip chup-ee chip
1¼″	(c) switty switty switty swit
1–1¼″	(d) sugar-tweet, sugar-tweet, sugar-tweet

Much individual and some geographical variation; (a) and (b) are eastern forms, (c) and (d) more westerly. Seton's often-quoted 'Beecher Beecher Beecher' interpretation is very rare and should not be used as a typical example.

MOURNING WARBLER

1½″	(a) cheese cheese cheese cheese sweet (*emphatic*)
1–1¼″	(b) cheery cheery cheery cheery cheery
1¾″	(c) chee chee chee chorry chorry chorry
1¼″	(d) trew-*lee* trew-*lee* trew-*lee* trew-*lee*
1½″	(e) choory choory choory choory (choory)

Also with considerable individual and some geographical variation. The 'truly, truly' song is rare in Ontario.

[*Comment:* The recordings I have studied (ours from Ohio and Dr. Gunn's from Ontario) consist of 3–5 trilly "cheeree" notes, and some have from one to three short "ti-di" phrases at the end. The "cheeree" notes rise in pitch at the end, and usually fall in pitch at the beginning; the "ti-di" phrases, when they are present, are at a lower pitch than the others. (D. J. B.)]

YELLOWTHROAT

3″	(a) witchety witchety witchety witchety witchet
2″	(b) witsety witsety witsety witsety
2″	(c) swee-bee *tweet,* swee-bee *tweet,* swee-bee *tweet*
2″	(d) te-*wee* bitsy, te-*wee* bitsy, te-*wee* bitsy
1¾–2¼″	(e) wee-bee *cheetie,* wee-bee *cheetie,* wee-bee *cheetie* (wee-bee *cheet*)

Songs of southern Ontario forms are quite uniform (a, b). Northern forms (c, d, e) are very variable and usually more complex.

[*Comment:* The songs of this species are subject to a great deal of variation, even in birds in the same geographic area. The phrases vary in number from 2 to 5, and the songs usually last from 1½ to 2½ seconds. The song may start or end anywhere in the phrase, that is, the first and/or the last phrase may be incomplete; different songs of the same bird may vary in this respect. The phrases of the song are often run together so that it is difficult to determine just which note marks the beginning of a phrase.

The following are some interpretations I would give to yellowthroat songs; the first three (a-c) consist of 3-note phrases, the next two (d-e) consist of 4-note phrases, and the last (f) consists of 5-note phrases.

(a) *wich*-a-tee *wich*-a-tee *wich*-a-tee

(b) *wee*-tee-to *wee*-tee-to *wee*-tee-to

(c) which-*is*-it which-*is*-it which-*is*-it

(d) *which*-en-is-it *which*-en-is-it

which-en-is-it

(e) which-en-*was*-it which-en-*was*-it which-en-*was*-it

(f) which-*one*-is-*on*-it which-*one*-is-*on*-it which-*one*-is-*on*-it

(D. J. B.)]

YELLOW-BREASTED CHAT

ch-ch-ch-ch-ch-ch-ch-ch-ch-ch-ch, quit, kew kew kew kew, chip-chip-chip-chip-chip-chip, pit, cheek, chee-chee-chee-chee-chee-chee-chee, mee-ow, chur, etc.

A long, rambling, un-warbler-like song something like that of a Catbird or Mockingbird.

HOODED WARBLER

1½″ (a) chew weet-you weet-it weet-it

1–1¼″ (b) weet-you weet-you weet-i-chew

1½″ (c) chew chew chee witchee witchee

Sung in unhurried fashion with clear enunciation.

[*Comment:* I would suggest adding the following:

1–1½″ (d) tawee tawee tawee-*tee*-to

1–1½″ (e) taree taree ta*ree*ree (D. J. B.)]

1001267

WILSON'S (PILEOLATED) WARBLER

1–1¼″ (a) chee chee chee chee chee che-che-che-ch-ch (wit-wit)

1″ (b) chew chew chew chew chee-chee-chee-chee

Two-parted, rapid, chattery.

CANADA WARBLER

1¼″ (a) chip chupety swee-ditchety

1¼″ (b) chip suey de swee-ditchety

1¼″ (c) chip swit-dee swee-deetchety

The 'chip' at the beginning is the same sharp, emphatic note that is used as a call-note; there is then a small but appreciable pause before the rest of the song explodes in staccato fashion. The middle part is variable, but the end is fairly constant. A short, sharp, explosive song. [*Comment:* Some songs begin with two "chip" notes. (D. J. B.)]

AMERICAN REDSTART

1″	(a)	zee-zee-zee-zee-zee-zee *zwee-oo*
1″	(b)	zee-zee-zee-zee swee-oo
1″	(c)	zee-zee-zee-zee-zee-zee *zwee*

Last 'zee' note is usually higher in pitch; last phrase drops and is down-slurred. Immature males often have quite atypical songs.

[*Comment:* The songs of this species are high-pitched and somewhat lisping, and are subject to a great deal of variation; one bird may sing songs of several different types. The songs are of two general patterns; in one the song consists of 4–7 similar notes or phrases, with a louder and lower-pitched note at the end; in the other the song consists of a series of 2–8 similar phrases, without the lower note at the end. (D. J. B.)]

W. W. H. GUNN AND DONALD J. BORROR

PLATE 3
SWAINSON'S WARBLER
Page 50

BACHMAN'S WARBLER
Page 68

Male

Female

Swainson's Adult

Semper's Warbler

THE GEOGRAPHICAL DISTRIBUTION OF WARBLERS

IT IS CLEAR that the present-day distribution of the New World families and subfamilies of nine-primaried Oscine Passeres is overwhelmingly tropical and that comparatively few species and genera reach North America at all, where they are markedly migratory. The Wood Warblers are a notable exception in that a high percentage of them *breed* in North America (north of Mexico), mostly retiring to the tropics to winter. A more or less exact distributional division of the family by species follows in the Distribution Table.

This may be contrasted with the Honey-Creepers (*Coerebidae*), wholly tropical; the Tanagers with 62 genera, of which only *one* genus and 4 species reach the United States; the *Icteridae* (Orioles, Blackbirds, Meadowlarks) with 34 genera, of which 10 reach the United States and only 4 have

resident species, the others highly migratory; and the subfamily *Richmondeninae* of the Finches, of which only 6 genera out of 18 reach North America, where all species are migratory except the Cardinal and Pyrrhuloxia.

These facts have given rise to the rather too facile theory that the *Parulidae* originated somewhere in the tropics, that the more "aggressive" members moved north into North America as the climate moderated and the Ice Age waned, and that they migrated south each winter to their ancestral home. This theory is endorsed in part in that warblers now occur in variety and abundance in areas positively known to have been formerly buried under a thick layer of ice, in other words under conditions which they could not conceivably have tolerated on the basis of their present

DISTRIBUTION TABLE

1. Breeding wholly in North America north of Mexico 42

2. Breeding throughout much of North America and southward to central Mexico: Yellow Warbler (*aestiva group*) and Audubon's W. (*Dendroica*), Common Yellowthroat (*Geothlypis*), and Yellow-breasted Chat (*Icteria*) 4

3. Breeding from southern U.S. or Mexico to Central America:
   a. Chiefly from Arizona to northern Nicaragua—Grace's W. (*Dendroica*), Olive W. (*Peucedramus*), Painted Redstart (*Setophaga*).
   b. From Arizona to Guatemala—Red-faced W. (*Cardellina*).
   c. From southern Texas to western Panama—the Ground-chat (*Chamaethlypis*).
   d. In southern Texas and Mexico—Colima W. (*Vermivora*).
   e. From Mexico to northern Nicaragua—Crescent-chested W. (*Vermivora*), Fan-tailed W. (*Euthlypis*).
   f. Mountains of Mexico and Guatemala—Red W. and Pink-headed W. (*Ergaticus*) 10

4. Breeding from southern Texas to Argentina: Olive-backed W. (*Parula pitiayumi*) . . . 1

5. Breeding in the United States and the West Indies: two *Dendroica* species—Yellow-throated W. (to Bahamas) and Pine W. (to Bahamas, Hispaniola) 2

6. Confined to the West Indies: five species of *Dendroica* (Adelaide's, Arrow-headed, Olive-capped, Plumbeous, and Vitelline Warblers); Whistling W. (*Catharopeza*), Semper's W. (*Leucopeza*); Yellow-headed and Oriente W. (*Teretistris*); and the Green-tailed and White-winged Ground Warblers (*Microligea*) 11

7. The Yellowthroats (*Geothlypis*): 5 species confined to Mexico, one in the Bahamas, 2 in Central America and South America 8

8. The Mangrove Warbler (*Dendroica*), including both the "Golden Warbler" *petechia* group of the West Indies, and the Middle American *erithachorides* group breeding from Baja California, both coasts of Mexico, the West Indies, and Central America to Peru and the Galapagos Islands 1

9. Confined to mountains of Costa Rica and Panama: Flame-throated W. (*Vermivora*), Collared Redstart (*Myioborus*), and Black-cheeked W. (*Basileuterus*) 3

10. The chats of the genus *Granatellus*: Red-breasted and Gray-throated Chats in tropical Mexico (*G. sallaei* extending to Guatemala); and the Rose-breasted Chat in the Amazonian region of Brazil and adjacent Venezuela, British Guiana, Bolivia, and Peru 3

11. Tropical Redstarts of the genus *Myioborus:* 9 species ranging variously in the highlands and mountains of Mexico and Central America to Andes of Argentina 9

12. Tropical warblers of the genus *Basileuterus:* between 19 and 27 species (depending on taxonomic judgment) ranging variously in Mexico and Central America (7 species), and South America 23

well-known requirements. It is further endorsed by the proved fact that their return to the ancestral home takes place in *late* summer, at a season when vegetation and insect food are at their maximum luxuriance and abundance.

This theory is too facile in that it ignores several other considerations. In evolutionary terms it takes time to evolve so many distinct species and peculiar genera, and it seems incredible that they could have evolved so rapidly, while the Ice Cap was receding, and the warblers were pushing north to occupy newly opened territory. The possibility arises, therefore, that *some* of the ancestral warbler stock originated in *old* North America, in a warmer pre-glacial climate, and that the refrigeration of the climate culminating in the Ice Age sent many of these warbler elements into various parts of present-day Central and South America. The fossil record proves this to have been true in other families, and it can be suspected of still other groups.

It has been frequently stated and often repeated that the genus *Dendroica* was probably of West Indian origin. One reason is that it is only in the West Indies that endemic species of the genus occur outside North America, and that a large number of species winter there primarily and abundantly, notably the Cape May, Black-throated Blue, Yellow-throated, Kirtland's, Prairie, and Palm. Of the six West Indian species, four are the only dull colored warblers of the genus. We have *D. pharetra* of Jamaica, suggesting a Black-and-White in color; and the drab *D. plumbea* of Dominica and Guadeloupe, from which the aberrant and drab *Catharopeza bishopi* and

Leucopeza semperi of St. Vincent and St. Lucia may be descended. Curiously enough, the Pine Warbler breeds in the northern Bahamas and Hispaniola; but it is represented in the southern Bahamas and Cuba by a very distinct species *D. pityophila*, the Olive-capped Warbler. There is general agreement that the Prairie Warbler is most closely related to *D. vitellina* of the Cayman Islands and the remote Swan Island in the middle of the Caribbean Sea. Oddly enough the Prairie Warbler regularly migrates in winter to the Cayman and Swan Islands, thus supposedly returning to its ancestral home!

Unfortunately, again, the remaining West Indian species is *D. adelaidae* of Puerto Rico and St. Lucia, which is so closely related to Grace's Warbler (southwestern United States to Nicaragua) that Hellmayr suggested they might be conspecific, and most certainly in the same *formenkreis* (polytypic species). Moreover, far too many species of *Dendroica* are casual to very rare in the West Indies and migrate in numbers to Central and South America either via Texas and Mexico or else by a trans-Gulf of Mexico route. So I fear that the West Indian origin of the genus is arrived at by a somewhat oversimplified reasoning. The fact that no resident species of *Dendroica* is now to be found exclusively in Mexico or Central America does not prove anything of necessity. We may gain here by considering the much better known fossil record of mammals, which proves over and over again that many living orders and families originated in areas where *none* now survive.

LUDLOW GRISCOM

CHAPTER 7

A COMPARISON OF THE FORAGING RANGES OF WARBLERS

Compiled by W. W. H. Gunn, Alexander Sprunt, Jr.,
James Bond, E. R. Blake, A. F. Skutch,
and H. L. Cogswell

The height at which warblers seek their food varies from the ground to the tops of tall trees. The following table, arranged alphabetically, concerns the vegetational level at which 82 of the warblers forage on their breeding grounds; some species which forage high nest on the ground, others at different heights in their winter homes and on migration. The arrows indicate this variability.

LOW RANGING	MEDIUM RANGING	HIGH RANGING
Bachman's ——→	Adelaide's ——→	←—— Bay-breasted
Belding's Yellowthroat	American Redstart	Blackburnian
Black-cheeked, Buff-rumped	Arrow-headed	←—— Blackpoll
Canada	←—— * Audubon's ——→	←—— Cape May
Chestnut-capped ——→	Black-and-White	Cerulean
Chestnut-sided ——→	Black-throated Blue	←—— Flame-throated
Colima, Connecticut	Black-throated Gray ——→	Grace's
Fan-tailed	Black-throated Green ——→	←—— Hermit
Golden-browed, Golden-crowned	Blue-winged	←—— Olive
Gray-breasted ground	Collared Redstart	←—— Olive-backed
Gray-throated Chat ——→	Crescent-chested ——→	←—— Pine
Ground-chat	←—— Golden-cheeked	←—— Red
Hooded ——→	Golden-winged	←—— Townsend's
Kentucky, Kirtland's	Magnolia	
Louisiana Waterthrush, Lucy's	←—— Myrtle ——→	
MacGillivray's, Mourning	←—— Nashville	
Northern Waterthrush	Olive-capped ——→	
Orange-crowned ——→	←—— Oriente	
Ovenbird ——→	←—— Painted Redstart	
Palm ——→	Parula ——→	
Prairie, Prothonotary	Pink-headed ——→	
Red-breasted Chat ——→	Plumbeous ——→	
Rufus-capped, Red-faced ——→	Tennessee	
Semper's, Slate-throated Redstart ——→	Whistling ——→	
Swainson's	←—— Yellow	
Three-striped	←—— Yellow-headed	
Vitelline, Virginia's ——→	Yellow-throated ——→	
White-winged ground, Wilson's ——→		
Worm-eating		
Yellow-breasted Chat, Yellowthroat		

* In Central America Audubon's W. forages on the ground and also in the tops of high trees. The Myrtle acts similarly in the West Indies.

60 WARBLERS BREEDING IN THE UNITED STATES, CANADA, AND BAJA CALIFORNIA

THE 1957 A.O.U. Checklist describes 57 different species of "North American" warblers, to which have been added the three hybrids: Brewster's, Lawrence's and Sutton's. These birds are described in the following 203 pages, which together comprise Chapter 8. The reason for the inclusion of Baja California as part of "North America" is not entirely clear; it dates from the '80s when the first Checklist Committee was formed. Very little was then known in the United States about tropical birds or their ranges; but the peninsula of Lower California had been relatively well explored. (L. G.)

1

BLACK-AND-WHITE WARBLER

Mniotilta varia

WERE all the members of this puzzling, provoking and altogether delightful avian family as readily recognized as this one, how much of doubt and confusion would vanish, and, one might add, fascination!

Few birds have been so well named. This warbler is black and white, just exactly that, no more, no less. If well seen, it can be mistaken for no other, but if indistinctly seen, confusion could arise because of its general resemblance to the Yellow-throated Warbler (were the throat color of the latter not seen) and to the Blackpoll.

The Black and White is a "creeper". Its actions and behavior are reminiscent of a nuthatch or Brown Creeper for it is a deliberate bird, always taking its time, searching diligently in crack or cranny of tree trunk, limb or leaf cluster for its insect prey. Compared with the usual dash and movement of many other warblers, such behavior is itself diagnostic. It seems always unhurried, undisturbed and methodical.

Black and white is ever a compelling combination and the trim, streamlined bird which sports it is not likely to be forgotten. Though appearing to prefer swampland habitat, it is also found in dry situations, always in deciduous growth (or broad-leaved evergreens, such as live-oak). In Florida in winter, it occurs in the oak and palm "hammocks" of the Kissimmee Prairie region and starts to sing there in early February in some warm winters.

In *Warblers of North America* (1907) Dr. F. M. Chapman gives the winter range as "Northern Florida (St. Augustine) and southern Texas; south throughout the West Indies to Venezuela and Ecuador."

Since he wrote that, this warbler has been established as wintering as far north as coastal South Carolina, as far west as Baja California and southern Arizona, and south through Central America and Colombia. This is a good illustration of the advance of ornithological knowledge by means of increased and more proficient observation on the part of bird watchers generally, for it is hardly to be supposed that the species has actually extended its winter range that far since Dr. Chapman wrote.

[*Comment:* The Black-and-White Warbler is one of the earliest spring warblers to reach its breeding-ground in the Transition Zone. Most of the other members of this family arrive in or pass through the region in mid-May or somewhat later, according to the season, when the oaks are in bloom and the opening flowers attract swarms of insects.

The Black-and-White Warbler, however, owing to its peculiar habit of feeding on the trunks and the large limbs of the trees, does not have to wait for the bounty supplied by the oaks but finds its special feeding ground well stocked with food long before the oaks blossom or their leaves unfold. It comes with the Yellow Palm Warbler late in April, when many of the trees are nearly bare, and not long after the Pine Warbler. . . . The fall migration is long-drawn-out. Again, the bird does not depend, like many of the warblers, on finding food among the foliage, so it may linger long after the trees are bare of leaves, sometimes, here in New England, well into October. I saw a bird in eastern Massachusetts on October 23, 1940, a very late date. (W. M. Tyler in Bent's *Life Histories*)]

Like many other warblers, the Black-and-White crosses the Gulf of Mexico on migration, an astonishing feat for a bird so small. I have seen it on the Dry Tortugas Keys, that great stop-over station where so many Gulf migrants pause in their overwater journey.

Unlike some other warblers, the Black-and-White is only occasionally victimized by the Cowbird; but George Byers (1950) describes (in Bent) a nest in Michigan that held two eggs of the warbler and eight of the Cowbird, on which the warbler was incubating.

Mniotilta varia (Linnaeus)
(Gr., *Mniotilta,* moss-plucking; Lat., *varia,* variegated)

Type Locality Santo Domingo

OTHER NAME: Black-and-White Creeper

FIELD CHARACTERS: *Male,* upperparts black, streaked with white, a white stripe down center of crown and white line over eye, which distinguish it from the Blackpoll in spring. Underparts white, streaked with black except in middle of belly.
Female, similar, but streaking below grayish rather than black.
Length, 4.75 to 5.25 inches.

NESTING DATA: Built in a slight depression in the ground, occasionally in crevice above ground, usually at base of stump, side of log or foot of forest tree, at times amid the roots of windfalls. Nest rather bulky, constructed of grass, dead leaves, bark-strippings and rootlets, lined with hair. Occasionally canopied or semi-arched over.
Eggs—4 or 5. Ground color, white or creamy, profusely spotted and speckled with reddish-brown and lavender, often in the form of a wreath about large end. Some specimens are very evenly marked over entire surface. Rounded oval in shape with less of a pointed small end than most warbler eggs.

VOICE: The descriptive words most often applied to the song of the Black-and-White Warbler are—thin and wiry. It is hard to choose any better. High and insect-like, the notes are fourth highest in pitch, after the Blackpoll, Blue-winged and Blackburnian, according to A. R. Brand who recorded 16 species in 1938. The song is, however, pleasing in effect, lisping syllables repeated from six to eight times in the same tone: *we see, we see, we see.* Varied and more elaborate renditions are sometimes heard from breeding birds.

[*Comment:* A commonly heard song in the breeding range in Ontario is one in which the song is split in two parts by a single note given at lower pitch, e.g.: "weezy weezy weezy weezy weezy weezy *bee* weezy weezy weezy etc." (Gunn)]

The call note is a single sharp "pit," which suggests the *chip* of the Blackpoll. This warbler is less vocal than many others. (*See Chapter 5*)

FOOD HABITS: Largely wood-boring insects, with bark and click beetles, moths and small caterpillars. The bird is a definite economic asset, sharing with woodpeckers and creepers in a constant check on insects inimical to tree growth.

GENERAL RANGE: *Breeds* from southwestern Mackenzie, central Saskatchewan, central Manitoba, southern Ontario, southern Quebec, and northern Newfoundland south to northeastern British Columbia, central Alberta, eastern Montana, southwestern South Dakota, central Texas, southeastern Louisiana, northern Mississippi, central Alabama, central Georgia, central South Carolina and southeastern North Carolina.

Winters from Baja California, southern Texas, cen-

tral Florida, coastal South Carolina and the Bahamas, south through Central America and the West Indies to Ecuador, Colombia and Venezuela. *Accidental* in Scotland.

ALEXANDER SPRUNT, JR.

2

PROTHONOTARY WARBLER

Protonotaria citrea

ALEXANDER SPRUNT, JR writes: "We are moving soundlessly in a place of silence. The dug-out slid onward under the impetus of the paddle thrusts with an occasional, all but inaudible hiss of water-drops striking the surface over which we cruised. A spell seemed to have fallen over us as we entered a world of soaring gray trunks, wine-brown water and swaying moss-banners.

"Then, occasional sounds began to break through the placid quiet. The far away scream of a hunting red-shouldered hawk drifting thinly downward; the drumming of a woodpecker on an ancient cypress. And then, distant though it was, came that clear, ringing call, that rising whistled cadence which, more than anything else, seemed to be coming from the pipes of Pan.

"Nearer it came, filling the air with mel-ody; then across the dugout's bow streaked an orange-yellow flash, to alight, only yards away atop a cypress knee, a glowing bit of animated color. Down it went into the knee itself, but actually into a narrow crevice which we had not noticed. We had seen a Golden-swamp or Prothonotary Warbler.

"Everyone who has ever watched birds knows full well that certain species are inevitably connected with certain habitats. To me the Prothonotary Warbler has al-

46

ways seemed the very essence of the cypress country. It fits eminently amid the gray-green gloom and dark waters of the cypress lagoons.

"However, any river bottom, lowland swale or willow brake within its range may be home to this exquisite bird, for all such habitats appeal to it. In all of them are the natural cavities, old woodpecker holes, some crack or cranny created by normal decay, which are essential to its nesting requirements."

The Prothonotary Warbler is also at home along the willow dotted streams of Louisiana where I have heard many singing as we drove along their borders. It is found along the lowlands bordering the Mississippi River and is exceedingly abundant in the cypress lagoons at Reelfoot Lake, Tennessee as well as the flooded bottomlands of that area. It is found in the Okefenokee Swamp in Georgia in the shaded flooded areas where its song livens the mornings along with the calls of the Florida Sandhill Crane. It is also found in bottomland woods along many northern rivers in southern Ontario, Michigan, Wisconsin and Minnesota. In Michigan it prefers a sluggish flowing area along a stream 50 to 200 feet in width, where the bottomland is thick with black mud, where maple and ash predominate. Here, deep in the shade they spend their summers, usually one pair remaining within a few hundred feet from where they first appeared in late April or early May until they depart in August. While I have canoed along these streams in June or early July, when mosquitoes were at their worst, the birds have been exceedingly conspicuous. As Sprunt

has written, "It is a low-ranging bird a bit of whose behavior makes observation much easier than with some others of its tribe. Its tameness, too, is quite pronounced. Now and then it clings to, and creeps about the trunks of swampland trees much like a nuthatch. Often it alights on floating bits of debris or aquatic plants, presenting a picture of woodland beauty that is unforgettable. Occasionally, I have been so near the bird that I could have touched it with a boat paddle."

Leaving its winter home from northwestern Ecuador east to northern Colombia, Venezuela, Trinidad and Surinam then north into Panama, Costa Rica, Nicaragua to Campeche and Cozumel Island Mexico the Prothonotary Warbler begins to arrive across the Gulf of Mexico usually in late March or early April, rarely in late February, until the northern part of its range is reached by mid-May. In Michigan the species sometimes arrives during late April when the vanguard of a few males show up singing and battling for territory for several days before the first females arrive.

In winter the species is found in the mangroves, fresh-water swamps and often it has been noted far from water in acacia-like trees near stump land and dry forest. However, it is a bird of streams, pools and stagnant water usually, both winter and summer.

In the summer, territory often appears to include the nesting site primarily. In one bird house I erected at Reelfoot Lake, Tennessee three pairs of Prothonotary Warblers raised young during one summer. The first pair settled on the territory,

brought up their family in May and departed somewhere else for a second brood·
the second pair took over and raised their
brood, then departed, when the third pair
came in and raised their brood. All of these
birds were banded except one of the last
pair. However, usually they remain all
summer on a certain definite territory nesting in many sites, holes, cavities in rotten
wood, etc., even in boat houses, in boxes,
glass jars, pitchers, in mailboxes and in
bird houses. The cypress knees are used in
many southern places.

Protonotaria citrea (Boddaert)
  (Lat., *protonotaria,* chief papal notary, who wears a
  yellow hood; *citrea,* lemon color)

Type Locality Louisiana

OTHER NAMES: Golden-swamp Warbler, Wild Canary,
Yellow Bird (Michigan).

FIELD CHARACTERS: *Male,* head, neck and breast bright
                orange-yellow; back olive-green; rump
and outer edges of wing- and tail-feathers bluish-gray;
under tail coverts and most of inner webs of outer tail
feathers white; bill black.
    Female, usually much duller, less yellow and less
blue-gray.
    Immature, resembles more the female and has some
gray in edgings of feathers (Roberts, *Birds of Minnesota*).
    Length, 5.25 to 5.75 inches.

NESTING: Mainly in cavities, either natural or aban-
          doned woodpecker holes, sometimes
under bridges, in boat houses, often in bird houses if
placed in right places along creeks or over standing
water where shady. I have found 43 nests in Michigan
in natural cavities, 41 in woodpecker holes, preferably
Downy Woodpecker holes. The highest nest was 10.4
meters above ground. Of 84 nests in "natural" locations, 29 were over standing water, 32 along the edge
of running water or over it and the remaining 23
over dry land from .61 to 137.8 meters from water and
usually in easily flooded areas.
    Elevations vary from practically water-level to as
much as 15 or 20 feet (Sprunt) (Hoke).
    Nest constructed of small twigs, moss, lichens, bark,

plant down, skeletonized leaves and in the south
cypress bark, lined with fine grasses or sedges.
    Eggs—3 to 8. Usually 4 to 6. In Michigan I have
found 106 sets of eggs which averaged 5.07 eggs per set
(5 x 3, 21 x 4, 44 x 5, 33 x 6, 3 x 7).
    The eggs are whitish with a slight yellow tinge,
glossy, boldly and liberally spotted and blotched with
"burnt umber," "bay," "chestnut brown," and "auburn," intermingled with spots and undertones of
"light Payne's gray," "Rood's lavender," "violet-gray,"
and "purplish gray." (Harris, Bent, 1953:23)
    Incubation—The incubation periods on marked eggs
was very similar in Tennessee and Michigan. In Tennessee the known incubation period averaged for 19
eggs 12 days and 10 hours varying from 12 to 13½
days. In Michigan 1937-1940, the incubation period
averaged for 64 eggs 12 days and 17 hours (12 to 14
days). The incubation periods of last laid eggs (which
were marked) always came between 12 and just under
14 days. Two broods are raised regularly in Tennessee
and if the first nest is successful in Michigan, attempt
of second brood is usually tried. Young remain in the
nest an average of 10¾ days in Michigan (21 young)
and 11 days at Reelfoot Lake, Tennessee (14 young).

VOICE: Loud and penetrating, "Tweet-tweet-tweet-
           tweet-tweet." An aerial song, much
longer sounds something like "Che-wee—che-wee-chee-
chee, chee-chee-che-wee—che-wee." While giving this
the bird hovers something like a butterfly, after flying
up from surrounding trees. After giving the song the
male again drops into the trees. The regular song is
given from perches (usually in trees) and about 85
per cent of the time in the shade usually less than 50
meters from the nest. One male sang from 9 to 10.6
meters above ground or water. The regular song has
from 7 to 12 tweets and was given at the rate of 7 or
8 songs per minute in the early morning down to one
to four during midday (*cf. Chapter 5*)

NESTING SUCCESS: Of 178 Michigan nests, 50 (28.1 per
                  cent) were successful in that at least one
young left the nest. Of 645 eggs, 262 (40.6 per cent)
hatched and 191 (29.6 per cent) young left the nest
(1937–1948). At Reelfoot Lake, Tennessee 25 of 36 nests
were successful (69.44 per cent) and out of 163 eggs,
100 hatched and all 100 left the nest (61.35 per cent).
Cowbirds parasitize nests where possible. Once I found
a Pilot snake eating the young in one nest. The House
Wren in southern Michigan takes over many nests
throwing out the eggs, young and nests. Other small
mammals and predatory birds which prey on small
birds are capable of doing so on this species.

FOOD HABITS: Chiefly insectivorous. In one stomach
              from a specimen taken October 31, 1915

at Sosa Hill, Panama, Thomas Hallihan (*Auk,* 41, 1924:324) found small seeds, insects and two small Lepidoptera. In Tennessee insects are carried to the young continuously as are they in Michigan—may-flies and many juicy larvae.

PARENTS: The female incubates the eggs and broods the young. She does most of the nest-building. The male often begins the first nest in the spring, occasionally feeds the female on the nest and assists in feeding the young after they hatch. After the young leave the nest he does much of the feeding.

POPULATION STUDIES: In one bottomland area studied by myself in southern Michigan there were around 14 pairs on an area of 88 acres with an average size of territory of 3.66 acres much of which was not used. Smallest territories were 1.9 acres. Males tried invariably to return to close proximity to their previous years' nest area. Females came back less often, 50 per cent of males returned the second year; 22.2 per cent the third year; 11.1 per cent the fourth and 11.1 per cent the fifth. None exceeded this date.

In Tennessee a greater density occurred in number of pairs in certain areas along Reelfoot Lake and pairs changed territories as evidenced by the using of one bird house by three banded pairs during one summer.

MIGRATION: From the north in fall across eastern United States, across the Gulf of Mexico to Yucatan south to Venezuela and Colombia, and return in the spring. Departure begins in Colombia in February (Bent, 1953:29) through March and early April across Yucatán, Cuba and the Gulf. Some arrive in Florida by March 18, in southern Mississippi (same date) and in southern Michigan they are sometimes found the last few days of April up to the 15th of May. Departure southward begins in July and by mid-August it usually is almost impossible to find any

Prothonotary Warblers in Michigan. A few have been found into the first week of September.

GENERAL RANGE: *Breeds* in Eastern United States, from central Florida, southern Louisiana through the Mississippi valley and Atlantic states to southern Ontario, central Michigan, Wisconsin, southern Minnesota, Iowa, eastern Nebraska and Kansas to Missouri, Arkansas, through eastern Oklahoma to southeastern Texas. *Winters* in Central America and northwestern South America: Costa Rica, Nicaragua, Venezuela, Colombia, northwestern Ecuador, Trinidad.

LAWRENCE H. WALKINSHAW

3

SWAINSON'S WARBLER

Limnothlypis swainsonii

To paraphrase an immortal poem could one say—Oh, warbler, shall I call thee bird, or but a wandering voice? Surely no lines ever written could so epitomize this little known, elusive dweller in the deep shades of southern river swamps and mountain ravines. Discovered by the Rev. John Bachman near Charleston, South Carolina, in 1832 and named by Audubon, it remained "lost" to science for nearly forty years. Although reported many times since its discovery few details of its life history have been made known.

Swainson's Warbler, like certain other rare or localized members of this family, is not a bird of bright plumage. Quite the reverse is true and it aptly deserves the description of an obscure "little brown bird". This lack of distinctive markings together with the type of habitat it frequents, has rendered it one of the more unfamiliar warblers to many bird students, even those residing within its range.

The flood plain swamps of the rivers of the southeastern states constitute the summer home of the greater portion of these warblers. These swamps which are subject to periodic flooding are composed of fairly large trees with a dense under-story of cane, briars, vines, scrub palmetto, herbaceous plants and young trees of the next succession. Amid the sometimes eerie gloom of such swamps this unobtrusive bird lives close to the ground, flitting here and there like a tiny, dark phantom—here one moment, gone the next. If one is fortunate it may flush from the ground to perch on a nearby twig above the surrounding growth and sit there perfectly motionless, like a miniature thrush. Then the observer will see the whitish line over the eye and note the lack of wing bars, as well as contrast the brownish back with the dull white underbody. Suddenly the twig is empty, the little brown ghost has gone; but, ringing out in startling sweetness among the shadows, comes a burst of melody which echoes in one's mind long after the notes have ceased.

In spring, the Swainson's usually arrive on the breeding grounds from their little known winter home the first week in April. Though to be looked for in suitable swamps, they may be seen during migration in the most unlikely places, a plantation garden or suburban yard, a brushy field edge or roadside ditch. One of the strangest places we ever saw one was the open parade ground of old Fort Jefferson on the Dry Tortugas. Flitting about in a portia tree, it fed actively and at close range permitted observation of every detail of its plumage.

The males are the first to arrive in the spring usually preceding the females by about ten days. On arriving they establish territories in the vicinity of those occupied the previous year. From singing posts varying in height from ground level to twenty or more feet they proclaim possession of their territories by repeatedly giving forth their remarkable song. Rather regular and frequent singing continues until the hatching of the eggs. After that singing is sporadic up to the middle of July when it ceases altogether with the beginning of the postnuptial molt. Occasional songs may be heard in the fall following the molt.

The territory defended by the male is used primarily for mating and feeding and not for nesting. The nest itself is usually located along the margin of the territory but may be entirely outside it, thus making its discovery more difficult. Territories are usually adjacent in suitable habitat and less than an acre in size. Four measured in Georgia ranged from .72 to .91 acres.

Mating having occurred the nest site is selected by the female. Characteristically she selects a mass of last winter's leaves caught in the "head" of a cane (*Arundinaria.*), or a windfall of Spanish moss lying across a cane, or small bush, as a foundation on which to build. The finished nests, never at any great elevation, are quite bulky and loosely constructed but well camouflaged. Nests have been found in Florida which were placed on the broad surface of fronds of the scrub palmetto (*Sabal eatonia*) overhung by others. Again, nests have been found in blackberry tangles and masses of vines in areas where neither cane nor palmetto was present. Anyone who searches for a nest must be prepared for rough going, wet and muddy clothes, and the definite possibility of encountering such undesirable swamp dwellers as the cotton-mouth moccasin, to say nothing of mosquitoes and their ilk.

The nest is constructed entirely by the female from materials gathered from the swamp floor in the immediate vicinity. Upon completion, the three, rarely four, eggs are laid on successive days and incubation begins with the laying of the last one. Without help from the male she incubates the eggs the necessary 14 to 15 days, often sitting continuously for periods of one and a half to two hours. Both parents then share equally in feeding the young which

John H. Dick
'55

John H. Dick
'55

remain in the nest 12 or more days. After their departure the young may be seen following the parents for two or three weeks still begging for food. As summer fades into autumn the Swainson's gradually disappear from their nesting haunts, there being a noticeable decrease in numbers by September 15 with practically all of them gone by October 1.

ALEXANDER SPRUNT JR., AND
J. FRED DENTON

[*Comment:* Since the early days of American ornithology this little-known warbler has been considered a resident of the cane brakes and coastal swamps of the deep South. However, recent discoveries are forcing us to re-orient our thinking as to the species.

Within recent years observers have learned that the bird also occupies a considerable area of the southern highlands in Tennessee, North Carolina, Virginia, and West Virginia. It nests at altitudes up to 3000 feet or more, and chooses sites that are tangles of rhododendron, mountain laurel, hemlock, and American holly. So far as is known, there are no connecting populations between the coastal or river swamps and the mountains. A more perfect set of conditions for racial separation could scarcely be asked for. We have regarded Swainson's Warbler as a stable species which has not undergone any racial differentiation. However, we have no idea how long this mountain population has occupied its present range. If this be a comparatively recent extension, then we may be witnessing a case where behavior change precedes morphological modification.

In an account of the birds of a region in northwestern Florida, Worthington and Todd 1926) wrote (*Wilson Bull.,* 33): "Its (Swainson's Warbler's) favorite haunts are the dense thickets on the edge of the lowland woods, where it contrives to keep so well concealed that were it not for its characteristic song its presence would go unsuspected. It is fond also of rank fern growth, where it is equally successful in eluding observation and capture. Only once did we find it in the dry upland, among the thick scrub oaks. The birds spend most of their time on the ground among the dry leaves, walking along gracefully, like the Ovenbird, and uttering their song at frequent intervals." With the necessary allowances made for differences in the topography of the two areas, this would make a very satisfactory description of the habits of the bird as we observed them in West Virginia. Even the fondness for dense fern growths is notable.

We found the birds difficult to observe, and extraordinarily difficult to collect in their favorite haunts. So dense are the shadows under rhododendron and hemlock thickets that only the closest observation revealed the movement of the birds. With their rather neutral brown coloration, their rapid movements, and their apparent liking for the centers of the thickets, they seemed to blend imperceptibly into their surroundings. Often enough when we were very close and would catch a glimpse of them in the tangles before us, they would fly without our catching the movement at all. Every time an attempt was made to follow the birds through the thickets they would fly, sometimes to a considerable distance, before we could see them. 'Squeaking' would bring them fairly close, usually much too close to make shooting feasible. The only good observations we made were from the edges of clearings, or from roads or trails.

Almost everyone who has written of the haunts of Swainson's Warblers has quoted the statement of Brewster (1885): "Briefly, four things seem indispensable to its existence, *viz.,* water, tangled thickets, patches of cane, and a rank growth of semi-aquatic plants." From the account given above, it will be evident that of these four only the first two are present in the West Virginia situations which the birds select, and that even water is scant or wanting in some cases. (MAURICE BROOKS)]

Limnothlypis swainsonii (Audubon)
(Gr., *Limnothlypis,* a marsh finch; Lat., *swainsonii,* for William Swainson)

Type Locality South Carolina

FIELD CHARACTERS: Top of head olive brown; upperparts and rump olive, a whitish line over eye; underparts buffy white, tinged with olive-gray on the sides. No eye-ring or wing-bars.
Length, 5.00 to 6.50 inches.

NESTING DATA: Often in stands of swamp cane, sometimes in low bushes or vines, or atop fronds of palmetto. Frequently, though not always near water at elevations of from 2 to 10 feet.

Nest very large for size of bird, made of leaves and lined with pine needles or moss. The leaves are arranged with the stems upward the result being an apparent mass of trash lodged in the surrounding vegetation.

Eggs—3 usually, 4 rarely. Cream or bluish white, with very little gloss. Generally unmarked.

VOICE: [The comparison of the song of this species with that of the Waterthrush or the Louisiana Waterthrush is an oft-made, and, to our ears, an apt one in many respects. Certainly the same quality is present, and the beginnings of the songs are sufficiently alike to suggest immediately a similarity. We are convinced that it would be very easy to pass the song by, believing that we were listening to

the somewhat unusual notes of a Louisiana Waterthrush, or even a Northern Waterthrush. In fact, Brooks and Lunk heard one series of songs from a bird (which sang at other times in a more usual fashion) that sounded almost precisely like a Waterthrush.

The song most frequently given by the birds we heard appeared, to the senior author at least, to consist of three or four sharp, high introductory notes, all well separated, followed by a phrase of four or five syllables uttered rapidly, and slurred. It might be transliterated as *whee, whee, whee, whip-poor-will,* the first two (or three) introductory notes on even pitch, the last *whee* a half-tone lower, and the slurred phrase with *will* separated into two syllables, and accented on the *whip* and on the *wi-* part of the *will.* The last phrase sounded at times remarkably like one of the songs of the White-eyed Vireo. (MAURICE BROOKS)] (*See Chapter 5*)

FOOD HABITS: Mostly an insectivorous-spider diet.

GENERAL RANGE: *Breeds* locally in northeast Oklahoma, Missouri, Illinois, Ohio, Maryland and central West Virginia south to Arkansas, Mississippi, southern Louisiana and northern Florida. Also in many parts of Alleghenies. *Winters* in Cuba, Jamaica, Yucatan and British Honduras.
ALEXANDER SPRUNT, JR.

4

WORM-EATING WARBLER

Helmitheros vermivorus

THIS warbler which, as Bent (1953) points out, was "poorly understood by the early writers on American birds . . ." might well be designated as still unfamiliar to many present-day bird watchers. It is certainly one of the lesser known warblers and as Chapman says "is far too inconspicuous to force itself on our attention and its presence is usually detected only by the watchful."

The name of this species was an unfortunate choice. No more partial to "worms" than many others of its kin, despite the common and scientific names, it does show characteristics which have led some students of it to conclude that Hillside Warbler would be a far better name. It frequents wooded hillsides and ravines, where medium sized stands of deciduous trees and undergrowth occur. Water is an added attraction and small streams and swampy bogs rimmed by tangles of bushes and vines attract the bird strongly.

Though securing some of its food in trees, the Worm-eating Warbler is largely terrestrial and is a *walker*. While not indulging the hurried, nervous movements of many of its family, it keeps steadily about its search for food and way of life, deliberate always without being lethargic. Its plumage blends well with its chosen haunts and its habit of walking might lead one to mistake it for an Ovenbird at first glance. However, any detailed observation will reveal the conspicuously striped head which is the bird's outstanding field characteristic. Further, the breast is not spotted like that of the Ovenbird, being plainly a uniform buffy-white.

Occasionally this warbler feeds like a

Black-and-White, circling the trunk or limb of a tree in a creeping manner, but more often walks about over logs and leaves of the forest floor, the tail carried at an angle above the back line. Nesting on the ground as it does, it is open to the depredation of small rodents such as squirrels, mice, weasels and the like, as well as snakes. It is not often victimized by the Cowbird, though such does occur at times. It is a very close sitter at the nest. Franklin L. Burns reports as follows in Bent: "I searched for 10 seasons before I found my first nest, and oddly enough it was through the parent bird carrying a 'worm' to its young; nevertheless I have since thought that a more fitting name for the species would have been Hillside or Laurel Warbler. . . . The nest, well hidden under a drift of dead forest leaves, never varied in composition in over a hundred examples examined by me, in partly skeletonized leaves and the characteristic reddish-brown lining of the flower stem of the hair moss. . . . One brood is all that is reared in a season, I think."

The spring migration is partially across the Gulf of Mexico from Yucatán and it occurs regularly along the Texas coast and uncommonly in Florida, arriving at both these points on approximately the same dates. It is uncommon on the Tortugas, those tiny islands west of Key West which are so indicative of migratory routes; most of these warblers pass to the westward. In former years the species figured extensively in losses at lighthouses during migration, the ratio being larger north of central Florida than in the southern region.

Helmitheros vermivorus (Gmelin)
(Gr., *Helmitheros,* worm-hunter; Lat., *vermivorus,* worm-eating)

Type Locality Philadelphia, Pa.

FIELD CHARACTERS: A wide stripe of olive-buff in center of crown, bordered on sides with stripes of blackish, a similar one through the eye. Upperparts olive-green; underparts buffy-white. Sexes alike. *Length,* 5.00 to 5.75 inches.

NESTING DATA: On the ground, usually on hillsides or banks of ravines, concealed under dead leaves at the base of a sapling, roots of larger trees, in cavities of banks or under shrubbery. Constructed of decayed or skeletonized leaves, lined with the reddish flower stems of hair moss, or fine grass and horsehair.
Eggs—3 to 6, usually 4. White, speckled with shades of brown and drab, sparingly or profusely, often with markings wreathed about the large end. Some eggs are immaculate.

VOICE: A monotonous simple trill, (che-e-e-e-e-e) usually on the same pitch and almost exactly like that of a Chipping Sparrow. Call-note resembles the word "chip." A flight song has been noted uncommonly, more musical than the ordinary delivery

John H. Dick
'55

John H. Dick
'55

PLATE 5
COLIMA WARBLER
Page 88

Adult

VIRGINIA'S WARBLER
Page 85

Adult

LUCY'S WARBLER
Page 93

Adult

Lucy's Immature

and somewhat varied. It is given below tree-top level. (*See chapter 5*)

FOOD HABITS: Largely insectivorous. Earth-worms do not figure to any extent. Grasshoppers, caterpillars, beetles and spiders are taken.

GENERAL RANGE: *Breeds* from northeastern Kansas, southeastern Iowa, northern Illinois, southern Indiana, southern and central eastern Ohio, southwestern and central Pennsylvania, central and southeastern New York, southern Connecticut, and western Massachusetts south to northeastern Texas, central Arkansas, central southern Louisiana, western Tennessee, northern Alabama, northern Georgia, northwestern South Carolina, and northeastern North Carolina. *Winters* from southern Florida and eastern Mexico to Panama, Bahamas and Greater Antilles.

ALEXANDER SPRUNT, JR.

5

GOLDEN-WINGED WARBLER

Vermivora chrysoptera

THE sprightly Golden-wing, with its black bib, its habit of swinging from branches and hanging upside down, suggests the chickadee. But that impression is fleeting, so distinctive is its flashing crown of gold, its trim mantle of pearl-gray, and its yellow wing-patch. The Golden-winged Warbler is easily recognized at any season.

To make the acquaintance of this charming little bird we must seek it in overgrown pastures, on hillsides with dense scrubby thickets, or along briar-grown borders of swampy deciduous woodlands. We find it busily gleaning insects from the ground to the tree-tops, but it is generally found in the lower tree levels. In the central Alle· gheny Mountains, however, Maurice Brooks found the Golden-wing a characteristic bird in high, dry areas of chestnut sprout, and in scrub pine.

In such haunts we should have no trouble locating a singing male. Mounting to a favorite perch, usually a high, bare branch, he sings persistently from the time of his arrival in May, until well into June. With upturned head, his bill pointing toward the zenith, he delivers his simple, insect-like song, a series of 4 or 5 drawling buzz notes, the first note higher and more prolonged than the others. A second song, lacking the buzzing character, is described by Winsor M. Tyler as follows: ". . . about a half dozen short notes given in a quick series on the same pitch, and ends with one long note on a higher key, *th-th-th-th-th-th-theee.*"

The Golden-winged Warbler builds its nest on the ground. Though coarse and bulky, and loosely-constructed of grasses, leaves and strips of grapevine bark, the nest is nevertheless artfully concealed against clusters of goldenrod or other sturdy weeds which provide the nest with support. The female incubates her 4 or 5 eggs for ten or eleven days. Both parents attend to the feeding of the young. Ten days after hatching the young leave the nest.

The Golden-wing winters mainly in Central America. It migrates across the Gulf of Mexico, avoiding Florida and southern Georgia, where it is very rare. It then moves northward, mainly east of the Mississippi, to its summer haunts. We are not apt to see conspicuous numbers of Golden-wings during the great warbler waves of spring, hence it is a red-letter day if we have the good fortune to 'mark up' several of these birds. Again in the fall it is generally overlooked, probably because of its early departure south. Yet the Golden-wing is a locally common species in its summer range.

Vermivora chrysoptera (Linnaeus)
   (Lat., *Vermivora*, worm-eating; Gr., *chrysoptera*, golden-winged).

Type Locality Philadelphia, Pa.

FIELD CHARACTERS: *Male,* forehead and crown bright yellow, bordered by a white line over the eye; throat and sides of head black, with a broad white streak on each side of throat; underparts dull white; upperparts slate-gray; wings slate-gray with conspicuous yellow patch. (The only warbler that combines a blue-gray back and yellow in the wing).
   Female, similar to male but crown and upperparts duller; throat and sides of head gray.
   Immature, similar to adults of respective sexes.
   Length, 5.00 to 5.30 inches.

NESTING DATA: On or close to ground, usually supported by ferns or weed stalks, made of leaves, grasses, grape tendrils, shreds of grape bark, and lined with a few hairs or fine grasses.
   Eggs—4 to 6; white, with brownish speckling about larger end.

VOICE: A simple, insect-like buzz: *zeee-bzzz-bzzz-bzzz-bzzz.* When excited, "a chattering *tchu-tchu-tchu*" (Winsor M. Tyler) (*See Chapter 5*)

FOOD HABITS: Probably entirely insects; minute bugs and larvae, canker-worms, spiders.

GENERAL RANGE: *Breeds* from southeastern Manitoba, central Minnesota, southeastern Ontario, central New York and southern Vermont, and Massachusetts south to southern Iowa, northern Illinois, northern Indiana, northern New Jersey, eastern Tennessee, and in the mountains to northern Georgia.
   Winters from Guatemala south to Colombia and Venezuela.

MAURICE BROUN

6

BLUE-WINGED WARBLER

Vermivora pinus

THE specific name *pinus* is a misnomer, for this warbler is not associated with pine trees; the *pinus* is derived from the "Pine Creeper," the name by which the Blue-wing was known to those early historians of American ornithology, Mark Catesby and George Edwards.

Although a bird of bright plumage, the Blue-wing is a rather unobtrusive warbler, even when singing from some favorite, exposed perch. It moves quietly, deliberately, and fairly near the ground. In its nesting too, the Blue-wing is retiring. Only the most diligent search, or accident, will reveal the deep, cup-shaped nest, built of leaves and grasses and well concealed upon the ground among coarse plants. The "song" is unlike that of any other warbler, except possibly that of the Golden-wing, being hardly more than a weak, wheezy,

insect-like buzz delivered in two parts.

Both the Blue-wing and the Golden-wing have much in common: they exhibit similar behavior, their nesting habits are identical, and they occupy much the same habitats. Like the Golden-wing, this species haunts old pastures and upland clearings, but it is equally at home along the bushy borders of low, swampy woods.

The Blue-wing bears no color resemblance to the Golden-wing, yet the two species are obviously very closely related; they are the best known examples of wild birds that interbreed. Wherever the ranges of the two species overlap, with consequent interbreeding, fertile hybrid descendants are produced: the Brewster's Warbler and the Lawrence's Warbler.

The Blue-wing winters in Central America and migrates across the Gulf of Mexico.

61

It migrates mainly through the Mississippi Valley, and occurs very rarely in the Southeast south of Virginia. Breeding chiefly in the Central States, the bird has spread northeastward to the lowlands of eastern Massachusetts in recent decades.

The phenomenon of anting is almost unknown among the wood warblers. Mrs. Eleanor E. Dater (*Auk,* 70: 89, 1953) has described in detail an instance of the Blue-wing anting, at Ramsey, New Jersey.

Vermivora pinus (Linnaeus)
(Lat., *pinus,* a pine)

Type Locality Philadelphia, Pa.

FIELD CHARACTERS: *Male,* crown and underparts lemon-yellow; a black line through the eye; upperparts bright olive-green; wings gray or blue-gray with two prominent white (sometimes yellowish) wing-bars; tail gray with large white patches on inner webs.

Female, similar to male but duller.

Immature, closely resembles the adults.

Length, 4.50 to 5.00 inches.

NESTING DATA: On the ground, among bushes or tufts of grass or ferns, in overgrown fields or woodland borders, built of leaves and grasses, strips of wild grape bark and lined with bark fibers and hair, firmly wrapped with leaves.

Eggs—4 or 5, rarely 6; white, thinly speckled with rufous, lavender or purplish.

VOICE: Two long, buzzy notes, the second usually lower in pitch than the first and rougher, *bzzzzzz—brrrrrr* (Aretas A. Saunders). This has been rendered as *beee* buzz (inhale and exhale). A less com-

mon song: *wee, chi-chi-chi-chi, chur, chee-chur* (F. M. Chapman). (*See Chapter 5*)

FOOD HABITS: Small beetles, ants, spiders, caterpillars.

GENERAL RANGE: *Breeds* from central eastern Nebraska, central Iowa, southeastern Minnesota, southern Wisconsin, southern Michigan, northern Ohio, northwestern Pennsylvania, western and southeastern New York, and southeastern Massachusetts south to northwestern Arkansas, central eastern Missouri, southern Illinois, central Tennessee, northern Alabama, northern Georgia, North Carolina, northern Virginia, central and northeastern Maryland, and Delaware. *Winters* from southern Mexico to Guatemala, and Nicaragua and casually to Panama and Colombia; also western Cuba.

MAURICE BROUN

7

BREWSTER'S WARBLER

Vermivora chrysoptera x pinus

PROBABLY no other North American birds have excited so much speculation as the Brewster's and the Lawrence's Warblers—the fertile hybrid offspring of the Golden-winged and the Blue-winged Warblers.

The type specimen of this warbler was taken by William Brewster in 1870, and in 1874 it was described by him as a new species. As more examples of this bird and the Lawrence's Warbler came to light, they provided a guessing game for various writers, some of whom maintained that they were color phases or atavistic forms of the Golden-wing. Other theories accounted for the birds as "incipient species," or mutants. Ornithologists puzzled over the status of the hybrids for nearly two generations.

Brewster, as early as 1881, had decided that the controversial warblers were hybrids between the Golden-wing and the Blue-wing. His belief was based on the fact that the hybrids occurred within a breeding area occupied by the parent species; that the characters of the hybrids were obviously borrowed from the supposed parent forms; and that complete stages of intergradation connecting the Brewster's and the Blue-wing indicated their affinity. Brewster's convictions ultimately proved to be correct.

In 1908, J. T. Nichols, taking for granted the hybrid parentage of the Brewster's and Lawrence's Warblers, found that their existence and relative abundance was in accord with Mendelian Laws. Thus, briefly, when typical Blue-wing mates with typical Golden-wing, the result should be a homogeneous brood of Brewster's, the Mendelian dominants (white-breasted

PLATE 6
TENNESSEE WARBLER
Page 75

NASHVILLE WARBLER
Page 81

Fall Plumage

Immature

Adult Male

Adult

EASTERN ORANGE-CROWNED WARBLER
Page 78

Adult

LUTESCENT WARBLER
Page 80

Immature

John H. Dick

birds); when impure Blue-wing is mated with typical Golden-wing, the offspring should be Golden-wing and Brewster's in equal numbers. Typical Blue-wing when paired with impure Golden-wing should produce Blue-wing and Brewster's in equal numbers; while a mixed impure parentage of Blue-winged and Golden-winged warblers should yield equal numbers of Blue-wing, Golden-wing, Brewster's and Lawrence's. The last named bird manifests recessive characters, hence its greater rarity.

This explanation satisfactorily accounted for the difficult question: how could a black-throated bird, mated with a yellow-throated bird, produce white-throated progeny? Genetically, the Brewster's Warbler has a plain throat because this feature is dominant over a black throat, and white underparts are dominant over yellow underparts.

Studies of the breeding of these warblers suggest that hybrids do not breed with hybrids, but only with one of the parental forms. In 1910, in a swamp in Lexington, Massachusetts, Walter Faxon found two female Brewster's Warblers, each mated to a male Golden-wing. More recently, in Passaic County, New Jersey, T. Donald Carter studied a banded male Brewster's Warbler for six seasons. During five of these seasons the bird was mated with a female Golden-wing.

Note: For a more detailed presentation of the significant facts in the interesting histories of the two hybrids, see the accounts in Forbush's *Birds of Massachusetts and Other New England States,* vol. 3. Also, Kenneth C. Parkes' "The Genetics of the Golden-winged x Blue-winged Warbler Complex," (*Wilson Bull.,* vol. 63, pp. 5–15).

Vermivora leucobronchialis (Brewster)
(Gr., *leucobronchialis,* white-throated)

Type Locality Newtonville, Mass.

FIELD CHARACTERS: *Male,* forehead and crown bright yellow; a black line from bill through the eye; upper plumage bluish-gray; wings gray tinged olive-green, with conspicuous white or yellow patch; tail bluish-gray with white patches on inner webs; underparts white, the breast often tinged with yellow.
Female, similar to male but duller.
Remarks: In general resembles the Blue-winged Warbler with *whitish underparts;* or the Golden-winged Warbler but *without the black throat.* Every degree of variation exists between the Brewster's and the Blue-wing. Most individuals tend to approach the Blue-wing but may have the underparts extensively tinged with yellow, especially on the breast. The wing patches are variable, being almost white in some birds.

VOICE: Similar to the Golden-wing or the Blue-wing.

GENERAL RANGE: In migration the Brewster's Warbler has been found in widely scattered localities from Louisiana and southeastern Oklahoma, northward to Wisconsin and Massachusetts. Its breeding range coincides with the northern part of the range of the Blue-winged Warbler, but its center of distribution is in the lower reaches of the Connecticut and Hudson River valleys, where heavy interbreeding of the parental forms occurs. *In winter* specimens have been taken in Costa Rica and Venezuela. (*See Chapter 14*)

MAURICE BROUN

8

LAWRENCE'S WARBLER

Vermivora chrysoptera x pinus

THE history of the Lawrence's Warbler dates to 1874, when a specimen was collected on the Passaic River, near Chatham, New Jersey. It was described as a distinct species by Harold Herrick. Since no definite knowledge of the bird's history was forthcoming, its validity as a species was questioned and, together with the Brewster's Warbler it became the subject of much theorizing and speculation. With the revelations of their hybrid status in 1908 these birds were dropped from the Check-list of the American Ornithologists' Union.

Lawrence's Warbler is a much rarer bird than Brewster's. It could hardly be expected to have any distinctive features of its own for it is essentially a Blue-winged warbler, with similar nesting habits, haunts, and song. It associates with both parent species, and has so far been found mated only with the Blue-winged Warbler; there is no record of a pair of Lawrence's Warblers mating together. The first knowledge of its home life was obtained in 1904, when a male mated with a female Blue-winged Warbler in the New York Zoological Park, producing "six vigorous young birds" which, according to C. W. Beebe, were in typical nestling plumage of the Blue-winged Warbler.

Vermivora lawrencei (Herrick)
    (Lat., *lawrencei,* after George N. Lawrence)

Type Locality near Chatham, N.J.

FIELD CHARACTERS: *Male,* forehead and forepart of crown bright yellow; chin, wide cheek stripe and lower parts of body, yellow; under tail coverts white; lores, region below the eye and ear coverts, black; throat and upper breast black; upperparts bright olive-green; wings bluish-gray, with two conspicuous white wing bars; tail bluish-gray, the three or four outer feathers marked with white.

Female, similar, but forehead dull yellow; wing bars white tinged with yellow; black patches of the male replaced by dusky olive-green or gray-green.

Remarks: A Blue-winged Warbler, wearing the characteristic black or dusky throat and head markings of the Golden-winged Warbler. The majority of Lawrence's Warblers conform to the above description, but intergrades occur which may bear closer resemblance to either the Golden-winged or the Blue-winged Warbler.

Voice: Similar to the Golden-winged or the Blue-winged Warbler. "Has three to five clos-ing notes dropping always at the last notes" (C. de Windt).

General Range: Examples of this vary rare hybrid have been found in Ohio, eastern Pennsylvania, northern New Jersey, southeastern New York and Connecticut. It may be anticipated wherever the parental forms co-exist. In migration, recorded south to Louisiana.

Maurice Broun

[*Comment:* Lawrence's Warbler has recently been reliably reported from Florida, three records from widely separated points (A. S., Jr.)]

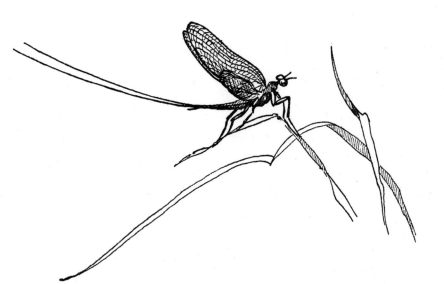

9

BACHMAN'S WARBLER

Vermivora bachmanii

THIS rarest of American warblers remains an unattained goal to many bird-students today. Though there are a good many records of its appearance over the years since its re-discovery, the species seems to be dropping off again recently and if there is one adjective which applies to it more than any other, it is—unpredictable.

The history of this warbler closely parallels that of Swainson's Warbler. Both were discovered by the Rev. John Bachman (a year apart) near Charleston, South Carolina (1832–1833). Both were described by Audubon and both became "lost species" for the ensuing half century. Both frequent heavily timbered swamps where water abounds; both are partial to the growth of cane (*Arundinaria tecta*). However, Swainson's Warbler is now far better known than Bachman's. Since I am one of the favored few to have seen Bachman's (in the same swamp where it was originally discovered), I can say at once that it is the hardest bird to see, even when constantly giving its song, of any of the avian tribe I have looked for.

Though the general range of this warbler is rather extensive, it is a highly local species, astonishingly so in fact, and it has been found nesting in but five states (Missouri, Arkansas, Kentucky, Alabama and South Carolina). South Carolina, originally the type locality, still figures in current history as the state where recent observations have been made more frequently. Arthur T. Wayne found the first nest in South Carolina in April of 1906, 73 years after Bachman had discovered the bird. Six nests were found that year and two in 1907. One each was discovered in 1916 and 1918 and *none since!* Three birds were noted in the

John H. Dick
'55

PLATE 7
PARULA WARBLER
Page 97

Female

Male

YELLOW-THROATED WARBLER
Page 156

Male

Female

years of 1938, 1946 and 1947. From 1948 through 1953 inclusive, Bachman's Warbler appeared every spring in the same swamp where it was originally discovered but though seen by numerous observers during that period, no nest was found.

The year 1954 went by with no appearance but a male was seen and heard in another locality in 1955. During the spring of 1955, a specimen appeared along the Potomac River near Washington, causing a veritable sensation among bird-watchers of that area. Such is the recent history of this remarkable species.

Some of the reasons why Bachman's Warbler is so hard to find are:

The character of the habitat (heavy swamps and dense foliage)
Abundance of insects (mosquitoes, ticks, chiggers, etc.)
Presence of venomous snakes (rattlesnakes and water moccasins)
The very small size of the bird, its quiet habits and ventriloquial song
Its utter unpredictability of occurrence.

I have spent as much as from two to three hours in swampy woods with a male singing ten times a minute at very close range and failed to get a glimpse of it. Response to the 'squeak' is the only reason I was ever successful. Most of the observations of this warbler have been while on migration.

The song has been compared to that of the Parula and Worm-eating Warblers plus the Chipping Sparrow. To my mind it is very like the Parula's. Delivered with great regularity (about every six seconds), it is definitely ventriloquial, this probably because the bird turns its head frequently while singing, and the body as well, so that directions from which it seems to be coming vary widely. Usually a high-ranging warbler, it nests as low as three feet and often feeds at between twenty and forty feet from the ground.

It is an early migrant, some of Wayne's nests were found in late March, which means that building must have been in progress about the middle of that month. Its spring route is north from Cuba over the Gulf, or along the west coast of Florida, as it reaches Louisiana and Florida at about the same time (late February to early March). Fanning out toward the Mississippi Valley, some birds proceed to Missouri and Kentucky while others veer eastward to reach South Carolina.

There is a correspondingly early departure, South Carolina birds disappearing by mid or late July. Rare instances of winter birds in southeastern U.S., are known (Okefenokee Swamp, Georgia, December 30, 1928 and Melbourne, Florida, January 27, 1898). Despite the fact that many migrational records have emanated from the Florida Keys, there is but one from the Dry Tortugas, where W. E. D. Scott recorded it in 1890. This indicates (only) that Bachman's Warbler crosses directly north from Cuba toward the central and western portions of the Keys with the boundary being Key West, then proceeding up and along Florida's west coast.

Certain names are as inevitably connected with this warbler as are the few known nesting sites. *Charles G. Galbraith* in 1886 secured the first specimen in the U.S., 53 years after Bachman discovered the bird.

[*Comment:* Galbraith was a professional plume collector who shot 38 of them in the springs of 1886, 1887 and 1888 and still others in 1891, all on dates between February 27 and March 20, and all in the vicinity of Mandeville on Lake Ponchartrain. The species must then have been exceedingly abundant for him to have obtained so many specimens of it. At about the same time it was plentiful, at least in migration, in southern Florida, where on March 3, 1889, alone, 21 birds struck the lighthouse on Sombrero Key. Since the time of Galbraith there have been fewer than a dozen records for Louisiana, despite an intensive search for it. (GEORGE H. LOWERY, JR.)]

Arthur T. Wayne in 1901 secured the first bird in South Carolina 63 years after Bachman collected his. Wayne also found the only nests in South Carolina and more than anyone else anywhere, the number being nine. [Wayne too collected many specimens, 50 on an 1892 Suwanee River trip and 8 more in 1894 along the Wacissa and Ancilla Rivers. He was convinced that the bird raises only one brood a season. (I. R. B.)] *Otto Widmann* found the first nest and eggs known to science in May of 1897 in Dunkin County, Missouri. *George C. Embody* found the nest in Kentucky in 1906 and *Ernest G. Holt* discovered the Alabama nest in Autauga County in 1920.

Though this warbler has been seen in its summer range on several occasions in recent years I know of no nest having been found since Holt's Alabama one. Thus, well over a generation has passed since anyone has discovered the home of this unpredictable bird.

Vermivora bachmanii (Audubon)
(Lat., *bachmani,* for John Bachman)

Type Locality near Charleston, S.C.

FIELD CHARACTERS: *Male,* forehead, chin and eye-ring yellow; forepart of crown black, bordered with gray; back of head and neck gray; upperparts olive-green; a black patch on chest. Wings and tail gray, latter with white tip markings on outer tail feathers.
Female, similar but lacking black on head and chest (except occasionally).
Length, 4.25 to 4.50 inches.

NESTING DATA: At low elevations (2 to 5 ft.) in bushes, vines or canes according to locality, sometimes on palmetto leaves. Nest of grasses and leaves, the latter skeletonized at times, moss and weed-stalks, lined with black fibers of *Ramalina* lichen. Missouri and South Carolina nests show same material.
Eggs—3 to 4. Pure white and usually glossy. Of the eggs thus far found only one was spotted (Holt's Alabama nest). It had a dozen minute dots of light brown mostly about the large end. Measurements average .63 x .49 inches.

VOICE: Song wiry and insect-like, strongly suggesting a "listless" Parula Warbler. Delivered about 10 times per minute seemingly from varied directions and resulting in a ventriloquial character. Exceedingly difficult to locate bird by. (*See Chapter 5 and comment below*)

FOOD HABITS: Little known but probably mainly insects. Remains of caterpillars and ants were found in stomachs of Alabama birds (Howell, 1924).

GENERAL RANGE: *Breeds* (probably) from southeastern Missouri and Kentucky, south to central Alabama and southeastern South Carolina. Has been recorded during breeding season from western Arkansas, Missouri, northern Kentucky, Virginia and North Carolina, south to Louisiana, Mississippi and southern Alabama. *Winters* in Cuba and on the Isle of Pines.
ALEXANDER SPRUNT, JR.

THE BACHMAN'S SONG *

The spirited singing of the Bachman's Warbler is remarkable even for a bird known to be a relatively continuous

* An interesting discussion of the Bachman's Warbler, from which the following is taken, appeared in the *Atlantic Naturalist,* Sept.–Oct. 1954.

singer. The typical song has been variously compared to that of the Parula and Blue-winged Warblers, the Chipping Sparrow, and the Worm-eating Warbler. Aretas A. Saunders describes the one definite record which he had as a short trill all on one pitch, *threeeeeeeeee,* and compared it especially with the first note of the song of the Blue-winged Warbler. However, he noted that this bird, like others of its genus, presumably had a second song of greater variety.

Brewster wrote of the singing:

"The song is unlike that of any other species of *Helminthophila* with which I am acquainted and most resembles the song of the Parula Warbler. It is of the same length and of nearly the same quality or tone, but less guttural and without the upward run at the end, all of its six or eight notes being given in the same key and with equal emphasis. Despite these differences, it would be possible to mistake the performance, especially at a distance, for that of a Parula singing listlessly. The voice, although neither loud nor musical, is penetrating and seems to carry as far as most warblers. Besides the song the only note which we certainly identified was a low hissing *zee-e-eep,* very like that of the Black-and-White creeper."

Howell describes the song as a short, buzzing trill, rapidly repeated without change of pitch, resembling the song of the Worm-eating Warbler, but with the quality of the Parula's song. And he mentions two, observed in Alabama, that "had the habit of singing on the wing, the song being delivered just before the bird alighted on a perch after a short flight."

Wayne reported one Bachman's singing exactly like a Prothonotary Warbler, the song lasting for more than 20 minutes, but no one else has described this song. Alexander Sprunt, Jr., characterizes it as high and thin, like a Parula's without the characteristic typical Parula ending and having a certain ventriloquial quality.

On May 9, (1954) when we first heard the song, (at Lebanon, Virginia), the bird was singing regularly, at almost ten-second intervals. The typical song consisted of seven or eight short notes, delivered quickly and spiritedly. We wrote the song down first as *zrr, zrrr, zrr, zrr, zrr, zrr.* Then Shirley Briggs noticed that some of the songs ended in a note with an upward inflection—*chwit.* When I imitated the song, the bird regularly repeated, adding the extra note.

Gilbert Benjamin observed that the Bachman's sang while hanging upside-down on a twig in chickadee fashion. It sang while feeding, without interrupting either the feeding or the singing, and it sang while preening. It continued singing when a kingfisher landed and rattled on the same branch within a distance of eight feet. Benjamin timed the duration of the song at about 1½ seconds.

IRSTON R. BARNES

ABOUT JOHN BACHMAN

The Reverend John Bachman, discoverer of the rare and beautiful warbler which Audubon appropriately named in his honor, was himself a rare spirit, and it may be said with truth that he still awaits discovery.

He is not known as he should be to the many thousands who nowadays are interested in American wildlife. How many are aware, for instance, that we owe principally to John Bachman the most important pioneer book on American mammals, perhaps the most fascinating book on that subject ever written—the *Quadrupeds of North America*? Though Audubon and Bachman are given, in that order, as the authors, Bachman's contribution to the text overbalances that of his friend, and his vivid, authentic chapters are among the best in the whole range of American natural history.

Never an adventurous wanderer like Audubon, who explored the American wilderness when it was still unspoiled, John Bachman, the busy pastor of a growing church, had to do most of his natural history work in the neighborhood of his home, Charleston, S.C. Indeed Bachman is almost as "local" as that other clergyman-naturalist, the Rev. Gilbert White, whose famous natural history of Selborne Parish is justly regarded as a classic. The modest pastor of St. John's in Charleston lacked the romantic appeal of Audubon, as well as his artistic brilliance, and compared with the latter's far-spread fame, Bachman's is confined today to a narrow circle. Yet because of his ever memorable *"Quadrupeds"* and because of his influence upon Audubon's great work on the birds of America, Bachman must always have a high place among American naturalists. A sober and careful man of the solid and steady German and Swiss stock, he was an invaluable check upon the soaring and poetic spirit of the cloud-capping French genius with whom his name will always be associated.

John Bachman was the youngest son of Jacob Bachman, a successful farmer of Rhinebeck, in Dutchess County, New York. "From my earliest childhood," he himself wrote, "I had an irrepressible desire for the study of Natural History." That was his first love, but a man could not in those days count upon making a living from the study of nature. After a brief trial at the law, young Bachman turned to the Lutheran ministry and knew at once that he had found his true vocation. For a year and a half he was in charge of three churches which formed the Gilead Pastorate in the beautiful Hoosac region of New York. Then considerations of health led him to accept a call to St. John's Lutheran Church in Charleston.

Thus began in the year 1815 a pastorate

which was to last 60 years, gloriously fruit-
ful in good works and fortunately allowing
time and opportunity for that other love of
his heart, natural history.

Another turning point came in 1831
when Audubon, whom he had previously
known only by correspondence, spent a
month in Bachman's house in Charleston.
This was the beginning of the long friendship between two kindred and yet dissimilar spirits which was to have so marked an
effect upon the work of each. It was a
friendship which ripened with the years,
no shadow of a cloud ever dimmed it, and
the two friends and their families were
united by even closer ties when Audubon's
sons, John and Victor, married two of
Bachman's daughters.

It was not long after his first meeting
with Audubon that Bachman discovered
Swainson's warbler in the spring of 1832
near the banks of the Edisto River in South
Carolina. In July, 1833, he capped this discovery with that of the far rarer black and
yellow bird which Audubon promptly
named *Vermivora bachmanii*.

HERBERT RAVENEL SASS

10

TENNESSEE WARBLER

Vermivora peregrina

IT is usually easy to make up one's mind whether or not a bird belongs to the warbler family, the main difficulty being in determining the correct species. However, the Tennessee Warbler is a little different in that few other warblers resemble it closely, whereas its gray cap, eyestripe and general color pattern do suggest the Red-eyed and Philadelphia Vireos in outward appearance.

The Tennessee Warbler is smaller than the vireos, and the bill is finer and more needle-like, but size evaluation is often a difficult thing in the field and the best criterion probably lies in the different behavior patterns of the two families—the rapid, restless vivacity of the warblers contrasting with the slower, more deliberate movements of the vireos.

In spring, the Tennessees travel from Central America northward through Texas and the Mississippi watershed, usually appearing with the middle and later portions of the warbler migration. In the northern states, their arrival often coincides with the time when fruit blossoms are at their best and the beauty of the fruit trees is enhanced by the presence of these birds as they move rapidly about the blossoms, expertly gathering tiny insects and singing their cheerful song all the while.

As they approach the Canadian provinces, they fan out broadly to reach their breeding range in the northern boreal forest, where they are abundant along a swath that extends across the continent but is rather narrow latitudinally. The habitat they select there ranges from fairly dense to quite open spruce or Jack-pine forest and to the smaller conifers about bog margins.

Their nests are usually set into sphagnum moss and located in such a manner that they are concealed from above by dead vegetation of the year before.

The male selects singing posts that are only about 5–30 feet from the ground—either on the tops of young conifers or near the end of a branch partway up larger trees. From such vantage points he gives forth quite a loud, ringing song that carries a considerable distance when not too heavily blanketed by forest. The song typically consists of a varying number of repetitions of three discrete phrases, presented in sequence, but sometimes only two of the three phrases are used. A typical song might be interpreted phonetically as follows:

Ticka ticka ticka ticka ticka swit swit swit chee chee chee chee chee chee chee chee

Mr. D. S. Miller, of Toronto, incorporates the bird's name in his interpretation:

Tenna tenna tenna tenna chip chip see see see see see

The winter range is reached by routes that largely retrace those of spring migration. Bent (1953) gives an interesting account by Dr. A. F. Skutch of the manner in which Tennessee Warblers winter in numbers amongst the coffee plantations of Central America, most commonly at an altitude of about 3000 to 5000 feet, where at times they appear to be the most abundant bird.

As is the case with other warblers, the choice of name for the Tennessee was based on an accident of geography, for it happened that the species was first discovered by Alexander Wilson in that state in 1832. The name therefore has no particular significance other than to indicate that the species does pass through Tennessee in spring and fall migration.

The Tennessee does not rank amongst the five most abundant warblers—a distinction that might be given to the Yellow Warbler, Myrtle Warbler, Ovenbird, Yellowthroat, and American Redstart—but it should qualify for a place in the next grouping of ten. Each observer will have his own ideas about relative abundance, but I would place the Tennessee slightly below the Black-and-White, Nashville, Chestnut-sided, and Palm Warblers, and more or less on an even footing with the Magnolia, Black-throated Green, Blackburnian, and Kentucky Warblers. It is certainly a common migrant within its limits.

Vermivora peregrina (Wilson)
　(Lat., *peregrina*, wandering)

Type Locality Cumberland River, Tenn.

FIELD CHARACTERS: *Male,* head gray, a light stripe over the eye and a dark line through the eye; upper parts bright olive-green and underparts grayish white or white, with no streaking.
　Female, similar to male, but some olive-green on crown and yellowish tinge to underparts.
　Immature, lacks gray cap; greenish above and yellowish below; eye-line yellowish.
　Length, 4.50 to 5.00 inches.

NESTING DATA: Built on the ground, usually in a damp, mossy situation such as in a sphagnum bog. The nest is made of dry grasses and lined with hair; it is well set into the surrounding vegetation and commonly with the protection of dried bog plants overhead.
　Eggs—4 to 7, commonly 6. White or creamy white, with brown speckles or small spots sometimes evenly scattered and on others concentrated to form a wreath at the large end.

VOICE: Song usually in three parts, but occasionally in two. Each part consists of a variable number of repetitions of a one- or two-syllable phrase and differs from the others in pitch, rhythm, and length. One of the louder warbler songs, with a duration of about three seconds. Sample interpretations:

(a) Ticka ticka ticka ticka ticka swit swit chew-chew-chew-chew-chew-chew-chew
(b) Chip chip chip chip ticka ticka ticka ticka ticka ticka tsee tsee tsee tsee tsee tsee

There is also a flight song. (*See Chapter 5*)

FOOD HABITS: As far as is known, their food is almost entirely composed of insects and similar small-animal material.

GENERAL RANGE: *Breeds* from southern Yukon, central MacKenzie, northern Manitoba, northern Ontario, northern Quebec, central Labrador, and western Newfoundland south to south-central British Columbia, northwestern Montana, central Alberta, central Saskatchewan, southern Manitoba, northern Minnesota, northern Wisconsin, northern Michigan, south-central Ontario, northeastern New York, southern Vermont, central New Hampshire, southern Maine, southern New Brunswick, and central Nova Scotia. *Winters* from Guatemala east to western Colombia and northern Venezuela. Spring migration takes it along the eastern coast of Mexico and also across the Gulf of Mexico, through Texas to the Mississippi Valley, then spreading out to cover its wide breeding range. Fall migration largely retraces the spring route.

W. W. H. GUNN

11

ORANGE-CROWNED WARBLER

Vermivora celata

THIS little warbler is one of the family which contributes much to the puzzlement and confusion of many bird watchers. It has none of the beauty and brilliance possessed by many of its relatives, no outstanding vocal ability, no obvious orange crown and is an extremely obscure, plain looking bird. In showing it to many observers not having seen it before, my favorite description is that the principal field mark of the Orange-crowned Warbler is that it does not have any! No eye-ring or stripe, no wing bars, just a little mouse-like bird.

None the less, there is much of interest about it and it is not really difficult to recognize when one becomes familiar with what to look for and where to look for it. It is known as only a winter warbler in much of the country and it occurs in some

abundance throughout the southeast and Gulf regions at that season. In migration it may be seen almost anywhere in a wide range from northwest Canada southward, and it is Canadian in its nesting.

The southeastward migration is quite prolonged often continuing into November. According to Forbush, "the bird may be found almost anywhere in New England during the fall migration, wherever there are trees and shrubbery, never very high up." (BENT).

It is fond of live-oaks, myrtle thickets, brushy field edges and patches of woodland. The distinctive "chip" call note helps to locate it but it is not otherwise vocal in its winter quarters. In recent years of field work in south central Florida I have found it one of the characteristic wintering birds of the Okeechobee-Kissimmee region. The mixed "hammocks" of oak and cabbage palms there, harbor many of these warblers throughout much of the winter, and they come occasionally to feeding stations.

The Eastern race of the Orange-crown does not nest in this country, penetrating far into Canada to indulge its domestic season. It seems remarkable that so fragile a bird would occupy the immense range that it does throughout a year, even normal migrational hazards not seeming to affect it as much as many other species. As with others of its genus, the bill is very delicate and needle-pointed and the orange of the crown is largely confined to the basal half of the feathers and can scarcely be seen except in a bird in the hand. However, at times this character is visible, though many who know the bird well have never observed it in life.

Vermivora celata celata (Say)
   (Lat., *celata*, concealed, referring to the crown patch)

Type Locality Omaha, Nebraska

LOCAL NAME: Eastern Orange-crowned Warbler

FIELD CHARACTERS: Upperparts dusky olive-green; underparts paler, at times dimly streaked with olive-gray. Crown patch brownish-orange but usually concealed on basal portion of feathers. It is lacking in immatures and some females. An inconspicuous, obscure-looking species. *Length,* 5 inches.

NESTING DATA: From the ground (usually) into low bushes a foot or two high. Nest composed of grass, bark-strippings and plant down, lined with fur, hair or feathers. Rather large for size of bird.
   Eggs—4 to 6. White, with small spots of reddish and lavender often in a wreath about large end.

VOICE: Difficult to render into words, but like that of the chipping sparrow on a higher key and more musical, ending on an ascending scale. Call note a *chip* suggesting the Tree Sparrow but sharper. (*See Chapter 5*)

A. Eastern. B. Rocky Mountain.
C. Lutescent. D. Dusky.

FOOD HABITS: Insects with some berries and fruit. Takes suet and other feeding-station provender, such as peanut-butter, crumbs, etc.

GENERAL RANGE: *Breeds* from central Alaska, northwestern and central MacKenzie, northern Manitoba, northern Ontario, and northwestern Quebec south to the Alaska Peninsula, Kodiak Island, and central eastern Alaska, central Yukon, central Alberta, southeastern Saskatchewan, southern Manitoba, and western and central Ontario.
   Winters from northern California, Nevada, Arizona, southern Texas, through the Gulf states, south to southern Florida, Guatemala and southern Baja California.

Vermivora celata orestera Oberholser
   (Lat., *orestera*, mountain-dweller)

Type Locality Willis, New Mexico

LOCAL NAME: Rocky Mountain Orange-crowned Warbler

This form of the Orange-crowned Warbler is similar to *V. c. celata* but larger and decidedly more yellow above and below.

RANGE: Mountain regions from New Mexico, Arizona, western Texas and eastern California, central Nevada, Utah, southwestern Saskatchewan to British Columbia and southwestern Yukon. *Winters* from southeastern California, Nevada, Arizona and Texas south into Mexico.

Vermivora celata lutescens (Ridgway)
   (Lat., *lutescens,* becoming yellow)

Type Locality Fort Kenai, Alaska

LOCAL NAME: Lutescent Warbler

This Pacific Coast Orange-crown differs in being brighter in general coloration than *V. c. celata,* both in the olive-green of the upperparts and much yellower beneath. The latter color appears predominant if the bird is seen in good light at close range. Its habits and behavior are like those of the others.

RANGE: Pacific Coast from southern California north to western Nevada, coastal British Columbia and southern Alaska; *wintering* from central California as far south as Guatemala.

Vermivora celata sordida (Townsend)
   (Lat., *sordida,* dirty, dark)

Type Locality San Clemente Island, Calif.

LOCAL NAME: Dusky Warbler

This very dark race inhabits the islands off the coast of California, especially Santa Catalina, but has nested at San Diego (mainland). *Breeding* range extends south to Todos Santos Islands off Baja California. *Winters* on the California mainland.

The whole plumage is darker than any other form of this warbler and both bill and feet are larger. It nests in low bushes rather than on the ground, sometimes as high as 15 feet. The eggs usually number three. It scatters rather widely in winter, occurring as far north as San Francisco.

ALEXANDER SPRUNT, JR.

12

NASHVILLE WARBLER

Vermivora ruficapilla

HERE is a smallish warbler that calls for the exercise of some care in field identification because its color patterns are not strikingly different from those of a number of other warblers. However, the gray head, white eye-ring, and yellow underparts reaching up to the throat combine to separate it from such similar species as the Connecticut, Mourning, and Canada Warblers.

The reddish crown-patch that gave rise to the specific name *ruficapilla* tends to be veiled in fall by the gray tips of new feathers. In spring, the crown-patch emerges as a distinct marking, but it is difficult to see in the field even at that season unless you happen to be looking down on the bird.

From their wintering gounds in Central America, the Nashville Warblers' migration takes them through Texas rather than the southeastern states, where they are rarely seen. Moving up through the central portion of the Mississippi watershed, they then disperse to breeding grounds that form a broad belt extending from the northern tier of states well into the coniferous forests of Canada, and from central Saskatchewan eastward to the Maritimes. Fall migration moves back over the same route. A western form of the species, known as the Calaveras Warbler, alternates between wintering grounds in Mexico and breeding grounds extending from high ground in the Sierra Nevadas northward to British Columbia.

Nashvilles are amongst the earlier warbler migrants to arrive in spring and the later ones to leave in fall, often travelling at about the same time as the Black-throated Green Warbler.

For most of the last century, it was evidently considered a rare bird. Nowadays, however, it is decidedly common in Ontario—in fact, it tends to be taken for granted by observers who can be heard to remark: "Oh, that's just a Nashville"—when they had obviously hoped that it would prove to be something more unusual.

In selecting nesting territory, Nashville Warblers show a preference for two quite different habitats. One of these is the northern type of forest-bordered bog with a sprinkling of conifers such as Tamarack and Black Spruce, and a ground cover largely of Sphagnum and Labrador Tea. The other habitat, more frequently used in the southern part of the breeding range, is quite dry by comparison and represents a fairly early stage of second-growth forest where deciduous trees such as White Birch and Trembling Aspen mingle with Balsam Fir in rather open stands with numerous small clearings.

As the second type of habitat has become widespread in the wake of extensive clearing and lumbering operations, this fact may have had a bearing on their increase in numbers during the past half century.

The well-concealed nest seems invariably to be placed on the ground, often in the cover of such plants as Bunchberry, Shin Leaf, club mosses and dead bracken. The area that the male bird defends about the nest-site may be exceptionally large for a warbler—sometimes twice as large as that of other warblers found in the same vicinity. The male bird spends a good deal of his time at mid-story level, shunning the tops of the highest trees.

The Nashville's two-part song is basically simple in design. One phrase is repeated from four to seven times in the first part, and another phrase sung from one to seven times (commonly 3 to 5) in the second part. The second part is sung more rapidly than the first, and usually in a lower pitch. As the entire song lasts less than three seconds, it is not easy to count the components in each part.

Two syllables per phrase are clearly enunciated by those birds that sing the first part more slowly:

see-bit, see-bit, see-bit, see-bit, see-bit

When sung more rapidly, the two syllables tend to be elided:

see-it, see-it, see-it, see-it, see-it

When the tempo is extremely rapid, the phrase is shortened to a single syllable:

seet, seet, seet, seet, seet

In the second part of the song, a single-syllable phrase is repeated very rapidly. Thus a fairly typical rendition of a full song might be:

see-it, see-it, see-it, see-it, see-it, ti-ti-ti-ti

Vermivora ruficapilla ruficapilla (Wilson)
(Lat., *ruficapilla,* red-haired)

Type Locality near Nashville, Tennessee

LOCAL NAME: Eastern Nashville Warbler

FIELD CHARACTERS: *Male,* head gray with partly veiled chestnut-red crown-patch and white eye-ring; back and wings and tail olive green; throat and underparts yellow with no streaking.
Female, similar to male but duller; chestnut cap-patch may be lacking.
Immature, resembles the adult female; crown-patch absent in immature female.
Length, 4.5 to 5.0 inches.

NESTING DATA: Built on the ground; a small, compact nest of rootlets and fibres, lined with hair; sometimes set in a concealing depression in moss or beneath a canopy of dried, dead bracken.

Eggs—4 or 5. White or creamy white, with reddish brown speckling often concentrated in the form of a wreath at the larger end.

VOICE: Song is two-parted; in the first part, one phrase is sung 4–7 times, and in the second part another phrase is sung 1–7 times. The second part is delivered more rapidly and usually in a lower pitch than the first. Sample interpretation:
see-it, see-it, see-it, see-it, ti-ti-ti-ti-ti (See Chapter 5)

FOOD HABITS: Almost entirely insectivorous; larval and adult forms commonly sought on the underside of leaves. Flying insects sometimes taken in flycatcher fashion.

GENERAL RANGE: *Breeds* from central Saskatchewan, southern Manitoba, northern Ontario, southern Quebec, Nova Scotia and Cape Breton Island south to Nebraska, northern Illinois, northeastern West Virginia, western Maryland, northern Pennsylvania, northern New Jersey and Connecticut. *Winters* southern Texas, south to Mexico and south and east to Guatemala. In spring migration, some populations apparently cross the western part of the Gulf of Mexico, then moving through Texas and the central portion of the Mississippi valley before fanning out to cover the breeding range. Migration in fall is a reversal of the spring migration.

Vermivora ruficapilla ridgwayi van Rossem
(Lat., *ridgwayi,* for R. Ridgway)

Type Locality E. Humboldt Mts., Nevada

LOCAL NAMES: Western Nashville, or Calaveras Warbler

A. Eastern Nashville. B. Calaveras.

This western form is similar to *V. r. ruficapilla,* but more yellowish olive-green above and brighter yellow below; lower abdomen more extensively whitish.

RANGE: Mountain regions of the western United States from the Sierra Nevada to British Columbia west of the Rocky Mountains, and from central California to Utah and northwestern Montana. *Winters* southern Sonora and Durango, south through Mexico to Guatemala.

W. W. H. GUNN

PLATE 8

SUTTON'S WARBLER

Page 159

Male

SOCORRO WARBLER (*male head*)

Page 104

Female

OLIVE-BACKED WARBLER

Page 99

GROUND-CHAT

Page 221

Male

Female

John H. Dick

13

VIRGINIA'S WARBLER

Vermivora virginiae

EVEN in full breeding plumage, Virginia's Warbler is so modestly attired that one might suppose that it still wore its dull winter dress. The gray male timidly displays chestnut on his crown and yellow on his rump and upper tail-coverts, but the chestnut feathers are tipped with gray and the yellow is clouded with olive-green. He wears his brightest color, a clear lemon-yellow, on the less exposed parts of his body, including the throat, chest, and under tail-coverts. The breeding female is even duller.

This inconspicuous gray warbler was discovered at Fort Burgwyn, New Mexico, by Dr. W. W. Anderson and named in honor of the collector's wife by S. F. Baird, who described the species in 1860. It breeds in the mountains of the semi-arid southwestern quarter of the United States, from northern Utah and Colorado to southern Arizona and New Mexico and from the White Mountains in eastern California to the eastern slopes of the Rocky Mountains in Colorado, chiefly in the altitudinal zone between about 6000 and 9000 feet above sea level. In the foothills of the Rockies in Colorado it is abundant and possibly the most common of the wood warblers. Here in the spring, as the scrub oaks on the hillsides put forth their gray-green foliage and greenish-yellow catkins, the males sing incessantly as they forage amidst the burgeoning trees whose colors they match. In a voice full for so small a bird, they pour forth a variety of animated verses. *Che-wé-che-wé-che-wé, ché-a-ché-a-ché*, the song sounded to one observer, while another wrote it as *zdl-zdl-zdl-zdl, zt-zt-zt-zt*.

For its nest-site, Virginia's Warbler

chooses the side of a narrow ravine or a steep and often rocky mountain slope that supports a dense growth of scrub oak, mountain mahogany or choke-cherry. Here, often beneath a tussock of grass, it finds or makes a depression in the ground litter, or even in the soil itself, to receive its open, cup-shaped nest, which is sometimes so deeply embedded that its rim is level with the surface. The structure is composed of leaves, strips of bark, thin grass stems, roots, mosses, lichens, and similar materials, and has an inner lining of fine vegetable fibers, horsehair, or even fur. In this excellently concealed nest the female lays, in late May or June, from three to five eggs; but most often the set consists of four. The white eggs are finely spotted or speckled with shades of reddish-brown, which on some are thickly sprinkled over the whole surface, whereas on others they are concentrated at the large end. Apparently no one has ever watched these warblers build their nest or incubate their eggs; but we know from the observations of Bailey and Niedrach that both parents attend the nestlings, nourishing them chiefly with the caterpillars which at this season devour the foliage of the trees and shrubs of the mountain slopes. The young are in the nest when these larvae are most abundant. As the caterpillars become scarce the parents lead their family, now able to fly, down into the foothills where other food is available.

After the close of the breeding season in July, Virginia's Warblers molt into a still duller and browner plumage, in which the chestnut crown-patch is concealed by brownish-gray tips of the feathers and the yellow of the breast loses its brightness. In late August or September they undertake their southward migration. Theirs is a journey far shorter and less hazardous than that of many other warblers; for they follow an overland route which takes them no farther than west central Mexico, from Jalisco and Guanajuato to Morelos and Guerrero, where they find semi-arid mountains similar to those in which they nest. Here they remain until the following April, passing the winter, according to William Beebe's observations, in flocks which keep close to the ground in the dense underbrush of the mountain sides.

Vermivora virginiae (Baird)

Type Locality Fort Burgwyn, N.M.

FIELD CHARACTERS: *Male in breeding plumage,* upperparts gray; crown chestnut, the feathers usually tipped with gray; rump and upper tail-coverts bright yellowish olive-green or olive-yellow; no wing bars nor tail patches; a conspicuous white eye-ring; sides of head paler gray than back; under tail-coverts, chest and usually also throat lemon yellow; rest of underparts dull white, becoming grayer on sides. *Female,* similar to adult male but duller. *Length,* 4.25 to 4.50 inches.

RECOGNITION MARKS: Gray upperparts distinguish from all but Lucy's W. Yellow areas of chest and tail coverts distinguish from *V. luciae,* which in other respects it closely resembles.

NESTING DATA: Nest an open cup, of leaves, grass, strips of bark, mosses, lichens, etc., on the ground or in a slight depression in the earth, among scrubby vegetation on mountain slopes, often hidden beneath a tussock of grass.

Eggs—4, less often 3 or 5, white finely speckled with shades of reddish-brown and vinaceous drab, these markings thickly covering the whole surface of some eggs but on others concentrated at the large end.

VOICE: Song bright and rapid, *che-wé-che-wé-che-wé, ché-a-ché-a-ché,* or *zdl-zdl-zdl-zdl, zt-zt-zt-zt.*

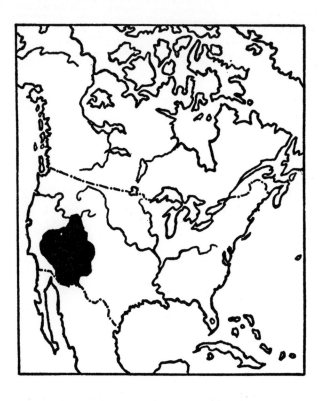

GENERAL RANGE: *Breeds* in western U.S. from central eastern California, northern Utah and northern Colorado to eastern slope of the Rocky Mountains and south to southwestern New Mexico and southeastern Arizona. *Winters* in western Mexico from Jalisco and Guanajuato to Morelos and Guerrero.

ALEXANDER F. SKUTCH

[*Comment:* The Virginia Warbler is more shy and retiring than the Colima Warbler. It feeds closer to the ground and does not appear in the tops of large trees to feed and to sing as much as does the Colima. The song of the Virginia Warbler has greater volume. In their respective habitats during the nesting season *Vermivora crissalis* in the Chisos Mountains is about four times as abundant as *Vermivora virginiae* in the Huachuca Mountains. This estimate is based on the careful counting of singing males of both species. (J. VAN TYNE)]

14

COLIMA WARBLER

Vermivora crissalis

THE Colima Warbler is probably the least known member of the warbler family in this country. There are other localized species, Bachman's being elusive, erratic and unpredictable; Golden-cheek limited but easily seen in readily accessible country, as is the case with Kirtland's. Few bird watchers have seen it, for the distance involved and physical effort necessary deter most. A glance at the Range tells the story.

Here, amid the pines, oaks and maples of the rocky slopes at elevations exceeding 6000 feet, lives this little gray and yellow warbler. Once the searcher for it is there, Colima is not hard to find or watch but when one has located it, all surroundings considered, he feels that the rest of the world is very far away!

I have been fortunate enough to visit the Chisos Mountains on three occasions, accompanied on one by John Henry Dick. We found a pair of Colima Warblers one day in late July, 1951, near famous Boot Spring at an altitude of about 6500 feet. The female put on one of the most convincing "broken-wing acts" either of us had ever seen. Fluttering about over the dead leaves on the ground, she passed between us several times, we being hardly more than a yard apart, and once came within eight inches of my feet. Search as we might, and did, we could not find the young birds.

In early September of 1950, I found two or three of these warblers at much lower altitudes, noting them about Kibbey Spring, just above the Basin at about 5300 feet. This was probably due to migration being at hand and the birds more dispersed. Colima is rather deliberate in its move-

John H. Dick
'55

PLATE 9
OLIVE WARBLER
Page 106

Male

Female

GRACE'S WARBLER
Page 163

Adult Male

Immature

ments and not shy. It responds to the "squeak" readily, at least such is my experience.

The Colima frequents oaks, though maples are used too, and the bird is a low ranger as a rule. It is not a striking looking warbler, rather plain I have thought it, but the grays, whites and yellows form a pleasing combination. The bird sings persistently, the notes carrying considerable distances. Much of the feeding and all of the nesting is on the ground, though search for food carries the bird into the limbs of trees frequently. Only certain areas in the Chisos are inhabited, the South Rim Trail from the Laguna to Boot Spring being a favorite. I have found it also in Pine Canyon and Kibbey Spring.

ALEXANDER SPRUNT, JR.

THE DISCOVERY OF THE NEST
OF THE COLIMA WARBLER

On July 20, 1928 Frederick M. Gaige collected an adult male *Vermivora crissalis* near Boot Spring, high in the Chisos Mountains of west Texas. It was the twelfth known specimen of this warbler and the first ever found in the United States. With the hope of learning more about this very rare bird and perhaps finding its undiscovered nest and eggs, William G. Fargo, who had supported the expedition of 1928, generously offered to send me to the Chisos Mountains again in 1932. As companions I was fortunate in securing Edouard C. Jacot of Prescott, Arizona, and Dr. Max M. Peet of Ann Arbor, Michigan. Both are exceptional field ornithologists, and they helped immeasurably in assuring the success of the undertaking.

Arriving in Marathon on April 26, 1932 we secured the necessary supplies and on April 28 drove south eighty-six miles to San Vicente on the Rio Grande, where we made our base with our friend Thomas J. Miller. With the assistance of Mr. Miller we soon engaged a reliable Mexican with a string of eight sturdy burros to pack the equipment and supplies up to Boot Spring, the highest good camp site in the Chisos Mountains, and the very place at which the Colima Warbler had been collected. At the end of a hard day of pulling by automobile and burro we reached the end of the last vestige of road and established camp at Upper Juniper Spring at the lower edge of the Chisos forest. During the next day and a half the hard-worked burros relayed the baggage 2000 feet up the winding precipitous trail to our Boot Spring camp.

On May 2 Peet began observations in the Boot Spring Valley, and by the next day we were all free to devote ourselves to the study of the birds of the mountain range and especially to the search for the nest of the Colima Warbler. We were delighted to find the species quite common in Boot Spring Valley. It frequented especially the young maples and deciduous oaks along the banks of the dry, boulder-strewn stream bed; and elsewhere on the steep mountain slopes we noted its preference for the clumps of small oaks. We saw no Colima Warblers below 6000 feet, but from there on up to the last good stand of oak at 7500 feet on Emory Peak nearly every large thicket of oak seemed to harbor one or two warblers.

On May 4 Peet noted pursuit behavior

which may have had some courtship significance, but we had no further evidence of nesting until May 7 when, as I was crossing the dry stream bed about a hundred yards below Boot Spring, I suddenly saw within twenty-five feet of me a female warbler with nest material in her bill. I stopped instantly and, remaining motionless, was greatly relieved to see the warbler continue undisturbed by my presence. In a moment she dropped to the ground and entered the nest which was on the sloping right bank of the stream about six feet back from the margin of the rocky stream bed. After working for about twenty seconds the warbler left the nest and flew down the stream bed a hundred and fifty feet. In twelve minutes she was back with more nest material to repeat the performance. Subsequent excursions for building material during the ensuing hour were of three, twelve, six and twenty-two minutes' duration.

Lodged between small rocks, the nest was deeply imbedded in dead oak leaves, and the dense ground cover of vines and other herbaceous plants which completely arched over it left an entrance only on the northwest side toward the stream bed. The nest was loosely woven of fine grasses, the outer portion on all sides containing many pieces of green moss. The rim included a large proportion of fine red strips of cedar bark. The nest cavity, which was five centimeters across the rim and four centimeters deep, was lined with fine grasses, a little white fur (apparently of a rabbit), and a few larger hairs of a fox or badger.

The call note of the Colima Warbler is a very sharp, almost explosive "psit." It is quite distinctive, and we frequently recognized individuals by their call note alone. The common song of the Colima Warbler is a simple trill, much like that of the Chipping Sparrow but rather shorter and more musical and ending in two lower notes. There is also another, more varied song which was much less frequently given. The males are persistent singers, even when the sky is overcast. Once we even noted several singing steadily in a dense fog which had silenced most other species. The song can be easily heard three or four hundred feet through the woods, although it does not seem loud when heard nearby. The males usually sing from the bushes and small trees, feeding and moving about between songs. Sometimes, however, an individual will maintain his post on some isolated perch as much as twenty feet from the ground and there sing at frequent intervals. The males were still singing when we left the mountains on May 27.

Vermivora crissalis (Salvin and Godman)
    (Lat., *crissalis*, of the crissum)

Type Locality Colima, Mexico

FIELD CHARACTERS: Similar to Virginia's Warbler but larger and darker; crown paler; rump darker and richer in color; little if any yellow on throat and breast. Crissum brighter yellow and back less gray. *Female* lacks yellow on breast. *Juvenal* lacks crown spot.
    Length, 4.25 to 5.00 inches.

NESTING DATA: On the ground, of fine grasses, dead leaves, moss and cedar bark, lined with grass, fur or hair. General ground cover of vines or leaves partly or completely conceals nest. Only a very few have as yet been found.
    Eggs—4. Creamy white, speckled and splashed about the large end with brownish and cinnamon drab in the form of a wreath.

A. Lucy's Warbler. B. Colima Warbler.

VOICE: Usual song a long trill somewhat like that of the Chipping Sparrow or Pine Warbler; of very musical character though difficult to render in words. Another song is more varied and louder in delivery, audible for some distance and quite persistent. "To our ears the notes more nearly resembled those of the Pine than the Chipping Sparrow's. The Pine Warbler-like trill was followed by two lower notes, the final one usually accented." (D. Snyder in the *Auk:* 74)

RANGE: The known distribution of the Colima Warbler includes the following places: Chisos Mountains, Texas; Sierra Guadalupe, Coahuila; Miquihuana, Tamaulipas; Patamba, Michoacan; Sierra Nevada, Colima. As Outram Bangs remarked, the two southern localities may well represent only the winter range. The dates involved are April 6, 1889 (Colima), and January 29, 1903, and, in spite of the passing thirty years, nothing has been added to our knowledge of the species in the southern part of its range. At the three northern localities (in Coahuila, Tamaulipas, and Texas) the records range from April 25 to July 25. For the present these three points in the mountains of northeastern Mexico and adjacent Texas represent the sum of our knowledge of the breeding range of the Colima Warbler.

JOSSELYN VAN TYNE

15

LUCY'S WARBLER

Vermivora luciae

THE Lucy's Warbler is the sole member of the wood warbler family that nests mainly in the hot Lower Sonoran desert of the southwestern United States and northwestern Mexico, and it could therefore be called the Desert Warbler. It is generally distributed wherever there are large mesquites, especially along the main watercourses, and may also be found in willows along such rivers as the San Pedro, Santa Cruz, Gila, and Colorado. In southeastern Arizona, it occurs also in the mountain foothills. Long fingers of its nesting range extend along the Virgin River valley into extreme southwestern Utah, along the bottom of the Grand Canyon, and even into the San Juan drainage in southeastern Utah. In the last fifteen years at least, it has occurred along the Rio Grande in New Mexico, where I first found it near San Antonio in 1942, and where a nest was discovered at Radium Springs, between Las Cruces and Elephant Butte Dam, by Lena McBee and Ruby Allen in June, 1948.

Lucy's is one of the smallest warblers. Its gray and white dress, with inconspicuous chestnut crown and rump patches, also mark it one of the plainest of warblers. The white eye-ring may lead to confusion with a Gnatcatcher, and its size and actions often remind me of a Verdin. It is usually found feeding at middle heights in its favorite mesquites, seldom in either treetops or near the ground.

During the nesting season it is quite shy, and does not readily disclose the location of its nest. This is a tiny affair, as befits so small a builder, and is generally placed in natural cavities, behind loose bark, or in woodpecker holes. Occasionally a deserted

Verdin's nest is utilized. It is ordinarily placed five or six feet from the ground, sometimes as many as fifteen feet, and now and then within a foot or two of the ground. Although a mesquite is the usual site, nests have also been found in holes in banks, in yuccas, in willows, in sycamores, and in elderberries. The four or five eggs have a white or creamy ground color with fine auburn speckles concentrated at the larger end.

The song reminds me of a Yellow Warbler's, especially when heard at a distance. Closer at hand, it is relatively not so loud and has a more wiry quality. An apt description is that of W. L. Dawson, who says "It is a *Warbler* song, rather than the song of the Lucy Warbler." Its scolding or warning note is loud for such a tiny bird, and resembles that of a White-crowned Sparrow or Blue Grosbeak.

The Lucy's Warbler arrives early in the spring, often in mid-March, and usually by the 20th. Its numbers diminish rapidly, following the departure of the last young from the nest in July. A few linger until the middle part of September, and now and then a bird may be seen until the latter part of that month. It is rare as a migrant away from its breeding grounds. Its winter home is imperfectly known, but is believed to be in central western Mexico.

Another species associated with the exploratory period of western ornithology, it was unknown until the first year of the Civil War, when J. G. Cooper discovered it at long-abandoned Fort Mojave, on the Arizona side of the Colorado River opposite the extreme southern tip of Nevada. In describing it, he named it in honor of Miss Lucy Baird, daughter of the illustrious Prof. Spencer F. Baird.

[*Comment:* Dwarf Cowbirds are prominent in the formidable host of enemies which this tiny bird must face. Sometimes the warblers are able to entrench themselves behind apertures so narrow that the Cowbird cannot get in; and once we saw the Cowbird's foundling resting unharmed, but also harmless, upon the "doorstep," not less than two inches distant from the warbler's eggs. Another nest, more exposed, contained three eggs of the arch enemy, and had been deserted by the troubled owners. The Gila Woodpecker is an especially persistent enemy. Accustomed as he is to poking and prying, he seems to take a fiendish delight in discovering and devouring as many Lucy Warblers' eggs as possible. We caught several of these villains red-handed, and we found reason to believe that more than half of the nests in a certain section had been wrecked by them. Add to these the depredations of lizards, snakes, and, possibly, rats, and the wonder is that these tiny gray waifs are able to reproduce at all. (W. L. DAWSON)]

Vermivora luciae (Cooper)

Type Locality Fort Mojave, Arizona

FIELD CHARACTERS: Sexes alike, and young very similar. Upperparts a clear ashy gray, underparts entirely white. Rich chestnut patch on crown and rump. White eye-ring. Small and active; might be confused with a Gnatcatcher, or immature Verdin. In general appearance suggests a Warbling Vireo.
Length, 4.00 inches.

NESTING DATA: Nest is built in a natural cavity, behind loose bark, in deserted Woodpecker or Verdin nests, or, rarely, in fork in a small branch.

Very small and frail, of grasses and fine plant fibers with a lining of feathers and hair.

Eggs—usually 4, small with white ground color, finely speckled with auburn concentrated at larger ends.

VOICE: Song somewhat similar to Yellow Warbler's and to the Pileolated. A lively, double-pitched, *whee-tee whee-tee whee-tee whee-tee whee-tee whee-tee wheet* (Bailey). Call note fairly loud, with some resemblance to Blue Grosbeak's or White-crowned Sparrow's.

FOOD HABITS: Insectivorous.

GENERAL RANGE: *Breeds* north to extreme southern Utah, and Nevada, possibly in extreme southwestern Colorado and northwestern New Mexico; west to California and Nevada banks of Colorado River, and probably Imperial Valley in California; east to Rio Grande between Socorro, New Mexico and El Paso, Texas; and south to northern Sonora and northeastern Baja California. *Winters* in western Mexico south to Jalisco and Guerrero.

GALE MONSON

PLATE 10
EASTERN YELLOW WARBLER
Page 109

Immature

Adult Male

Adult Female

ALASKA YELLOW WARBLER
Page 110
Immature

MANGROVE WARBLER
Page 111, 292
Adult Male

Adult Female

John H. Dick
'55

16

PARULA WARBLER

Parula americana

IF any bird deserves the term "dainty" this is the one. Tiny as it is, it has undergone much ponderous nomenclatural variation in its history. Catesby called it "Finch Creeper," Bartram referred to it as "various colored little finch creeper," while Audubon and Wilson denominated it "Blue yellow-backed Warbler." Its generic, as well as common name, means "little titmouse." Quite a weighty array for this fragile bird!

Small as it is, it frequents a tremendous range, the latter covering nearly all of this country east of the Great Plains, plus parts of southern Canada. In its summer home, whether a woodland bird as it often is, or a dweller of open orchards, estates or parks, two plant forms appear essential to its needs. The northern bird rarely nests anywhere except where the tree lichen, *Usnea,*

"old man's beard" occurs. The southern race's distribution is largely governed by the presence of Spanish moss (*Tillandsia usneoides*). Though apt to be seen almost anywhere during the migrations, deciduous woods seem to be preferred, where it ranges high up amid groups of other migrant warblers. At these seasons it visits both urban and suburban areas and can be seen at bird baths and feeding stations.

The Parula is not only one of the smallest of the wood warblers but certainly one of the most attractive, though not as brilliant in plumage as many. Its characteristic and explosively terminated song is the essence of moss-bannered live oak groves in the South and the Usnea-hung woods of the North. It is often very tame and has nested several times within a few yards of my porch. When the young are being fed, it flits in and out of the drapery of moss with no concern for people sitting closely adjacent.

One of the more deliberate warblers, it examines crack and cranny of limb and trunk with methodical precision and is reminiscent of both nuthatch and titmouse in many of its postures and actions. It is not surprising that early observers likened it to the latter, as well as the creeper. Its confiding nature is further illustrated by the fact that it will feed young held in one's hand, an experience which many have delighted in.

Recognition of this tiny warbler should present no problem. Its size, or rather lack of it, the blue back with the yellowish "saddle-patch," two white wing bars and dark banded yellow breast are infallible field marks. Females and immatures might cause some confusion but practice will resolve doubt.

As it travels southward in late summer and early fall, it often falls victim to man-made migration hazards, such as radio beacons, tall buildings, ceilometers and bridges. Such dangers, together with the usual predation and the rather infrequent victimization by the cowbird in the north, appear to be the principal limiting factors to its population. To these, however, must be added the ever-increasing advance of civilization in eliminating habitat.

Parula americana (Linnaeus)
    (Lat., *Parula*, little titmouse; *americana*, of America)

Type Locality South Carolina

LOCAL NAME: Blue Yellow-backed Warbler

FIELD CHARACTERS: *Male*, crown, sides of head and neck and nape, blue-gray; upperparts the same but paler shade; patch on back yellowish-green; two white wing bars; throat and chest bright yellow, a band of dark brown across latter, a fainter band of tawny below. Belly white, flanks washed with gray.
    Female, pattern similar but duller in color, breast bands often lacking.
    Immature, like female but with olive greenish wash on back.
    Length, 4.25 to 4.90 inches.

NESTING DATA: In northern range nest is placed in festoons of *Usnea*, in the south, in clumps of *Tillandsia* moss, often completely concealed. Elsewhere in coniferous trees such as hemlock and occasionally mixed hardwoods without lichen. Made of fine grasses, bark-stripings, plant down, flowers of moss, lined with feathers. Elevations vary from 6 to over 100 ft.
    Eggs—4 or 5. White, speckled and spotted with chestnut and drab, at times in a wreath about the end. Some eggs are almost without markings.

VOICE: A buzzy ascending trill ending in a sharp, emphatic "zip." Variations occur but general pattern similar, with ending always abrupt and louder. (*See Chapter 5*)

FOOD HABITS: Almost entirely insects and spiders. Beetles, moths, flies and larvae make up the bulk of food. Flutters and hangs head down in chickadee fashion at times, and occasionally forages on the ground.

GENERAL RANGE: *Breeds* from southeastern Manitoba, central Ontario, southern Quebec, Maine, Prince Edward Island, south to eastern Texas, Louisiana, Mississippi, Alabama and central Florida. *Winters* from central Florida, and the Bahamas south through Mexico, Central America to Nicaragua and the Antilles to Barbados. *Accidental* in Iceland. (*Range Map*, see Socorro W.)

ALEXANDER SPRUNT, JR.

17

OLIVE-BACKED WARBLER

Parula pitiayumi

THE avid bird watcher who travels widely through tropical America will probably meet the Olive-backed or Tropical Parula Warbler more often, and at more widely scattered points, than any other representative of the family. It occurs in suitably wooded localities across the whole breadth of the tropics, from Capricorn to Cancer, and it even extends beyond them, reaching southern Texas at one extreme of its far-flung range and Uruguay at the other. Yet despite its abundance over an immense area, it is a rather elusive bird, not easy to know well; and surprisingly little has been recorded about its way of life. As a rule, one's attention is first drawn to it by its bright, hurried song, floating down from treetops high above him. If fortunate, he will catch a glimpse, all too often fleeting, of a small bird that rather closely resembles the related North American Parula Warbler in its blue or blue-gray upper plumage, and bright yellow throat and breast. Like the Parula, it has a triangular greenish patch in the middle of the back and (in some races) two white bars on each wing. But the male lacks the Parula Warbler's conspicuous white eyelids, and he bears on his lores and cheeks a prominent black area which his northern relative lacks. Although his chest is often washed or tinged with orange-tawny, he is without the well-defined dark pectoral band of the male Parula. The female *pitiayumi,* although duller in color, often more closely resembles the male than is true of the migratory Parula Warbler.

In at least the wetter parts of the tropics, the Olive-back appears to reside the year around in the districts where it breeds. Although not only at the northern limit of its range but even well within the tropics this warbler is found near sea level, it is far more often encountered in somewhat elevated regions. Thus in Costa Rica it occurs chiefly from 1000 to 6000 feet above sea level on the Caribbean slope, while on the drier Pacific slope of the southern part of the country it is rare below 3000 feet. In the Santa Marta region of Colombia, Todd and Carriker found it from 1000 to 4000 feet or more, rarely lower. In Trinidad, however, Belcher and Smooker met it in wooded areas at all levels. In various parts of its far-flung range this warbler lives in low, dry woodlands and even in semi-arid, cultivated valleys with scattered trees. But most often I have met it, as in Costa Rica and Ecuador, well up in the crowns of the great trees of the high rain-forest, where it flits about so restlessly in search of food that it is difficult for the earth-bound watcher to discover just what it eats. Once, however, I saw a Pitiayumi pluck the tiny, pearl-like protein bodies from the hairy cushions at the bases of the stout leafstalks of a Guarumo or Cecropia tree. These dainty morsels are the special food of the Azteca Ants that dwell in the wide, hollow stems of this hospitable tree so widespread in tropical America; but if ants happen to be absent, they accumulate to the benefit of small birds.

Although a large share of the resident, breeding warblers of tropical America remain with their mates throughout the year, as far as I have seen the Olive-backs in Costa Rica lead a solitary life during the months when they are not engaged with nests and young. Yet it is difficult to make quite certain of this point in the case of a bird that moves so restlessly through the high treetops.

The bright, rapid song of the Olive-back reminds me somewhat of that of the Yellow Warbler, but it is more complex, ending with a flourish very like a trill. In the Costa Rican mountains this warbler sings more or less throughout the year. On the exposed northern slopes of the Cordillera Central, a mile above sea level, I have heard it from time to time even in the gray, stormy months of November and December, when most of the birds foraged in silence through the chill, gloomy, dripping forests. In August and September it was one of the most persistent songsters of the region.

The few available records indicate that this species breeds from late April to July in northeastern Mexico and Texas and in June and July in the island of Trinidad. For its nest-site it selects some epiphytic growth, such as a hanging tuft of gray "Spanish moss" (*Tillandsia*), pendent cactus plants, mistletoe-like orchids, and similar "air-plants." In these compact masses of aerial vegetation the warbler either finds a niche or forces apart the stems to make one. The amount of actual building which it performs appears to be determined by the adequacy of the walls resulting from this process of separation. Some nests are described as being simply hollowed out of a mass of moss, with the addition of a few horsehairs as lining. Others are made by carrying in rootlets, vegetable fibers, shredded bark, fine grass, animal hairs, or the like to line the hollow and provide a firm receptacle for the eggs. Sometimes a

John H. Dick
'55

PLATE 11
MAGNOLIA WARBLER
Page 113

Adult Male

Adult Female

Immature

few feathers are added to the lining. The nests found in hanging cacti in Trinidad by Belcher and Smooker were built of green moss. All of the nests appear to be domed or roofed above and to be entered through a narrow, round opening in the side. In northern Mexico and southern Texas they are often placed only eight or ten feet up in open woodland; but those in Trinidad were about thirty feet above the ground, beneath horizontal limbs of Ceiba trees. From my failure to find a nest in the lofty Costa Rican forests, I surmise that here this warbler usually builds higher.

Each of the two nests in Trinidad contained only two eggs, but in the valley of the Rio Grande this warbler lays sets of three or four. The eggs are white or creamy white spotted and blotched with shades of brown and chestnut, usually in the form of a wreath or cap on the thick end. The good fortune of being the first to make a detailed study of the nest life of this elusive warbler awaits some enterprising bird watcher.

ALEXANDER F. SKUTCH

[*Comment:* This bird penetrates the U.S. only in the lower Rio Grande Valley of Texas. For its inclusion in our United States list, we are indebted to George B. Sennett who, on April 20, 1872, secured specimens at Hidalgo, Texas. Since that time it has been variously known as Sennett's Warbler (A.O.U. Check-list, 1931), Sennett's Olive-backed Warbler (Bent, 1953), Tropical Parula Warbler (Blake, 1953), and now under the name given above, Olive-backed Warbler (A.O.U. Check-list, 1957).

I have, on many field trips in the Brownsville, Texas area, seen this small warbler in June (1935–1941) and while it bears a definite resemblance to our Parula Warbler, it can at once be distinguished therefrom by the black lores and cheeks and complete absence of a breast band.

(ALEXANDER SPRUNT, JR.)]

Parula pitiayumi (Vieillot)
(*pitiayumi,* an Indian name based on Azara)

Type Locality Paraguay

LOCAL NAME: Pitiayumi Warbler, Tropical Parula

FIELD CHARACTERS: *Adult male,* upper plumage blue-gray to blue, with a large contrasting area of olive-green in center of back; two (or in some races one) white bars on wings and more or less extensive white areas on outer tail feathers; lores and more or less of cheeks black or blackish with no white on eyelids; throat, breast and forepart of abdomen bright yellow, fading to white on under tail-coverts, the chest more or less deeply suffused with orange-tawny.
Female, similar to male but duller.
Length, 4 inches.

NESTING DATA: A rounded hollow with an opening in the side is formed in a cluster of epiphytic vegetation, such as "Spanish moss," small orchids or hanging cacti. Here a nest is built of green moss, fine grasses and rootlets, hair, or similar materials; or if the surrounding stems are sufficiently close together, very little material is carried in.
Eggs—2 in the tropics, 3 or 4 at the northern limit of the species' range. They are white or creamy white, speckled with shades of brown or rich chestnut, these usually forming a wreath or cap on the large end, sometimes scattered rather evenly over the whole surface.

VOICE: Song clear and rapid, accelerated almost to a trill. (*cf. Chapter 14*)

FOOD HABITS: Largely insectivorous.

GENERAL RANGE: Occurs from southern Texas and nothern Mexico through Central America and South America to Peru, Bolivia, northern Argentina, Uruguay and southern Brazil.

Parula pitiayumi nigrilora Coues

Type Locality Hidalgo, Texas

LOCAL NAME: Sennett's (Olive-backed) Warbler

RANGE: From southern Texas south to northern Hidalgo and Vera Cruz. (*Range Map, see Socorro*)

ALEXANDER F. SKUTCH

18

SOCORRO WARBLER

Parula graysoni

THIS bird, also known as Socorro Parula, is the insular representative of the wide-ranging Tropical Parula or Olive-backed Warbler (*Parula pitiayumi*), and many ornithologists prefer to treat it as a subspecies. The A.O.U. Check-list of North American Birds (1957) still regards it as a distinct species. So far as known, it breeds only on Socorro Island in the Revilla Gigedo Islands, a rather isolated group of small volcanic islands off the Pacific coast of Mexico, some 250 miles southwest of the southern tip of Baja California.

The most recent ornithological report on these islands (B. H. Brattstrom and T. R. Howell, *Condor* 58: 107–120, 1956) describes Socorro as about nine miles long and rising to a height of 3700 feet, with the lower elevations mainly dense masses of shrubbery and cactus, but with larger broad-leaved trees, and some bromeliads and orchids on the more humid northern side and at elevations above 2000 feet. Regarding this warbler, which these authors treat as a subspecies of *P. pitiayumi,* they say:

"These little warblers were fairly common on Socorro, but they seemed scarcer than other endemic land birds although equally tame and easy to approach. They were abundant in bushes and low trees four to five feet above ground, although they were often seen hopping across piles of lava. No singing or territorial behavior was noted in either March or November. One unsexed bird was collected on March 14; it was slightly fat."

The only basis for inclusion of this bird in the A.O.U. Check-list is the collection by Chester C. Lamb of two specimens at Todos Santos, in the Cape region of Baja California (Pacific side), one on November

3, 1923 and the other on July 23, 1924. Lamb also reports seeing a third bird on February 5, 1924 at El Oro some thirty miles from Todos Santos. He suggests that the capture of a July specimen may indicate possible breeding in Baja California. It would, however, be most surprising were an endemic form of the Revilla Gigedo Islands to be found breeding on the mainland so far away; for every breeding land bird of these isolated oceanic islands is sufficiently differentiated from its mainland relatives to be given either subspecific or specific rank.

The Socorro bird differs from *Parula pitiayumi nigrilora* of south Texas and northeastern Mexico in having gray, instead of black, lores and cheeks, and in having much less white on the inner webs of the outer tail feathers.

Parula graysoni (Ridgway)
   (Lat., *graysoni*, for A. J. Grayson)

Type Locality Socorro Island, Mexico

A. Parula. B. Olive-backed. C. Socorro.

RANGE: Socorro Island, Revilla Gigedo Islands, Mexico, recorded also from Cape region of Baja California.

EUGENE EISENMANN

19

OLIVE WARBLER

Peucedramus taeniatus

ALTHOUGH one of the duller members of his colorful family, the male Olive Warbler is easily recognized by his orange-brown head, neck and chest, which contrasts so strongly with the gray of his upper plumage and the dull white and pale olive-grayish of his underparts. As additional distinguishing marks he wears on each side of his head a broad black band extending from the base of his bill to the ear-coverts, on his wings two broad white bands, and much white on his outer tail feathers. The female's head and neck are yellowish rather than ochraceous and the bands through her eyes are faint, but otherwise she resembles the male.

The only species in its genus, the Olive Warbler dwells in the coniferous forests of the high mountains from Nicaragua northward through El Salvador, Honduras, Guatemala, and Mexico to central Arizona and New Mexico. In Guatemala I sometimes met these birds in open stands of pine and cypress from 8000 to 10,000 feet above sea level. In the winter months, when frost formed on clear nights, they flocked with other small birds, including wintering Townsend's Warblers and resident Hartlaub's Warblers, but they were usually a subordinate element in the flock, far less abundant than these other species. Most of the time they foraged well up in the tall trees where they were difficult to observe. I did not see them creeping over the branches and twigs of the pine trees, searching for small insects in the manner of the Pine Warbler, as they do in the mountains of Arizona. In the spring months I sometimes heard their clear, vibrant song, which sounded to me like *teacher, teacher,*

teacher. Another song consisted of a single whistle rapidly repeated in the same clear tone. When flocking together they chattered with low, sweet notes, which reminded me of one of the calls of the American Goldfinch.

To my regret, I did not discover the nest of the Olive Warbler in Guatemala. Although it resides permanently in Middle America, apparently no one has found its nest in the tropical portion of its range. Fortunately, however, we have accounts of its breeding in the Chiricahua and Huachuca mountains of Arizona, where it nests in the open forests of yellow pine, sugar pine, and fir from 8500 to possibly 12,000 feet above sea level. Although some warblers of the treetops place their nests on or near the ground, the Olive Warbler chooses a high site, usually from 30 to 70 feet up in the pine and fir trees, among clustering needles well out from the trunk. Sometimes the nest is situated in a clump of mistletoe on a pine tree. Only the female has been seen to build. As she gathers her varied materials, often on or near the ground, she is followed by her mate, who sings and sometimes feeds her. The open, cup-shaped nest is a beautiful structure, composed of lichens, mosses, dry flower stalks, bud scales, plant down, and fine rootlets, of which the last two are used both in the outer wall and to form the lining. The eggs, three or four in a set, are grayish or bluish white, or even very pale blue, thickly speckled and blotched with shades of olive, brown, and gray. In the mountains of Arizona they are laid chiefly from late May to the end of June. The female sits very steadfastly in her well concealed nest, which is often ex-

tremely difficult to find even when one knows the tree in which it is hidden. Apparently no one has yet watched the Olive Warbler incubate its eggs and rear its family.

The sequence of plumages in the Olive Warbler differs from that in other wood warblers. In many of the species that reside permanently in the tropics the young acquire, a few months after leaving the nest, the colors of their parents; while in the migratory species they usually take on the adult colors in the spring before their first nesting. But young Olive Warblers, of which the sexes differ slightly even in the juvenal plumage, are more tardy in donning the adult attire. Young males approximately a year old breed in a plumage hardly different from that of the females, then acquire the deeper colors of maturity in their second autumn, or perhaps even later. All adults molt after the nesting season, chiefly in July, into fresh plumage which resembles that in which they breed but is somewhat duller. The clearer hues of spring are acquired mainly by the wearing away of the dull edges of the new feathers.

Although it is believed that there is a southward migration of those Olive Warblers which nest at the northern extremity of their range, this is at best only partial; for this hardy bird has been found in February on the snow-covered mountains of Arizona. In late fall it hunts for insects in the pine trees in close company with Mexican Bluebirds.

Peucedramus taeniatus (Du Bus)
   (Lat. *taenia*, headband. Gr. *peuce*, pine. Gr. *dramon*, to run. *i.e.* banded pine runner)

Type Locality Vera Cruz

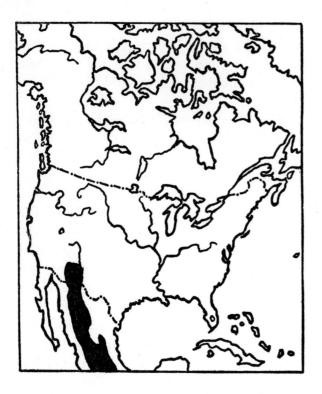

FIELD CHARACTERS: *Adult male,* foreparts of body, including head, neck and chest, orange-yellow or ochraceous, with a broad band of black on side of head from lores to ear-coverts; lower hindneck and extreme upper back yellowish olive-green; back, rump and upper tail-coverts plain mouse gray; wings blackish with two conspicuous white bars on coverts and light margins on the larger feathers; tail blackish with light edgings and large areas of white on outer feathers; breast and abdomen dull white in center becoming grayer on sides.

Female, similar to male but head and chest much paler, olive-green and yellowish, and the facial band or mask not nearly as distinctive; wing bars indistinct.

Length, 4½ to 5 inches.

NESTING DATA: Nest an open cup, of lichens, moss, flower-stalks, plant down, fine rootlets, etc., usually in a coniferous tree, sometimes in a clump of mistletoe, usually high from 30–80 feet up and out near end of branch.

Eggs—3 or 4 in the north; grayish or bluish-white or very pale blue, thickly speckled or blotched with shades of olive and brown, the markings usually scattered over the entire surface but often heavier or more crowded at the thick end. In Arizona, nesting takes place in May and June.

VOICE: Song a clear, vibrant *teacher, teacher teacher,* or *quirt, quirt, quirt* (Price) or a single clear whistle rapidly repeated. Call notes low and sweet, resembling the tufted titmouse's *peter.*

FOOD HABITS: Largely insectivorous.

GENERAL RANGE: Southwestern U.S. to northern Nicaragua, Guatemala and Salvador. Range in U.S.—southwestern and central Arizona and western New Mexico.

Peucedramus taeniatus arizonae Miller and Griscom

Type Locality Paradise, Arizona

LOCAL NAME: Northern Olive Warbler

This race differs from *P.t.* in coloration. Upper parts plain mouse gray, in spring plumage almost never tinged with olivaceous; head and throat plain ochraceous, duller than the type race.

RANGE: *Breeds* from central Arizona, southwestern New Mexico, south through mountains of northern Mexico. *Winters* in breeding range north as far as Santa Catalina Mts., Arizona and southwestern New Mexico.

ALEXANDER F. SKUTCH

20

YELLOW WARBLER

Dendroica petechia

THIS beautiful species is the best known and most widely known of all of our wood warblers. While this statement may be questioned in regard to some localities, where the bird appears only briefly on migration, it is certainly true in a continental sense. If one were to ask anyone at random whether he was familiar with the yellow warbler, the answer might be no; if asked whether he knew the "wild canary," the answer would probably be yes. While this local name is also applied to the goldfinch it is more generally connected with the warbler. "Summer yellow bird" or "summer warbler" are other localisms familiar to many.

There are good reasons for the bird to be as well known as it is. Aside from the vast range frequented, it comes freely into yards and gardens of towns and even cities, nesting close to human habitation. Actually, in the span of a year, this warbler occurs from northern Alaska to western Peru and from Newfoundland to eastern South America. It is a welcome spring migrant, an admired summer resident and a reminder of coming winter when it leaves in the fall. Very confiding and gentle in its behavior, it will sometimes alight on one's hand and feed its young if held there.

One of its most striking characteristics is the fact that it regularly persists in attempts to defeat that potent parasite, the cowbird. Frequently victimized by the latter, the yellow warbler has learned to build a floor over the cowbird's egg when the latter appears in a nest, and so isolate it. Multi-storied nests of this warbler are often found, not only of two or three stories, but as many as six! Photographs of such nests in cross-section well show the manner in which the unwanted egg is sealed off.

It is difficult to see how anyone could fail to recognize the yellow warbler at sight. Even those who know little or nothing about wild birds, do know canaries and the warbler's local name of "wild canary" is very fitting. A supposed "loose" canary flitting about in the shrubbery of an urban garden is more than apt to be a yellow warbler.

As familiar as it is about civilization however, its original haunts and nesting sites were not those bounded by streets and fences. The typical habitat, in North America, is along watercourses, edges of swamps or wet brushlands amid growths of willows, alders and small trees in low situations. The numerous resident races of continental tropical America, found south to Venezuela and Peru, inhabit mostly the coastal mangrove swamps. (*See Chapter 14*) Blueberry and raspberry patches are also frequented and, at times, hedgerows and thickets. In migration the yellow warbler might be seen almost anywhere.

Dendroica petechia aestiva (Gmelin)
(Gr., *Dendroica*, tree-dweller; Lat., *petechia*, island-seeking; *aestiva*, summer)

Type Locality Quebec City

LOCAL NAMES: Eastern Yellow Warbler, Wild Canary, Summer Yellow Bird, Summer Warbler

FIELD CHARACTERS: *Male,* forepart of crown yellow, tinged with orange; rest of upperparts olive green; sides of head and underparts bright yellow, streaked with chestnut; wings and tail edged with yellowish-green.
Female, similar to male but pattern duller, underparts faintly, if at all streaked.
Immature, resembles the female generally.
Length, 4.50 to 5.25 inches.

NESTING DATA: A neat compact cup of milkweed fibers, Indian hemp, grasses and bits of rotten wood and plant down. Firmly felted inside. At elevations of from 2 to 12 feet (sometimes as high as 40 feet) in crotches of willows, alders and cottonwoods. In urban situations shrubbery such as lilacs and occasionally grapevines and raspberries.
Eggs—4 or 5. Grayish or bluish white, spotted and splashed with various shades of brown and gray, often showing "warbler wreath" about large end.

VOICE: A series of musical notes, about 8 in number, a sort of "see-see-see-see-tititi-see" (A. A. Saunders). Also a shrill *wi-wi-wi-wi-wi-chee.* (*See Chapter 5*)

FOOD HABITS: Almost wholly insects. Caterpillars, cankerworms, beetles, weevils and plant lice form much of the diet. Raspberries are sometimes taken.

GENERAL RANGE: *Breeds* from northern Mackenzie, Minnesota, Michigan and Ontario east to Nova Scotia; south to Nevada, Montana, Oklahoma, New Mexico, Missouri, northern Alabama, Georgia and South Carolina. *Winters* from Mexico south through Central America and to Peru, the Guianas and Brazil. *Accidental* in England.

Dendroica petechia amnicola Batchelder
(Lat., *amnicola,* river-dweller)

Type Locality Curslet, Newfoundland

LOCAL NAME: Newfoundland Yellow Warbler

This race which lives almost throughout Canada, differs from *D.p. aestiva* in having duller yellow underparts and heavier streaking thereon.

RANGE: *Breeds* from central Alaska and British Columbia across to Newfoundland and Nova Scotia. The migration is mainly through the Mississippi Valley; *winters* in Mexico and northern South America.

Dendroica petechia rubiginosa (Pallas)
(Lat., *rubiginosa,* rusty)

Type Locality Kodiak Island, Alaska

LOCAL NAME: Alaska Yellow Warbler

This subspecies is smaller and much duller in coloration than *D.p. aestiva.*

RANGE: *Breeds* from the coast region of southern Alaska to Vancouver Island, British Columbia and northwestern Washington. Migrates through California to Mexico and Central America. *Winters* from Baja California, western Mexico south to Panama.

Dendroica petechia morcomi Coale
(Lat., *morcomi,* for J. F. Morcom)

Type Locality Fort Bridger, Wyoming

LOCAL NAME: Rocky Mountain Yellow Warbler

This bird was described many years ago but was only accepted in 1944 (*Auk,* 61:459). It differs in being darker above with less yellowish green and the female is more buffy below and grayish above.

RANGE: *Breeds* from Western Washington, British Columbia and Montana south to southern California, southern Nevada, Arizona, New Mexico and western Oklahoma. *Winters* in Mexico, Central America, Venezuela, Colombia, Ecuador, and French Guiana.

Dendroica petechia sonorana Brewster
(Lat., *sonorana,* of Sonora, Mexico)

Type Locality Sonora, Mexico

LOCAL NAME: Sonora Yellow Warbler

This is the palest of the yellow warbler group, living as it does, in the southwestern deserts, where lightness of color is the rule. In habits and behavior it resembles the other forms.

RANGE: *Breeds* from southern Nevada, Arizona, New Mexico, southwestern Texas, northeastern Baja California southward into Mexico. *Winters* from Mexico to Costa Rica and south to Colombia and Ecuador.

Dendroica petechia gundlachi Baird
(Lat., *gundlachi,* for Dr. Gundlach)

Type Locality Cuba

LOCAL NAME: Cuban Yellow (or Golden) Warbler

This form of the Yellow Warbler was added to the bird list of this country on June 15, 1941, by Roger T.

Peterson and Earle R. Greene, on the Bay Keys, near Key West, Florida. A singing male was watched for some time. Greene subsequently found a nest.

In appearance it is much like the Eastern Yellow Warbler but the lower throat shows streaking and the crown has a tinge of rufous. Since the 1941 appearance, it has been noted in the Keys by a number of observers. At this writing it has not yet been reported from the Florida mainland.

RANGE: Cuba, Isle of Pines, and the Bahamas. The U.S. range as of the present, composes the area from the Mullet Keys (west of Key West) to Poor Joe Key in the eastern portion of Florida Bay.

Dendroica petechia castaneiceps Ridgway
(Lat., *castaneiceps,* chestnut headed)

Type Locality La Paz, Baja California

LOCAL NAME: Mangrove Warbler

FIELD CHARACTERS: Similar in habitat to the Cuban Yellow Warbler, the Mangrove Warbler is included because of its occurrence in southern Baja California. It spends its life among the mangroves on the opposite side of the continent from *gundlachi.* It is a handsome bird, but the difficulty of penetrating its haunts has resulted in few observers ever seeing it. Because of its chestnut colored head it was once thought to be a separate species; some think it should be so classified now (*cf. Chap. 14*).

It spends its life among the lower branches of tangled growth of the red mangrove and often descends to the mud-flats beneath the arching roots where it is even more difficult to see. The dappled sunlight, filtering through the branches and leaves, the latter often yellowish, blend with the bird's plumage to the extent of rendering it highly inconspicuous. The song suggests the yellow warbler but is less shrill and given with a rising inflection.

The outstanding field character of this race is the bright red-chestnut of the head and throat, black wings margined with yellow and rich yellow, brown streaked underparts.

RANGE: Resident of both coasts of Baja California south of Lat. 27° North, and the Pacific coast of Mexico from Sinaloa to Guatemala.
ALEXANDER SPRUNT, JR.

[*Comment:* The Yellow Warbler group is considered by some ornithologists to comprise more than one species (from 2 to 6 have been recognized). However, all of the many forms are allopatric, *i.e.* have separate breeding ranges. Morphological differences among them are those of degree, and for the most part concern the extent of rufous on the head and underparts of adult males. Physiologically, they resemble one another closely, and might be expected to interbreed if their ranges were to overlap. In accordance with modern specific concepts, there is no reason why they should not be regarded as constituting a well defined, conspecific assemblage included in the diversified genus *Dendroica*. (JAMES BOND)]

21

MAGNOLIA WARBLER

Dendroica magnolia

LOOKING on certain bird names today from a background of more experience with the species than was had by their discoverers, we often wish the names bestowed upon them could be changed to more appropriate ones. Wood Stork for Wood Ibis, Common Gallinule for Florida Gallinule, Kestrel for Sparrowhawk, and so on. This warbler, one of the handsomest of the family, has always seemed a case in point to me. Balsam or Spruce Warbler would be better by far, than Magnolia.

Certainly, in its summer home, the great coniferous north woods form the typical backdrop for this brilliant bird, for among such it lives and moves and has its being. Alexander Wilson, in making it known to science, secured one in a magnolia tree in Mississippi and in describing it, gave it the specific name of that great plant, though calling it "Black-and-Yellow Warbler" in common parlance. Though the latter was in use for many years by other ornithologists as well, the bird is Magnolia Warbler today.

Few birds are as spectacular in their habitat as this one. Seen amid the semi-gloom of the silent ranks of evergreens, it seems to glow with living color. Despite the strong contrasts in its plumage pattern, there is no sense of gaudiness, simply a beautifully striking bit of brilliance against a somber background.

[*Comment:* In Ontario, the Magnolia is associated with balsam and white spruce, but with a good mixture of red maple, white birch, young sugar maple, and hazel. (GUNN)]

It is an easy warbler to watch, for it lives

at low elevations and shows little fear of an observer. The redstart-like habit of drooping the wings and spreading the tail shows off the beauty of the plumage to excellent advantage. Although I have watched it nesting amid the spruce woods of the Maine coast and practically had it alight on my hand to feed young, one of my most vivid bird memories is of this warbler in late May in the tamarack bogs of the Adirondacks. It is not often met with along the south Atlantic coast as the bulk of migrating warblers pass to the westward, but even there I can recall a day when, in November, a belated Magnolia all but alighted within a yard of me, the first specimen I had seen in my native state. Occasional birds stop briefly at the Tortugas.

The Magnolia is one of the "unmistakables." The gray crown, black back and cheeks, yellow breast and rump, white wing bars and tail patches all add up to infallibility of recognition. Even the female is similar in pattern though the colors are duller. In fall plumage, however, adults and immatures are much alike.

Dendroica magnolia (Wilson)
(Lat., *magnolia,* a genus of plants)

Type Locality Fort Adams, Miss.

LOCAL NAME: Black-and-Yellow Warbler

FIELD CHARACTERS: *Male,* crown slate-gray; white stripe behind eye; wide band through eye and nape; back black; rump yellow. Underparts bright yellow streaked with black; under tail coverts white. Wings and tail brownish-black, a white patch in wings and broad band of same across middle of tail, except for central feathers.
Female, similar to male in pattern but colors duller.
Immature, similar to female but much brownish-olive on head, neck and back. White areas reduced.
Length, 4.45 to 5.10 inches.

NESTING DATA: Usually in small conifers such as spruce, balsam or hemlock, at low elevations, but also rarely in oak-hickory-chestnut forests. Nests are placed 1-15 feet off ground, but higher nests have been found. Composed of small twigs, evergreen needles, grass and spider silk, lined with fine black rootlets.

Eggs—3 to 5, usually 4. Creamy white, spotted and splashed with shades of reddish-brown, hazel, purplish and lavender. Many eggs are wreathed about the large end.

VOICE: One of the so-called "full voiced" warblers. Song with much variation often rendered as "weeto-weeto-*wee*-tee-eet" and "witti-witti-wit" (G. H. Thayer). A "chip" call note and another like "tlep," metallic and somewhat lisped but musical in quality. William Brewster gave his interpretation of the song as "she knows she was right; yes, she knows she was right," and earlier, as "pretty-pretty-Rachel." (*See Chapter 5*)

[*Comment:* Magnolias seem to change their song patterns as the season progresses. The early, middle, and late portions of the breeding period seem to have their own characteristic song types. The first is emphatic and relatively loud: "Been been *been* dichew." The second is about the same length, but is less em-

phatic and contains more sibilants, notes resembling the word "sweet" appearing at the beginning and end. The third is short, weak and colorless, resembling an abbreviated song of the myrtle warbler. (W. W. H. GUNN)]

FOOD HABITS: Almost entirely insects. Beetles, worms, flies and plant lice seem favorite items. A definitely valuable destroyer of many injurious forms.

GENERAL RANGE: *Breeds* from Newfoundland across Canada to central Mackenzie region, south to central British Columbia, Alberta, and east to Wisconsin, southern Ontario and Massachusetts; southward in the mountains to southwestern North Carolina. *Winters* from Mexico south to Panama. Also in the West Indies.

[*Comment:* A dramatic example of the hazards migration presents to small birds is found in Pauline James' account of warbler destruction on Padre Island, Texas, on May 7, 1951 (*Wilson Bull.,* 1956, 68:224–227). "Over 10,000 exhausted small birds perished here this day, about 85% of them warblers. Of 2421 birds actually collected, 1109 were Magnolia Warblers." (ROLAND C. CLEMENT)]

ALEXANDER SPRUNT, JR.

PLATE 12
CAPE MAY WARBLER
Page 117

Immature

Female   Male

John H. Dick
'55

22

CAPE MAY WARBLER

Dendroica tigrina

MORE gaudily colored warblers there certainly are, but in any contest for honors as the most handsome warbler, the male Cape May must surely be given consideration. The rich, harmonious blending of colors, the striking pattern on throat and breast, the black cap and chestnut ear-patches—all these combine to make the bird a favorite with many observers.

Alternating as they do between the islands of the West Indies in winter and the northern continental spruce forests in summer, one might expect them to be highly adaptable to a variety of living conditions but, as in the more extreme case of Kirtland's Warbler, they seem to have rather strict requirements for nesting habitat in the north.

The selected habitat is normally in fairly open coniferous forest with a good percent-

age of mature spruces or in dense spruce forest with a scattering of taller spires above the canopy level. In either situation, the male establishes a few adjacent spires as song perches, singing from the very top or just below it. Usually the singer is fully exposed and can be seen at a considerable distance from a vantage point.

Cape May songs are high-pitched and weak, having less than half the volume of, say, the songs of Tennessee Warblers. The song most commonly heard is a simple repetition of a "zee" or "zeet" phrase five or six (3–11) times in the same pitch and at a rather slow tempo. In some songs, the phrases have two or three syllables, in which case the tempo is increased proportionately.

The nest, comparatively large for a warbler, is built in the dense terminal clump

117

of vegetation at the top of one of these spires, perhaps 30–60 feet high, and is virtually invisible from the ground. It is usually composed largely of Sphagnum moss with a thick lining of hair and feathers.

When feeding in the spruce forest, Cape Mays may fly-catch at treetop level or descend to considerably lower levels to hunt larval insects. Along with the Bay-breasted Warbler, the Cape May is known to reach dense populations in areas of forest where an infestation of Spruce Budworms is taking place. Kendeigh (1947) calculated a density of 28 pairs per 100 acres in spruce-fir forest near Lake Nipigon, Ontario, and Stewart and Aldrich (1952) found almost identical densities in spruce-fir forest in northern Maine under similar conditions of budworm infestation. In neither case was it clear whether this was a natural increase built up over the several-year cycle of a budworm outbreak or whether it occurred through infiltration of birds from surrounding areas.

Although Cape Mays are known to nest as far west as Alberta, the main body of the population summers in Quebec and the Maritime Provinces. West of the Quebec border, it is an uncommon warbler except under conditions of budworm outbreak.

With such a geographical distribution, the main flow of migration is naturally through the eastern United States, with probably more birds travelling east of the Alleghenies than west of them. Working up through Cuba, the Bahamas, and Florida through February, March, and April, they then fan out to some degree, a few reaching as far west as Missouri. They mingle with the middle or later groups of migrant warblers in May, arriving on the breeding range in late May or early June. The molt takes place in July after nesting and they are on their way south again before the end of August, moving rather rapidly through the eastern United States in September. At that time, the yellow rump is a useful field-identification mark.

Bent (1953) quotes several reports of Cape Mays in fall migration feeding on (or drinking from) ripening grapes in vineyards—one of the few instances of warblers departing from an insect diet.

The name "Cape May," incidentally, was given to the bird in 1831 by Alexander Wilson, who formally described and sketched a specimen collected by his friend George Ord at Cape May, N.J., twenty years previously.

[*Comment:* It is of interest that neither Wilson nor Audubon ever saw this warbler alive, and after Ord secured his specimen at Cape May (1811) it was not recorded from there again until almost a century had passed (1920). (ALEXANDER SPRUNT, JR.)]

Dendroica tigrina (Gmelin)
(Lat., *tigrina*, like a tiger, in markings)

Type Locality in Canada

FIELD CHARACTERS: *Male,* crown black; upperparts olive-green spotted with black; rump olive-yellow; sides of head chestnut; underparts and sides of neck yellow, heavily streaked on sides and breast with black; conspicuous white patches in wings; outer tail feathers spotted with white.

Female, head and upperparts olive with no chestnut cheek patches; little white in wings; underparts dull yellow, streaked with grayish-brown; rump olive-yellow.

Immature, similar to female but much duller.

Length, 4.70 to 5.65 inches.

NESTING DATA: In coniferous trees, usually near the top, 30 to 60 feet from ground. Compact cup of mosses, fine twigs, grasses and plant down, lined with hair, feathers or fur. Usually invisible from below.

Eggs—4 to 9, usually 6. Creamy white, spotted and splashed with rich brown, with under markings of drab, gray, and black, concentrated about the larger end.

VOICE: High-pitched, sibilant, and rather weak, the notes on one pitch and varying from 4 to 11 in the commonly presented song type. *Seet seet seet seet.* (*See Chapter 5.*)

FOOD HABITS: Generally insectivorous, but known to do damage to vineyard grapes in fall migration.

GENERAL RANGE: *Breeds* from southern Mackenzie, northeastern British Columbia, northern Alberta, central Saskatchewan, central Manitoba, northern Ontario, central Quebec and Newfoundland south to northern Wisconsin, northern Michigan, northeastern New York, New Hampshire, Maine and Nova Scotia. *Winters* in the West Indies north to the Bahamas.

W. W. H. GUNN

23

BLACK-THROATED BLUE WARBLER

Dendroica caerulescens

THERE is much of attraction in this "neat but not gaudy" warbler. It **is** an abundant migrant through much of the East but, aside from the mountain form (*cairnsi*) is a rather northern nester.

During the migrations from Florida, through the Atlantic States as well as west of the Alleghenies, it may be seen almost anywhere—woodlands, gardens, suburban yards and city parks. Its very name is distinctive and descriptive and even the dun-colored female is easy to recognize, thanks to the conspicuous white spot in the wings.

Once on its nesting grounds this warbler prefers heavy woodlands or mature forests of mixed conifers and hardwoods, the latter predominating, with an under-cover of laurel, hazel, or maple or other brushy saplings. In tracking down its "trees, trees, trees" song in the Adirondacks I have crawled through thickets of "witch-hobble," to find myself within a few feet of the singer as it rested on a low branch, giving its song several times a minute.

The tameness of this species is one of its most striking behaviorisms. One has little difficulty in approaching it closely, especially about the nest, and it indulges the "broken-wing" tactic to a marked degree. It is deliberate in its movements which are so different from the excessively active behavior of the Redstart. Much of the time this seems to be reflected in the song which is delivered lazily and with a very definite husky quality. Though the one most often uttered is not hard to remember, this warbler departs from custom and sometimes voices a variation one would not connect with it, despite familiarity. Therefore, when tracking down the "unknown" song,

PLATE 13
BLACK-THROATED BLUE WARBLER
Page 120

Young Male

Adult Male

Adult Female

the observer is sometimes surprised. Here after all, is no new bird at all—only a Black-throated Blue singing unlike anything the listener ever heard before.

Though hardly to be confused with any other species, this warbler so often allows close approach that no observer need ever be in any doubt as to its identity when seeing the male. Bent (1953) says of the female that she "is one of the most difficult of the warblers to recognize . . . the only distinctive marks are the white patches in the wings . . . sometimes obscure." This is no doubt true in cases where the white wing spot is lacking; but it is my experience and impression that if all female warblers were as generally recognizable as this one, there would be far less confusion about the family as a whole.

Migration hazards are hard on this warbler. Lighthouses once took a heavy toll, Sombrero Light off the Florida Keys, being one of many. On the Dry Tortugas Keys some 70 miles west of Key West in the Gulf of Mexico, I have seen the bird in the fall migration in such numbers and tameness that it constituted one of the avian sights of that remarkable area. Scores of them were to be seen on the parade ground of old Fort Jefferson, others hopping about in the galleries and gun emplacements, on the very porch of the guest quarters and in the sea-grapes and gumbo-limbo trees overhanging it.

ALEXANDER SPRUNT, JR.

THE BLACK-THROATED BLUE IN MICHIGAN

Arriving in northern Michigan after mid-May this bird is found usu-ally in cut-over deciduous forests. Through these forests grow a few scattered hemlocks and balsam fir, but they consist chiefly of red maple, sugar maple and yellow or gray birch. On only one occasion have I found the species in an uncut forest. In this area the canopy consisted of virgin maples and the undercover of very small maples. They seem to prefer deciduous areas which have been cut during the last five to ten years. Sometimes we have found nests in dead beech leaves; in a live beech less than two feet tall or in a similar maple where the forest floor is almost solid with these very small trees.

The young birds, when first hatched, have darker colored skin than most warblers that we have observed. When they left the nest we noted that two of the birds had feathers much darker than the third, indicating that the sexes are discernible even at that age. When the young were small they made little or no noise, but during their last day in the nest they made so much noise that we found the nest from some distance away. They called in unison with a rapid 'chur-chur-chur-chur.'

The chipmunk is apparently one of the animals feared most by this bird in the nesting season. On two occasions we were almost certain the young were taken by chipmunks. One young was gone each morning and we watched the chipmunks underneath the nests. On both occasions the birds went through the broken-wing ruse ahead of the chipmunks trying to lead them from their nest. The chipmunks caused no damage while we watched but by next morning another young was missing and the conclusion seemed obvious.

Dendroica caerulescens caerulescens (Gmelin)
(Lat., *caerulescens,* blue)

Type Locality Santo Domingo, W.I.

LOCAL NAME: Northern Black-throated Blue Warbler

FIELD CHARACTERS: *Male,* upperparts blue; wings brownish black, a conspicuous white patch at the base of the primaries; throat, sides of the face and sides of the body black; rest of the underparts white. Bill and legs dark.

Female, upperparts, olive-green showing the white wing spot; underparts, buffy.

Length, 4.50 to 5.50 inches.

NESTING DATA: Nest in small trees or in fallen tree tops, in maples, hemlocks, mountain-laurel, beeches, even in small spruces, blackberry bushes, yews, rhododendrons, all very near the ground from one to three feet up. Nest bulky, of rotten wood, strips of bark, dead-leaf fragments; lined with hair, black rootlets, at times even fine porcupine quills.

Eggs—Usually 4, less often 3 and rarely 5. White or creamy white, speckled blotched, or clouded with tones of brown, russet, or auburn. Measurements ranged between 15.2 x 12.2 and 18.9 x 13.0 mm. (Bent).

Incubation of eggs required 12 days according to Miss Cordelia J. Stanwood (Bent) and the young remain in the nest for 10 days.

VOICE: Aretas A. Saunders (in Bent) wrote: "The song of the black-throated blue warbler, in its more typical forms, is one of only three or four slowly drawled notes in a peculiarly husky voice, the last note commonly slurred upward." The length of the songs was from 1⅕ to 2 seconds. He also wrote that this warbler sings unusual songs more than most warblers. He found that the black-throated blue discontinued singing about July 21 but began again in late August after the molt. The common song consisting of from two to seven syllables sounds like "sweee-sweee-sweee-sweee" with the last syllable ending in an upward slur. Others have said it sounds like "zur-zur-zree" or "zero-zero-zee," the last syllable rising. (*See Chapter 5*)

FOOD HABITS: Largely insects but occasionally seeds and berries. Actual foods listed by Dr. Alexander Wetmore from eight stomachs of birds taken in Puerto Rico in December and January consisted of 75.5 percent animal matter and 24.5 percent vegetable matter.

A. Black-throated Blue. B. Cairns'.

GENERAL RANGE: *Breeds.* The known breeding range extends from northern Minnesota eastward through Ontario, Quebec (southern) to Cape Breton Island and Halifax, Nova Scotia, southward through New England, northeastern Pennsylvania west through northern Michigan and Wisconsin to Minnesota. However, the species has been found in Manitoba and Saskatchewan and is a regular migrant through North and South Dakota. *Winters* from southeastern South Carolina through southern Florida, south to Guatemala and northern Colombia; but chiefly in the West Indies, the Bahamas, Cuba, Jamaica, Hispaniola, Puerto Rico and the Virgin Islands.

LAWRENCE H. WALKINSHAW

Dendroica caerulescens cairnsi Coues

Type Locality Buncombe County, N.C.

LOCAL NAME: Cairns' Warbler

This mountain race of the Black-throated Warbler has been known to me practically since boyhood, as summers were spent for many years in what may be called the heart of its range, the high Blue Ridge. Two general areas, the Grandfather Mountain section to 5964 ft. altitude, and the Mount Mitchell area which is the highest east of the Mississippi River, 6684 ft., are typical habitats. It is a thoroughly characteristic bird of the hardwoods and conifers, as well as the great thickets of laurel and rhododendron.

This warbler was described by Elliott Coues in 1897 and named by him for its discoverer, John S. Cairns of Weaverville, N.C. Many of my observations of it were made within twenty miles of where Cairns lived.

Though birds in the northern part of the range intergrade with *d.c. caerulescens,* those of the Carolina mountains are typical of the race and all but invariably marked with black spots on the back. The female is darker and duller olive above and with less yellow below than *caerulescens.*

It lives at altitudes from about 2500 to 5200 feet and generally arrives ten days ahead of the passing *D.c.* migrants. The lowest I ever found a nest was about at 2200 feet, in a laurel sprout eight inches from the ground. It has been established as breeding in Pickens County, S.C., at even lower altitudes. The eggs are like those of *caerulescens.*

RANGE: *Breeds* from northern Maryland and south central Pennsylvania and West Virginia, south to northern Georgia and northwestern South Carolina. *Winters* in Cuba, the Bahamas and Dominican Republic.

ALEXANDER SPRUNT, JR.

24

MYRTLE WARBLER

Dendroica coronata

OF the great family of wood warblers the Myrtle might well be said to be at the top rung of familiarity even in its varied plumages; for it inhabits a tremendous range and shows itself to observers from one end of the country to the other, even at one's very window sills and porches. The South knows it as well as the North, the East as well as the West. Bent (1953) places it next to the yellow warbler and the yellowthroat as being known to most people, but in some areas it definitely exceeds both species in such category. It seems very strange that, in view of its general abundance, neither Audubon nor Wilson ever found it nesting.

I have often wondered if it is not the commonest North American warbler—it simply swarms in winter all over the southeastern part of the country as well as wintering further north than any other of the family.

Though Audubon called it the Yellow-rumped Warbler, a name still very distinctive, it has become so associated with the wax myrtle (*Myrica cerifera*) and its relative the northern bayberry (*Myrica carolinensis*) that many observers automatically connect the bird and the shrubs.

Though mostly a bird of the woodlands in the nesting period, the Myrtle Warbler is not so much so in winter. Broken forests, field edges, roadside hedges and thickets are frequented and it is often to be seen on beaches of mainland and island, where it feeds among the dunes. In the dense myrtle tangles of the Carolina barrier islands it can be observed in incredible numbers during the cold months and, while a berry-picker to a degree, combines fly-catching in its feeding behavior, as well as indulging in butterfly-like hovering about cracks and crannies of trees or buildings. It evinces remarkable tameness about human habitations, resulting in an ease of observation not possible with many other warblers. It is not infrequently seen on the ground and, as with most of the family, exhibits "broken-wing" tactics in the attempt to lure intruders from the nesting site.

One of the easiest warblers to recognize, its outstanding field mark is the bright yellow patch on the rump. Whether seen in the handsome blue-gray, black, white and yellow of the breeding dress, or the rather drab and dull winter plumage, the rump patch is ever present and easy to see. In winter, its tendencies toward ground feeding, or low elevations, remind one of the Palm Warbler with which it often associates in its winter range in the east.

It is a very active bird, seemingly on the go constantly. Of the very few species of Passerine birds I have found entangled in tough spider webs, this warbler has figured in two instances. One was dead, the other still struggling feebly. Both of these observations were in coastal South Carolina. The Myrtle Warbler is occasionally killed in considerable numbers on migration by striking obstructions, radio towers, ceilometers and the like, and is apt to be victimized by the cowbird.

Dendroica coronata coronata (Linnaeus)
  (Lat., *coronata*, crowned)

Type Locality Philadelphia, Penna.

LOCAL NAMES: Eastern Myrtle Warbler, Yellow-
    rumped Warbler

FIELD CHARACTERS: *Spring*—Upparts blue-gray, streaked with black; wings black with two white wing-bars; tail black, marked with white spots on outer feathers; underparts whitish, streaked with blackish; throat black; spot on crown, at sides of chest and on rump, bright yellow.

Winter—Upperparts gray-brown, faintly streaked with dark brown; sides of head brownish; yellow crown lacking or concealed, chest patches very dull but rump conspicuous. Underparts dull white or gray, with obscure streaking. *Length,* 5 to 6 inches.

NESTING DATA: Usually in coniferous trees such as spruce, cedar and hemlock. Nest of small twigs, strips of bark, plant-down and fibers, lined with hair and feathers. Elevations vary from 4 to 50 feet, the average about 20.

Eggs—4 or 5. White, speckled with shades of brown and lilac forming a wreath about large end.

VOICE: A rather loud, silvery trilling, rising or falling at the end, broken at times into separate notes and carrying for some distance: wheedle wheedle wheedle wheedle wheedle (Bent) whee whee whee whee whee whee whee hew hew (Allen). A sharp, metallic call note like "chep" often uttered in winter and very distinctive.

A. Eastern Myrtle. B. Alaska Myrtle.

[*Comment:* In Ontario, many observers agree that the diagnostic call-note of the Myrtle, so different from that of other warblers, has an 'r' quality to it, as in 'turk.' (Gunn)] (*See Chapter 5*)

FOOD HABITS: Largely vegetable in winter, berries of wax myrtle, cedar, yaupon (Ilex) poison ivy and sumach. Insects are also taken and form bulk of summer food among which are beetles, plant lice and flies.

GENERAL RANGE: *Breeds* from northern Alberta across Canada to central Labrador and Newfoundland, south to central Alberta and across to northern Minnesota, Massachusetts and Pennsylvania (Poconos). *Winters* from central Maine and southern Nova Scotia west to Kansas and Missouri south through the U.S., Central America to Panama, Bermuda, Bahamas and the Virgin Islands. Has been recorded in Siberia and Devon, England.

Dendroica coronata hooveri McGregor

Type Locality Palo Alto, California

LOCAL NAME: Alaska Myrtle Warbler

This far western race, having longer wings and tail, resembles the Eastern Myrtle in habits and behavior. Bent (1953) says of it "It appears to be a quite finely drawn subspecies." Since there is an overlap in its range and that of Audubon's Warbler, the two occasionally interbreed with resulting hybrids.

RANGE: *Breeds* from northwestern Mackenzie to western Alaska and south to southern Alaska and northern British Columbia. *Winters* from Oregon south to California, Arizona, east to Missouri and has been found at such season as far east as South Carolina. Also Baja California to Vera Cruz, Mexico, Central America as far as Panama.

ALEXANDER SPRUNT, JR.

PLATE 14
AUDUBON'S WARBLER
Page 129

Male

Female

BLACK-FRONTED WARBLER
Page 131
Male

MYRTLE WARBLER
Page 125
Female
Male

Myrtle Immature

John H. Dick
'55

25

AUDUBON'S WARBLER

Dendroica auduboni

THIS handsome species takes the place in the west, of the familiar Myrtle Warbler of the east. Very similar to the Myrtle, there are definite differences aside from the diversification of range. Audubon's Warbler has a bright yellow throat, making five yellow areas against four for the Myrtle; it also shows more white in wings and tail. Its breeding range does not extend as far north as *coronata's* but penetrates further south and to higher altitudes. It is, in the nesting season, a truly mountain warbler breeding at close to 12,000 feet in Colorado. In Yosemite it nests from 3300 to 10,000 feet; in southern California from 9000 to 10,500 feet, and in New Mexico from 7500 to 11,000 feet. In Washington similar altitudes have been noted to at least 8000 feet.

In early September of 1955, John H. Dick and the writer found this warbler in numbers in the Chiricahua Mountains of southeastern Arizona, at altitudes of between 8000 and 9000 ft. They were in flocks, and were feeding from the ground itself all the way to the tops of lofty Ponderosa pines in the Rustler's and Barfoot Parks area. Audubon's Warbler descends to the lowlands only in winter.

There is a definite resemblance to the Myrtle Warbler in its quick and active way of life. It seldom seems to stop its constant flitting to and fro, hovering here, darting there, uttering the sharp, metallic "chip" so reminiscent of the eastern bird. It "flycatches" adroitly, either weaving through a swarm of gnats or midges, snapping them up, or launching out from a perch to secure a passing insect and returning to the lookout stand.

Sometimes nesting close to human habitation it is not particularly shy. Defense of nest or young is pronounced and Audubon's Warbler indulges the usual "broken wing act" in the vicinity of its home. Some of these performances are very elaborate.

It is a very hardy bird, many wintering almost as far north as the nesting range extends, although it does not then frequent high altitudes. It is one of the more successful of the warblers in maintaining a population status. In many parts of the west and particularly the southwest, it is one of the most abundant wintering birds, again paralleling the Myrtle Warbler of the southeast at that season.

The outstanding field mark is its yellow throat, the only species possible to confuse with it being the Myrtle which lacks this character. The fall and immature plumages of Audubon's Warbler show much more white in the tail than the Myrtle (4 or 5 areas against 2 or 3) but the yellow rump patch is conspicuous in both species. Even in obscure winter plumage this mark stands out well and of course the locality in which either bird is observed (east or west) is indicative of identity.

Dendroica auduboni auduboni (Townsend)
(Lat., *auduboni,* for J. J. Audubon)

Type Locality Fort Vancouver, Washington

LOCAL NAME: Pacific Audubon's Warbler

FIELD CHARACTERS: Very similar to Myrtle Warbler but with bright *yellow throat* and more white areas in tail.
Length, 5.10 to 5.25 inches.

NESTING DATA: In both conifers and deciduous trees and bushes, at times in cavities (J.K.

Jensen, New Mexico, 1932). Elevations vary from 9 to 30 ft. Nest usually "a beautiful structure" composed of small twigs, rootlets, bark-strippings and weed-stems, lined with hair or feathers, often the latter.

Eggs—3 to 5, usually 4. Gray or creamy white, spotted and marbled with varying shades of brown, drab and gray. Frequently wreathed about large end.

VOICE: Song similar to Myrtle, varies with locality, described as "chwee-chwee-chwee-ah-chwee" to "tsil-tsil-tsil-tsi-tsi-tsi-tsi." Somewhat louder and more pronounced than Myrtle. Call note a quick, metallic "chip."

FOOD HABITS: Largely insects. Of 383 stomachs examined in California, animal matter was present in 85% (insects-spiders), while vegetable was represented by 15% (wild fruits and weed seeds). Grapes are taken at times but damage to domestic fruit is negligible.

GENERAL RANGE: *Breeds* from central British Columbia, south along the coast to southern California and Baja California. *Winters* from southwestern British Columbia, coastal Washington south to Baja California and Mexico to Guatemala.

A. Audubon's. B. Black-fronted.

Dendroica auduboni memorabilis Oberholser
  (Lat., *memorabilis,* noteworthy)

Type Locality Boulder Co., Colo.

Local Name: Black-fronted Warbler

This form, the Black-fronted Warbler, was thought
for some time to be a distinct species but is now recognized as being sub-specific to *D.a. auduboni.* It has
much more black in the plumage than Pacific Audubon's Warbler, with the forehead, sides of crown
and head uniformly of that color, with the black area
of the breast unrelieved with lighter color. The female,
though duller, is much darker in this sex than in
auduboni.

This warbler nests in some of the high mountain
ranges of southeastern Arizona, notably the Santa
Catalinas, Huachucas and Chiricahuas, from about
8500 ft., upward. Nest and eggs are similar to those
of Audubon's Warbler and the general behavior of
this form is like it as well, though it averages larger
in size.

Range: *Breeds* from British Columbia, Alberta and
          Saskatchewan south to eastern Califor-
nia. Nevada, southern Arizona, New Mexico and
Texas. *Winters* from Central Washington, Nevada,
Utah, Arizona, New Mexico and southern Texas
south through Mexico to Guatemala and Costa Rica.

Alexander Sprunt, Jr.

26

BLACK-THROATED GRAY WARBLER

Dendroica nigrescens

THERE is much about this exquisitely neat, trim warbler that appeals on first acquaintance, and on any subsequent observation, no matter how frequent such may be. It is an easy warbler to watch, as it is not at all shy and often allows close approach. It frequents both tall and low-growth conifers in the northern parts of its range (which extends into southern British Columbia) but in the southern portions (Arizona and New Mexico) it is frequently found in low vegetation such as scrub oak, Manzanita thickets, Juniper and Pinyon Pines. In the Chiricahua Mountains, it is found in shrubby oaks and small conifers, sometimes bushes. It is a dry area bird, preferring rocky slopes and thickets along old stream beds.

Compared to many other warblers, the Black-throated Gray does not show the constant, nervous activity characteristic of its tribe, but is rather methodical and deliberate in its movements, varying between marked indifference to an observer and outright secretiveness. Though I have not had the opportunity of watching it at the nest, behavior there seems to differ widely. C. W. Bowles (1902) has examined a nest while the female fed on caterpillars in an unconcerned manner about five feet away, following him for about twenty feet when he left the vicinity, almost within arm's reach. W. L. Finley (1904) on the other hand, at a nest he discovered, says that "The moment the mother returned and found me at the nest she was scared almost out of her senses. She fell from the top of the tree in a fluttering fit. She caught quivering on the limb a foot from my hand. But unable to hold on, she slipped through the branches

John H. Dick
'55

Immature

Male

Female

Female

and clutched my shoe. I never saw such an exaggerated case of the chills. I stooped to see what ailed her. She wavered like an autumn leaf to the ground. I leaped down, but she had limped under a bush and suddenly got well. Of course I knew she was tricking me! But I never saw higher skill in a feathered artist."

The song is simple in quality and drowsily pleasing, usually delivered from the top of a bush or tree for some considerable period of time; then a shift of position to another such perch and a repeated performance.

The Black-throated Gray is an easy warbler to recognize. The black and white pattern of the head and throat is very conspicuous, and with the gray back, thinly streaked white breast and two white wing bars, identifies the male at once. There is a very small yellow spot in front of the eye, by no means easy to see except at close range. The female lacks the black throat, her's being white. It is certainly one of the most characteristic warblers of the west, easily found and well remembered.

Dendroica nigrescens (Townsend)
    (Lat., *nigrescens*, blackish)

Type Locality Near Fort William (Portland) Ore.

FIELD CHARACTERS: *Male,* head, chin and throat black, small yellow spot in front of eye; a white line behind and below cheeks. Upperparts blue-gray, underparts white with thin black streakings. Two white wing-bars; outer tail feathers heavily marked with white.
    Female, similar but with throat white.
    Length, 4.70 to 5.40 inches.

NESTING DATA: In conifers, manzanita bushes, oaks, usually at low elevations (3 to 10 ft.) but

sometimes as high as 25 to 50 ft. Nest of plant fibers, weed-stalks, grasses and leaves. Often presents a gray appearance because of the dead weeds and grass of such color. Lined with fur, feathers or hair.
    Eggs—3 to 5, usually 4. White or creamy, speckled and spotted with browns and drabs, often in a wreath at large end. Markings vary much in intensity.

VOICE: A simple, pleasing song of four or more notes, the last syllable may ascend or descend: "swee, swee, ker-swee, sick" or "wee-zy, wee-zy, wee-zy, wee-zy-weet" have been used to describe the song. Call note a low "chit."

FOOD HABITS: Largely if not wholly insects. Oak worms and caterpillars appear to be favorite diet.

GENERAL RANGE: *Breeds* from southern British Columbia, Washington and Oregon across to Nevada, Utah and northwestern Colorado, south to northern Baja California, Arizona, and New Mexico. *Winters* from coastal and southern California, southern Arizona south to southern Baja California into Mexico and casually to Guatemala.
    ALEXANDER SPRUNT, JR.

27

TOWNSEND'S WARBLER

Dendroica townsendi

THOUGH the nesting range of this beautiful warbler extends southward from Alaska into the Pacific Northwest of this country, it will always be connected in my mind with the high mountain ranges of southeastern Arizona during the migrating season. From the lofty reaches of Mt. Graham in the Penalinas to the fantastic canyons of the Chiricahuas, the glowing brilliance of *townsendi* will ever remain a vivid memory.

Though a high-ranging bird much of the time, Townsend's Warbler can be seen at low elevations and indeed, often nests in such. Evergreens (firs) are more utilized than any other growth and need not be of any great height. Nests have been found from 8 to 15 feet from the ground in these trees, but the bird has also been noted carrying nesting material into firs as high as 100 feet.

I have watched this warbler in the Arizona mountains as low as from 8 to 10 feet, feeding in scrubby growth and evincing a degree of tameness which allowed observation at no more than 15 or 20 feet. In good light, the striking markings stood out as if painted in bright blacks, yellows and whites; the birds being rather deliberate in movement, I was afforded ample opportunity for detailed study.

It appears very evident, from the literature, that Townsend's is one of the lesser-known warblers. This is true in several respects but especially in regard to its nesting habits.

The early reports of its breeding in willows, which are of course, of low growth, appear now to be erroneous. Subsequent observations confirm that the fir tree is much the preferred if not the only nesting situation, therefore Major Bendire's supposed nests of this warbler, taken from willows in southwest Oregon in 1875, and those collected by Walter Raine in 1892 at Vancouver, British Columbia, also in willows, leave room for doubt as to correct identification.

Another memory I treasure regarding this warbler is the sight of it amid the immense firs and cedars of Stanley Park in Vancouver City, B.C. Though not in the nesting season, the observation in such magnificent surroundings, where flashing sun-rays alternated with drifting wisps of fog, leaves the impression that Townsend's Warbler, almost more than any other species, typifies the grandeur of great trees, sunlight and shadow. The bird's predilection for great heights is notable under these conditions, and it appears hardly larger than a hummingbird in the crowns of the towering evergreens.

It is usually a very active warbler, flitting about restlessly from tree to tree on its all but constant search for food. Exceptions make rules however, and occasionally a specimen evinces a degree of deliberation that is definitely noticeable.

The song has been likened to that of both the Black-throated Green and Black-throated Gray Warblers, having a drawling tendency (but less than *D. nigrescens*) and composed of from five to seven notes or more, variously rendered as "dee," "zee," or "swee":

"swee, swee, swee, zee" or "dee, dee, dee—de, de," or "weazy, weazy, weazy, tweea."

Townsend's is a distinctive warbler. The alternating blacks and yellows of the head and throat; olive-green back and yellow underparts with black streakings, together with prominent wing-bars and much white in the outer tail feathers at once identify it. A similar pattern appears in the female but is much duller and she lacks the black throat. It certainly stands alone in appearance among western warblers.

As in the case of certain other western birds this warbler has appeared in the east in what seem utterly incongruous localities, notably Prospect Park in Brooklyn, N.Y. There are also extralimital records for Long Island, N.Y., and Gulfport, Miss.

Dendroica townsendi (Townsend)
    (Lat., *townsendi,* for J. K. Townsend)

Type Locality Fort Vancouver, Wash.

FIELD CHARACTERS: Male, crown, cheeks and throat black with alternating areas bright yellow. Upperparts olive-green, spotted or streaked with black; underparts yellow and streaked. Two distinct

white wing-bars and much white in outer tail feathers.

Female, pattern similar but duller and without black on throat.

Immature, similar to female but washed with brown.

Length, 4.60 inches.

NESTING DATA: Almost entirely in fir trees, though possibly in other conifers. Known elevations vary from 8 to 15 feet; birds have been noted carrying nesting material as high as 100 feet.

Nest compact and bulky, composed of plant fibers, bark-strippings, moss, grasses, lichens and slender twigs, lined with hair or stems of moss blossoms. Interior of cup rather shallow.

Eggs—3 to 5. White, or pinkish white, speckled and spotted with various shades of brown and lavender, mostly about large end but not in the often noted warbler "wreath."

VOICE: Rather drowsy in character and deliberately uttered, persistent. Variously described by the words "weazy," "dee" and "swee" repeated, usually five notes sometimes running to seven or more. Likened to both *D. virens* and *D. nigrescens.* (Bent, 1953.)

FOOD HABITS: Almost wholly insects with a marked preference for weevils (snout-beetles), one of which is very detrimental to evergreens (conifers). Engraver beetles, caterpillars and spiders are also taken with a small amount of vegetable food (about 5 per cent) such as seeds.

Feeding-station diet has been known to embrace cheese, marshmallows and peanut-butter. (Bent, 1953.)

GENERAL RANGE: *Breeds* from upper Yukon and Prince William Sound, Alaska, south to Washington, western Montana and Wyoming to southwestern Alberta. Migrates through Rocky Mt., region east to west Texas and west to Pacific Coast. *Winters* in California, western Mexico, Guatemala, El Salvador and Nicaragua. Alexander Skutch states that it occurs in Guatemala "in vast numbers" and he considers it "the most abundant of all birds" from September to May between 7000 and 10,000 ft. (Bent, 1953.)

ALEXANDER SPRUNT, JR.

28

BLACK-THROATED GREEN WARBLER

Dendroica virens

THIS handsome, often hard to see, warbler is rightly connected in the minds of many observers with the coniferous north woods. Though frequenting hardwoods also, conifers are favorites; but in any growth the bird is apt to be a high ranger. It is therefore more often heard than seen. Its small size, the height of the trees and screening foliage all combine to render the bird inconspicuous. It is not particularly shy and sometimes evinces a curiosity regarding an observer at close range, but it still remains more of a voice than an actuality to many who look for it.

The song is as distinctive as any warbler delivery can be, and easily learned. It has a drowsy quality which is appealing and, to some, musical as well. The notes vary from about five to eight, the last ascending, and the bird sings frequently. Mrs. Nice (1932) has counted 466 utterances in an hour. Albert Brand (1938) states that in vibrations per second in the highest note, the figure 6750 is reached, which compares well with the Black-polled Warbler whose performance "is the shrillest passerine bird song."

Whether heard on the spruce-clad islands of the Maine coast, the high hardwoods of the Adirondacks, the maple-hemlock forests of eastern Canada, or the cypress swamps and mountains of the Carolinas, the notes are instantly recognizable, though variation often occurs.

This warbler shows a strange quirk of behavior regarding invasion of its nesting territory in not tolerating certain intruders while disregarding others. Pitelka (1940) and Reading and Hayes (1933) are quoted by Bent (1953) on this characteristic. The close proximity of a red squirrel was seen to be ignored by a female Black-throated Green which had young, while a Black-and-White Warbler nearby was set upon and driven away at once (Pitelka). Reading and Hayes saw Chestnut-sided and Blackburnian Warblers and a Red-eyed Vireo driven off, while a family of Chickadees very close by was completely ignored. The Black-throated Green is occasionally victimized by the Cowbird.

[*Comment:* This and *D. caerulescens* occupy quite similar niches in Ontario, often being found within sight and sound of one another, but *D. virens* tends toward a slightly higher percentage of conifer. (GUNN)]

Once under observation, it is an unmistakable warbler, the yellow cheeks, olive-green back and black throat rendering the male unlike any other species, while the female's pattern is very similar though duller. The migration route indicates that it is a trans-Gulf traveler since it appears in eastern Texas from its winter home in Central America, and follows up the Mississippi Valley toward the northeast. The southern race (*waynei*) probably veers more to the eastward when making landfall in this country.

Dendroica virens virens (Gmelin)
   (Lat., *virens,* green)

Type Locality Philadelphia, Pa.

LOCAL NAME: Northern Black-throated Green Warbler

FIELD CHARACTERS: *Male,* upperparts yellow olive-green; wings dark brown with two white bars. Sides of head and neck lemon yellow; throat and breast black, rest of underparts white. Flanks and sides heavily streaked with black.

A. Black-throated Green. B. Wayne's.

Female, color pattern similar to male but much duller; cheeks and throat light yellow.
   Immature, like adult female but with more yellow on upperparts and white beneath.
   Length, 4.25 to 5.25 inches.

NESTING DATA: Usually in conifers but at times in maples, birches and other hardwoods, even alders and grapevines. Elevations vary from practically ground level (8 in.) to 70 feet. Nest a compact, often beautiful structure of twigs, grass, plant down, bark-strippings and moss, lined with hair, feathers or fur.

Eggs—4 to 5. Creamy white, speckled, spotted and scrawled with reddish brown, purplish and lilac, often wreathed about large end.

VOICE: A slow, rather drowsy series of 5 to 8 notes, the last on ascending scale. Easily learned and very distinctive. The words *zee zee zee zo zee* fit in most cases. (*See Chapter 5*)

FOOD HABITS: Largely insects with occasional berries. Many insects injurious to trees figure in the diet.

GENERAL RANGE: *Breeds* from central Mackenzie, Saskatchewan, northern Manitoba, central Ontario across to Newfoundland, south to central Alberta, Manitoba, Minnesota, Virginia, Ohio, Pennsylvania, New Jersey and eastern Massachusetts, south in the mountains to Alabama and Georgia.

Winters from southern Texas and south central Florida, south to Greater Antilles, eastern Mexico to Panama, with a single record for Colombia (see *waynei* below). One record for Heligoland, Germany.

Dendroica virens waynei Bangs
(Lat., *waynei* after Arthur T. Wayne)

Type Locality Mount Pleasant, S.C.

LOCAL NAME: Wayne's (Black-throated Green) Warbler

The thought of a Black-throated Green Warbler living in a cypress-magnolia association would hardly occur to anyone knowing the bird in the spruce-hemlock of the North Woods. When Arthur T. Wayne found this bird amid the "backwaters" of the Carolina Low Country in summer and secured specimens, he sent them to Outram Bangs of the Museum of Comparative Zoology at Cambridge, Mass., with the conviction that they represented a new race. Such proved to be the case and Bangs described the subspecies, naming it for its discoverer.

It differs from typical *virens* principally in the bill which is much smaller and more delicate, and the black area of the throat which is more restricted. The general color pattern is duller and the yellows paler. *Waynei* is a high-ranging bird. Aloft amid the cypress limbs, magnolia crowns or terminal twigs of tupelo gums, it seems minute and far away. Active and secretive aside from its tiny size, the almost constant song is the best means of locating it. In its coastal range this warbler nests in the old growth, heavily timbered swamps, while in the mountains it is a conifer dweller like the northern bird. The nest, of usual warbler appearance, is saddled on a limb at heights varying from 30 to 65 feet. The eggs number four and are like those of *virens* but average slightly smaller. The song is almost exactly similar to that of the northern bird except that it may be somewhat longer in delivery.

Once thought to be confined to the coast of South Carolina, study of this form has revealed it to have a much wider range, breeding birds of the mountains of the Carolinas now being assigned to it. It has been found as far north along the coast as the Dismal Swamp of Virginia. Typical *virens* occurs in the lower Atlantic region only as a migrant. It arrives on the coast (S.C.) in late March and in the Mt. Mitchell area of the high Blue Ridge (N.C.) in April, sometimes when still cold. Young birds have been seen on the wing in the Dismal Swamp (Va.) on May 24th but nearly a month earlier in the Charleston (S.C.) area.

RANGE: *Breeds* along coastal plain in southeastern Virginia, eastern North Carolina and southeastern South Carolina. *Winters* in western Cuba.

ALEXANDER SPRUNT, JR.

[*Comment:* The Northern Black-throated Green is one of the common warblers of the Boreal Forest Region north of Lake Superior. Although it has arrived as early as May 7 and delayed its arrival until May 22, it usually appears about the middle of the month, associating with the other species invading the region during that period. By early June it is occupying its breeding territory where it remains until late August or early September. In this area it prefers second growth, mixed forests of Black Spruce, Balsam Fir, Aspen Poplar and White Birch and we have rarely encountered it in the pure stands of Jackpine although elsewhere in its range stands of pine are said to be its favorite habitat. In these partially open woods, its lazy song is heard throughout the day at the intermediate and upper levels of the trees.

The peak of the breeding season is the third week in June when most nests will contain four or five eggs. All nests which we have observed have been in Black Spruce trees of moderate size, placed at relatively low levels on horizontal limbs a few feet from the trunk. The majority would have been overlooked in the half-shade of the forest had they not included white outer bark of the White Birch. Actually these were the only coarse portions of material utilized in their well-built, compact nests which consisted principally of slender twigs of spruce and fine grasses. They were lined by rather stiff, fine stems and rootlets so interwoven as to produce perfect cups. The Cowbird is not abundant in this region and is probably an unimportant factor in the life of the northern individuals of the Black-throated Green. (A. E. ALLIN)]

29

GOLDEN-CHEEKED WARBLER

Dendroica chrysoparia

THIS beautiful warbler is one of the very localized species of the country which results in many people thinking of it as "rare." Certainly, it is little known but not so much because of scarcity of numbers as by reason of its restricted breeding range. It is another warbler, occurring only in Texas and, as in the case of the Colima, in but a small portion of that vast commonwealth.

Having been fortunate enough to spend three consecutive summers in the midst of this bird's range, I came to know it well, and acquaintance with it can hardly result in any other conviction than that it is among the most attractive of the family. On the rough, rocky, juniper-clad hillsides of the Edward's Plateau near Kerrville, west central Texas, I saw many adults and young during the summers of 1949–1951. While occurring in several areas of this section, the Bell Ranch about three miles west of Kerrville was the spot more often visited and the birds were watched from early June until late July.

The Golden-cheek is essentially a bird of the cedar (juniper) brakes. And though such growth is its favorite, it frequents the small live oaks and Spanish oaks and the shin oak brush which are typical of the region. It arrives from the south about mid-March or late March. The nesting season was well along when most of my observations were made. Adults feeding young were noted about June 20th. The bird (male) was located rather easily by the song which is uttered frequently. Though I was never successful in finding a nest, Samuel A. Grimes of Jacksonville, Florida, that indefatigable nest-finding bird photographer, visited there in June 1950, and discovered three nests in two days! These were on a ranch near Ingram, some six miles northwest of Kerrville.

This warbler is actually the commonest species in that part of the Edward's Plateau, at least the one most readily found. Amid the cypress growth of the river-bottoms (Guadalupe River) Kentucky, Parula and Sycamore (Yellow-throated) Warblers occurred as well as Chats, but such growth was avoided by the Golden-cheek.

It is an active species, more or less constantly on the go, though the male is not hard to follow due to the rather open surroundings it seeks. The female, however, is shy and elusive.

The song period falls off sharply while the young are being fed and when the latter are first a-wing; then it ceases entirely. The birds then become scattered and are harder to find, seldom being seen in fact, after mid-July. Early August is the latest I have noted them in the Kerrville area. The handsome Golden-cheek is called "elegant" by Bent (1953) and so it is. Though reminding one of the black-throated green warbler in some respects, the black back of the golden-cheek is distinctive, as well as the contrast of black throat and white underparts. The brilliant yellow of the cheeks is of course, obvious.

Dendroica chrysoparia Sclater and Salvin
   (Lat., *chrysoparia,* yellow-cheeked)

Type Locality Vera Paz, Guatemala

FIELD CHARACTERS: *Adult male,* upperparts black, including tail, the outer feathers of which are largely white. Wings edged with gray. Cheeks and line over eye bright yellow, a black line through the eye. Throat and upper breast black, sides with black streaks. Underparts white.

Adult female, upperparts olive green; crown and back with black streaks. Area above eye, cheeks and sides of neck yellow. Tail with less white than male. Upper breast black, mingled with whitish tips, other underparts white.

Length, 4.50 to 5.00 inches.

NESTING DATA: A well-made cup of juniper bark-strippings, grasses, plant down and weeds and/or hair. Usually at low elevations, under 20 feet to as low as 4 or 5. Often in cedars (juniper) but at times in live oaks or cedar elm. Sometimes victimized by the Dwarf Cowbird.

Eggs—4. White, marked with spots and splashes of reddish brown, lilac and gray, often a wreath about the large end.

VOICE: Song like that of Black-throated Green Warbler. Difficult to render into words but with a definite ventriloquial quality. Has been rendered as "tweah, tweah, twee-sy" (Chapman). Call note a sharp "chip."

FOOD HABITS: Wholly insects as far as known.

GENERAL RANGE: *Breeds.* Several counties of south central Texas in the Edward's Plateau region. *Winters* from Pueblo, Mexico south to Guatemala, Honduras and Nicaragua.

ALEXANDER SPRUNT, JR.

30

HERMIT WARBLER

Dendroica occidentalis

MOST sought-after of all western warblers, both by earlier day egg-collectors and modern "bird-listers," this attractively garbed species is not rare, as so many writers have suggested. Rather, it is because so much of its foraging and singing is carried on at such great heights and amid the dense branchwork of the forest canopy that a good view of the bird on its nesting grounds is difficult to obtain. In the tall Douglas-fir forests of western Oregon and Washington the Hermit sings regularly from over 100 feet above ground, and most observers do not have the stamina exhibited by Dawson, who climbed well above that height to hear and watch the singers on their own level (*Birds of California,* 1923, p. 492). Also contributing to the idea of rarity, perhaps, has been the habit of so many western bird students of not bothering to look up at birds high in the treetops, because so many other lower and more open habitats are available. Hence the inhabitants of tall trees are frequently passed over, especially when their voices do not loudly command attention.

The nesting activity of the Hermit Warbler is apparently carried out at somewhat lower levels, on occasion even to within a few feet of the ground. Foraging birds also sometimes range into the lower tree branches or even into understory shrubs, the shier females perhaps covering this "beat" more regularly than the males, who must declare their territory from higher stations. In the Sierra Nevada of California I have found, however, that even the males can be called down to eye-level by a patient and quiet observer imitating the call of a Saw-whet Owl.

For breeding habitat Hermit Warblers show definite partiality to moderately dense canopies of true fir or Douglas-fir. Through much of the mountain area of California, where the forest of average density is composed of the more sparsely-crowned pines, they thus inhabit the denser glades and northerly slopes. Yet in the still denser Redwood forests of coastal regions they seem to be all but absent.

By the time the young are on the wing in July the male Hermits have ceased singing; and there is, as with so many other mountain species, a definite up-mountain movement. In August in the Donner Pass area in Placer County, California, where I spent three summers, Hermits frequently were exceeded in numbers only by the omnipresent Audubon's Warbler in the aggregations of small insectivorous birds roving the forest and meadow borders. At such times, by a combination of "squeaking" and "owl-calling," one can easily have as many as a dozen Hermit Warblers in sight at once. These up-mountain wanderers gradually move southward and eastward following the high mountain areas where meadow and creek-border areas are still moist. At this season they forage in willows and alders as well as in the adjacent conifers. On the fall migration they are usually not found in the dry foothill and lowland areas unless an early onset of cold weather in the higher country in September drives them downward. However, in spring in southern California the foothill oak woodland and even the chaparral-covered slopes and the scattered creosote-bush of desert plains are taken in stride by the northward migrants. They arrive in small numbers in southeastern Arizona by early April in some years, and by mid-April in southwestern California. At the peak of the migration, usually near the end of April, this and other warblers may be present along the favorable foothill lanes in real "waves," as are warblers in the East.

Whether on migration or in its less accessible breeding haunts, the male Hermit, once seen, is easily told from all other warblers occurring within its range by the pure yellow cheeks, black throat, and whitish underparts; and even the females and young show enough of this pattern to distinguish them from the more prominently marked Townsend's Warbler or the plainer species.

Dendroica occidentalis (Townsend)
(Lat., *occidentalis*, western)

Type Locality Fort Vancouver, Washington

FIELD CHARACTERS: *Adult male,* upperparts gray, the back streaked with blackish and overlain in fall with olive. Wings and tail blackish with narrow white edgings to the long feathers; wings with two conspicuous white bars; the outer tail feathers mostly white, and smaller white areas on the next two pairs of feathers. Sides and top of head bright lemon yellow, merging to drab blackish or dark olive-gray on nape. Sharply defined triangular throat patch pure black in spring and summer, partly overlain by whitish feather tips in fall. Rest of underparts white, sometimes with a few short dark streaks on the sides.

Adult female, upperparts olive-gray, with or without interrupted blackish streaks. Wings and tail as in male, but white less extensive. Sides of head yellow, sometimes with obscure dusky areas, but these not forming a definite cheek patch as in the female Townsend's. Crown yellowish with more or less dark olive-gray mottling. Throat yellow or whitish, with similar dark mottling, especially posteriorly. Underparts dirty white.

Young, in fall, resemble adults in general pattern, but with more olive above and browner below and on cheeks; little or no dusky on throat.

Length, 4.50 to 5.00 inches.

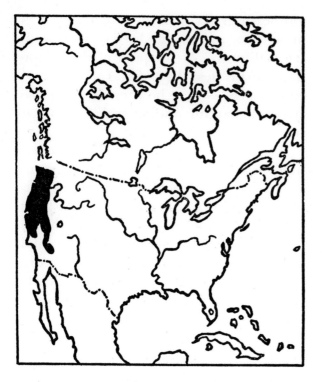

NESTING DATA: A 4 by 2½-inch cup of fine twigs,
          plant fibers, and needles or small stems
or bits of moss or lichen, lined with bark strips and
fine grasses or often some animal hair. Nearly always

in conifers, saddled on horizontal branches at moderate heights (20 to 40 ft.) but varying from 2 to 50 feet.

Eggs—3 to 5. Whitish, rather heavily marked particularly near the large end with irregular reddish
brown or lavender spots.

VOICE: Song with pattern like that of the Townsend's
          and Black-throated Gray Warblers, but
is usually less wheezy and ends more briskly: *tsilli,
tsilli, tsil, tsee-tsee tsip;* or a somewhat huskier *seezle,
seezle, seezle, seezl, zeet-zeet.* Although given with a
similar slight rise in pitch, it has more definite pattern than the song of Audubon's Warbler. Call notes
include a soft liquid *tilp* or *tsilk,* used in migration
as well as on breeding grounds, which is similar to
calls of Townsend's, Black-throated Gray, and Myrtle
Warblers but distinct from that of Audubon's Warbler.

FOOD HABITS: Entirely insects and small spiders, so
          far as known.

GENERAL RANGE: *Breeds* in the moderately dense coni-
          fer forest areas of southwestern Washing-
ton and Oregon, southward in mountains to central
California (chiefly in the Sierra Nevada, but sparingly
also near the coast) and possibly rarely in southern
California. Occurs in Nevada and Arizona and
throughout southern California in migrations (Apr.-
early May; Aug.-early Sep.). *Winters* from central
Mexico to Nicaragua.

HOWARD L. COGSWELL

31

CERULEAN WARBLER

Dendroica cerulea

THIS bird was discovered by Wilson apparently as a straggler in eastern Pennsylvania, and he claimed to have found it subsequently along the Cumberland River during the spring migration. Audubon found it during spring migration in Louisiana, where he claimed that he could sometimes see 5 or 6 specimens in a single walk. Later, on his adventurous trip to Galveston Island, Texas, he encountered another migrating flock. Everything that he has to say about the song, nest and eggs is largely imaginary and palpably in error.

At the beginning of ornithological history in America, therefore, the Cerulean Warbler was actualy rare and little known. It turned out to be an abundant summer resident in the rich Mississippi bottomlands, and in the Ohio River Valley. Ridgway found it abundant in the lower Wabash River Valley between Illinois and Indiana, where without any fanfare or publicity he quietly accumulated a fine series. It was William Brewster, however, who really put this bird on the map in his beautifully written biography *Birds of Ritchie County, West Virginia*. The nest and eggs were first taken in 1878. The nest is notoriously difficult to find, and virtually uncollectible, since it is usually well out on a limb on some terminal twig. Perhaps it is best discovered by watching the singing male leading the observer to the practically undiscoverable female, which will occasionally fly to the nest to brood. The world's record appears to have been made by P. W. Smith, Jr., who found 40 nests in one season near St. Louis, Mo., which is bound to remain a performance of great virtuosity.

Plate 16
TOWNSEND'S WARBLER
Page 135

Male

Female

HERMIT WARBLER
Page 144

Male

Male in Winter

Female

Immature

John H. Dick
'55

The Cerulean Warbler is sensitive to ecological change, particularly from white man's disturbance. Widmann in *Birds of Missouri* pointed out the bird disappeared the moment the big timbered swamps were logged, and Jones and Troutman made the same observation in Ohio. Todd commented on its decrease in historic times in western Pennsylvania. The species has long been known for its tendency to form isolated colonies in the East, and these colonies have become more and more prominent, especially in western and central New York state. Horton discovered an apparently breeding bird in Dutchess County, New York, in the upper Hudson River Valley, in 1894. Since then the species has increased steadily there, and it is currently possible to find up to 12 singing males in a day in 5 or 6 scattered localities. Chubb found a summering male in the Catskills in 1919. Other stray summering males turned up in northern New Jersey, and even in Holderness, New Hampshire, where a singing male was collected June 8, 1929, by Richard B. Harding.

Formerly the Cerulean was one of the rarest of spring warblers in Washington, D.C. It now occurs there regularly, and apparently nests in various localities near the District. It has been found breeding in northern New Jersey (Bergen County) since 1947, and has also been breeding across the Delaware River at Bowman's Hill, Pa. In New England, where it was recently appraised by Lincoln in Bent's *Life Histories* as of purely casual status, the number of sight records by experienced people has greatly increased (spring only). I agree heartily with Chapman's prediction that should this easterly trend continue, the bird might be found nesting in western Connecticut, southwestern Massachusetts, and possibly even in extreme southwestern Vermont, where favorable habitat still survives.

The cerulean arrives in the United States in late March and April. A famous member of the so-called "coastal hiatus," the bird is believed to fly across the Gulf of Mexico and rarely stops near the coast unless weather conditions are unfavorable. It flies further inland without pausing to rest, reaches the Ohio Valley as early as April 30, arrives in central and western New York by early May. By late May all birds are dispersed on their breeding grounds. During migration it is almost never reported in any large numbers on any one day. The highest counts I can find are 20 birds at Grand Isle, La., and a maximum of 18 in a day at Buckeye Lake, Ohio. On its breeding grounds it often gives a false impression of colonialism, due to the fact that all birds tend to gather in localities with especially favorable habitats. Thus on May 30, 1915, in an ideal swamp at Cayuga, N.Y., I found 20 singing males and 2 females; and at Howland's Island on June 8 I found 18 singing males and 1 female.

The breeding season, as is usual with warblers, is completed with extreme rapidity, after which the birds are at once on the move, gathering into flocks and roaming through the woods in early July, when they are largely overlooked. There is a recrudescence of the song period in late August, and the birds virtually disappear by early September, with only stragglers remaining by the end of the month. Actually, however, the fall departure is so extremely early that the bird has been collected at Key West on July 15, 1889, and it has reached eastern Ecuador by August 10.

South of its breeding range the Cerulean Warbler is well known as a common fall transient in Louisiana and the adjacent Gulf Coast states, where it arrives regularly in late July, and becomes common in the first two weeks of August. In northwestern Florida, at Pensacola, Francis M. Weston reports it 18 times in 36 years. It is virtually unknown, in the fall, in the true coastal plain. There are almost no records for Mexico other than 2 recent spring records from Vera Cruz; and it is an excessively rare warbler in Central America. In South America it is well known to winter in Colombia, Ecuador and Peru, where it is found in flocks of considerable size, and it has straggled to Venezuela and northwestern Bolivia.

The Cerulean Warbler has been widely advertised in the literature as our only true-blue or cerulean warbler. People have expatiated at some length on its alleged beauty and attractive markings. Actually most of this is not true. Many adult males are china-blue or grayish-blue on the upperparts, brightening to true cerulean-blue only on the back of the head. Chubb (1919) has observed how difficult a warbler it is to see and study well. It favors the tallest trees in rich swamps and bottomlands, and there is hardly any other warbler which ranges so exceedingly high and which gives the observer both a neck- and a back-ache in his attempts to study it. Fortunately it is a loud and persistent singer and can be readily found with a cer-

tain amount of intelligent search. Over and over again, however, all that one sees is an exceedingly small and chubby *Dendroica* with bright white underparts, some streaking on the flanks, and a conspicuous pectoral collar. Actually it is a rare occurrence to find this warbler at a lower altitude and see the sunlight bringing out the cerulean-blue tone of the upperparts. Everything that I have said here about the male applies equally to the even more inconspicuous female, which is actually much more difficult to identify correctly.

Both sexes turn out to be astonishingly variable. There is the variation already mentioned between china-blue or grayer males. Some birds have a distinct superciliary line of white over the eye, which in others may be individually lacking. Also it is well known that the pectoral collar may be broken or interrupted. In adult females the principal variation is that the upperparts may be greener or of a more bluish cast, and such birds seen on migration are occasionally recorded as purely imaginary immature males, although I am not aware that any such authentic plumage actually exists, and I am inclined strongly to doubt it. As a matter of fact, with experience and knowledge every single one of these variations can be observed in life through a good glass, and those readers who think they know this warbler well can mark themselves on the honor system as to whether they have actually observed all of these variations or not.

Dendroica cerulea (Wilson)
  (Lat., *cerulea,* blue)

Type Locality Philadelphia, Pa.

FIELD CHARACTERS: Both sexes exceedingly variable. *Male,* upperparts china-blue or grayish blue, brightening to cerulean on back of head; back streaked with black; underparts white with conspicuous blue-black band which may be interrupted or broken, across upper breast; flanks streaked with black; two white wing bars; tail dark with white spots on each feather except the two middles ones. Some males have a distinct superciliary line of white over the eye.

Female and immature, varying greatly, upperparts bluish-gray or bluish green, without black streaking; underparts white or faintly pale yellow without marks; wings and tail as in adult male; pale line over the eye and a dark line through it. May resemble female

Black-throated Blue Warbler but lacks white spots on wings of latter.

Length, 4 to 5 inches.

NESTING DATA: Favoring the tallest trees in rich swamps and bottomlands. Nest very dainty, compactly built of fine grasses, plant fibres and lichens, bound by spiders' webs, lined with hair, feathers or mosses, and placed in fork of coniferous or deciduous tree, 15 to 90 feet up.

Eggs—3 or 4, pale blue or greenish-white, speckled with reddish-brown or lilac, chiefly around large end.

VOICE: A loud and persistent song, resembling that of the parula warbler. *See, see, seep* (Forbush). "The syllables *tse, tse, tse, tse, te-e-e-e-e-e-e-e,* serve to recall it to mind. The song rolls up the scale quietly and evenly." Alarm note a sharp *chip.* [Rev. J. J. Murray (in Bent) writes of the two songs in Virginia: "The songs of the Parula and Cerulean are very similar but not difficult to distinguish. The pattern is reversed in the two; the Parula's song is *bzz, bzz, bzz, trill,* while that of the Cerulean is a *trill, trill, trill, bzz.* The Cerulean's song can be expressed by the phrase, '*Just a little sneeze*'."] (See Chapter 5)

FOOD HABITS: Chiefly insects.

GENERAL RANGE: *Breeds* from southeastern Nebraska, northern Iowa, southeastern Minnesota, southern Wisconsin, southern Michigan, southern Ontario, western New York, eastern Pennsylvania, southeastern New York, and northern New Jersey south through southeastern Kansas, eastern Oklahoma, eastern Texas, and southeastern Louisiana, central Alabama, central North Carolina to central Virginia, southern Maryland, and Delaware. *Winters* in South America from Venezuela to Peru and Bolivia. Casual in Cuba and the Bahamas.

LUDLOW GRISCOM

32

BLACKBURNIAN WARBLER

Dendroica fusca

THE very name of this exquisite bird is almost as attractive as the subject itself for, as Bent (1953) says, it seems "a doubly appropriate name, for its (the bird's) upperparts are largely black and its throat burns like a brilliant orange flame amid the dark foliage of the hemlocks and spruces. A glimpse of such a brilliant gem, flashing out from its somber surroundings, is fairly startling." So it is, indeed! No one ever forgets his first sight of a Blackburnian.

Bagg and Elliott (1937) have given a clear account of the naming of this warbler, the essence of which follows. In the late 18th century a specimen was sent from New York to England and was there described and named for a Mrs. Blackburn who was much interested in ornithology. Later, it was discovered that in a German publication of 1776, a specimen from British Guiana had been given the name *fusca* (blackish). Alexander Wilson had become familiar with the bird as a migrant near Philadelphia but, when he took a female (which he called a male) in Great Pine Swamp, Pa., he named it *Sylvia parus* or Hemlock Warbler. Audubon was also confused about this species for he thought the Blackburnian of English description and the Hemlock Warbler of Wilson to be different species.

In eastern United States, the Blackburnian is known mainly as a migrant from the Mississippi Valley to the mountain ranges of the Blue Ridge and Alleghenies, in which it breeds as far south as Georgia, in the Transition and Lower Canadian Zones. Although largely coniferous in its preferences it shows some variation in this,

John H. Dick
'55

PLATE 17
BLACKBURNIAN WARBLER
Page 152

Immature

Male

Female

CERULEAN WARBLER
Page 147
Male

Female

for Maurice Brooks has pointed out that in West Virginia, as low as 2500 ft., it is "thoroughly at home in the deciduous second-growth timber that in many places has replaced the coniferous forests." My own experience with this warbler has been almost entirely amid coniferous suroundings, the high Blue Ridge of North Carolina, the Adirondacks and the coastal islands of Maine. Hemlocks seem to be the favorite tree.

Singing perches are often at the very summit of a lofty hemlock or spruce. To see a male performing there, in bright sunlight, is a red-letter experience and when the bird descends into the gloom of the lower levels it almost seems to glow as Bent says, like some animated jewel. The song is very high-pitched and wiry, to my ears very insect-like. The notes vary from 7 to 25. Nesting as it does, at considerable elevations amid the thick-needled conifers, the Blackburnian is not often parasitized by the cowbird, but examples of it are known. Strangely enough, the highest known nest on record (84 feet) held a cowbird's egg which, as Herbert Friedmann remarks "is probably the altitude record for a cowbird egg, bettering by some twenty feet my highest record at Ithaca (N.Y.), a cowbird's egg laid in the nest of a Pine Warbler about sixty feet up."

The Blackburnian's designation as a "deep-woods" warbler is shared by the Black-throated Blue, Northern Parula and Canada Warblers.

The spring male is one of the unmistakable warblers, the black back, white patches in the wings and flaming orange of the throat and breast catching the eye at once.

The female is similarly patterned but much duller, while the immature is duller still, with the back brownish. Though a bird of eastern Canada and the U.S., it has appeared, as birds do, at very unlikely places, notably Frederickshaab, Greenland; Ogden, Utah; Fort Bayard, New Mexico and Libby, Montana.

Dendroica fusca (Müller)
(Lat., *fusca,* blackish)

Type Locality Guyane, French Guiana

FIELD CHARACTERS: *Male,* center of crown, line over eye, sides of neck and breast brilliant orange. Upperparts black, back streaked with white. Tail black, edged with gray; wings black with large white patches; sides streaked with black; abdomen light.
Female, similar but paler, wing patches reduced to white bars.
Immature, similar to female but duller, black areas less pronounced and mixed with olive-brown.
Length, 4.50 to 5.50 inches.

NESTING DATA: Almost always in coniferous trees at widely varying elevations (5 to 84 ft.), frequently hemlocks, but also fir, spruce, tamarack and pine. In the Appalachians it prefers the oak-hickory ridges lacking conifers. Nest of twigs, plant down and *usnea* lichen, lined with hair, fine grass and black rootlets.

Eggs—4 to 5. White, spotted and splashed with shades of brown and undertones of drab and gray. Often in a solid wreath about large end but sometimes spotted over entire surface.

VOICE: High-pitched, thin and wiry; not loud but penetrating, rendered as "ser-wee" repeated four times, or "chiddle" repeated twice, ending with "chick-a, chick-a, cheet" (F. H. Allen); sissi vit, sissi vit, sissi vit (Chapman). (*See Chapter 5*)

FOOD HABITS: Mainly insects, "feeding almost entirely on the forest pests that are so injurious to the trees" (Bent, 1953). Berries are consumed at times when insects are scarce.

GENERAL RANGE: *Breeds* from south central Saskatchewan and Manitoba across to northern Nova Scotia; south to central Minnesota, southern Ontario, central Pennsylvania, New York, Massachusetts and Maine; south in the mountains to South Carolina and Georgia. *Winters* from Guatemala south through Central America to French Guiana, Peru, and the mountains of Colombia and Venezuela. Transient in West Indies.

ALEXANDER SPRUNT, JR.

33

YELLOW-THROATED WARBLER

Dendroica dominica

To my mind this is one of the handsomest and most attractive of the wood warblers. Perhaps life-long association with it is responsible, because it nests in the moss banners of the live oaks in my yard, at times within 15 feet of the porch. Be that as it may, it is a beautiful avian creation and typifies to a degree, the entire family. If the Prothonotary Warbler is the essence of the cypress country, the Yellow-throated is the animated spirit of the Spanish moss and live oaks in the Carolina Low Country. Among them it feeds, in them it builds its home and rears its young. One of the pleasantest tasks the writer was ever asked to do was to prepare the life history of this exquisite bird for his friend, the late Arthur C. Bent's *Life Histories of North American Wood Warblers*. Inland, where the moss is lacking, this warbler frequents the pinelands and saddles its nest on a horizontal pine limb, but in any coastal area where *Tillandsia usneoides* is lacking, one will look in vain for the bird.

Somewhat creeper-like in movement, the Yellow-throated is a deliberate bird, searching methodically in crack and cranny of limb or trunk for its tiny insect prey. Now and then it pauses, throws back its head and pours forth its haunting melody of "sweetie-sweetie-sweetie." During long experience in south central Florida (Okeechobee region) I have found it wintering regularly; it diminishes as one goes further south. Curiously enough, it does not sing there, even in migration; but as one proceeds north of Orlando and the rest of the state into Georgia and South Carolina the song is a concomitant of any section of highway which traverses a cypress-pine-land-live oak association. As far as the Dismal Swamp (North Carolina-Virginia line) it may be encountered regularly, but once across Chesapeake Bay the bird becomes less and less common.

Superficially, this warbler might be likened to a black and white with a yellow throat. Many people to whom I have shown it for the first time have been impressed with this description. Any reasonably close view will at once reveal the differences.

At times the bird meets what might be termed unusual hazards. In much of its southern breeding haunts amid the cypress lagoons, there lives a huge spider which spins a wonderful golden web sometimes stretching it as much as fifty feet between tree trunks. This is the Carolina Silk Spider, a great black and yellow creature the size of a saucer. Twice I have seen this warbler entangled in the golden strands of the web. In both cases the bird was dead. On the other hand it does not appear to figure to any extent in migrational hazards as typified by lighthouses, high bridges and skyscrapers.

Certainly this warbler is one of the great avian attractions of the Southeast. Three other races occur in different sections, including a West Indian one.

Dendroica dominica dominica (Linnaeus)
(Lat., *dominica,* of Santo Domingo)

Type Locality Santo Domingo, W.I.

LOCAL NAME: Eastern Yellow-throated Warbler

FIELD CHARACTERS: Forehead and sides of head black, a white line over the eye being yellow anteriorly. Upperparts slate-gray; wings blackish-brown with two white bars; tail with white markings on outer feathers. Throat and breast bright yellow;

sides streaked with black, abdomen white. *Female* similar with less blackish markings.

Length, 4.75 to 5.75 inches.

NESTING DATA: In coastal areas nest always placed in clumps of Spanish moss and composed of grasses, weeds and feathers, lined with strands of moss and the flowers thereof. Inland nests usually saddled on horizontal branches of pines. Elevations vary from about 15 to 60 feet, but one nest in the writer's yard (Charleston, S.C.) was only 3 ft. 1 in., from the ground.

Eggs—4 rarely 5. Ground color greenish-white, marked with spots and splashes of reddish-brown and purplish.

VOICE: A ringing, melodious series of about seven notes of high carrying quality. Has been compared to song of Louisiana Water-Thrush and Indigo bunting. "Tee-ew, Tew Tew Tew Tew—Tew wi" or (western race) "see-wee, see-wee, see-wee, swee swee swee swee. The words "sweetie-sweetie" have always appealed to the writer as descriptive of the rendition. (*See Chapter 5*)

FOOD HABITS: Entirely insects, such as grasshoppers, crickets, flies, beetles, scale insects, bugs and occasional spiders.

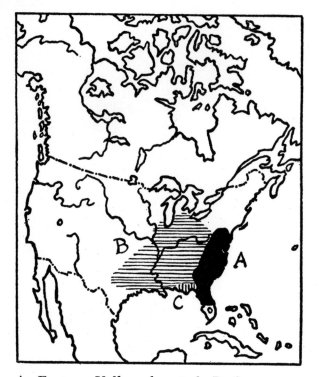

A. Eastern Yellow-throated. B. Sycamore. C. Stoddard's.

GENERAL RANGE: *Breeds* from eastern Maryland and central New Jersey south to central Georgia, southern Alabama and north central Florida. *Winters* from South Carolina, Georgia, Florida, south to Greater Antilles, and Bahamas.

Dendroica dominica albilora Ridgway
    (Lat., *albilora,* white-lored)

Type Locality Belize, British Honduras

LOCAL NAME: Sycamore Warbler

This is the mid-western form of the Yellow-throated Warbler, living west of the Alleghenies, mainly in the Mississippi Valley. It is very similar to *D. d. dominica* but differs in having a much smaller bill and the superciliary stripe having no yellow, or very little. In habits, behavior and nesting there is practically no difference.

It is fond of bottom-lands and the close proximity of streams, showing a preference for sycamores, cypress and elms. Always a high-ranging bird it nests as high as over a hundred feet, but the average would be between 30 and 75 feet. At times it nests as low

as 10 to 15 feet. It is a very early migrant, reaching Louisiana the first week in March. I have seen this warbler in summer in the high Blue Ridge of North Carolina (Watauga County) for it occasionally spills over into the Piedmont sections of the Carolinas.

In September (2nd-6th) 1949, I noted several at the Dry Tortugas Keys. In the fall migration there I have watched it at distances of from 3 to 6 feet, at which times not a trace of yellow was visible in the eye-stripe.

Along the banks of the Guadaloupe River at Kerrville, Texas, I saw this warbler for three summers (1949–1951) and it frequented the tall cypresses there, always high up.

RANGE: *Breeds* from central Oklahoma, Missouri, northern Illinois, northern Ohio, eastern Kentucky, eastern Tennessee and West Virginia south to east Texas and southeastern Mississippi, central Alabama, northern Georgia to northwestern South Carolina. *Winters* further south than *D. d. dominica,* from Cameron County, Texas, south through Mexico and Central America. Also in Cuba and Jamaica.

[*Comment:* Sycamore Warblers appeared in St. John's, Newfoundland, on October 24, 1953, and specimens were obtained. The flight must have been a spectacular one because as many as fifty individuals were recorded in one locality. The last were seen on November 11. (LESLIE TUCK)]

Dendroica dominica stoddardi Sutton
    (Lat., *stoddardi,* for Herbert L. Stoddard)

Type Locality Walton County, Florida

LOCAL NAME: Stoddard's Yellow-throated Warbler

This slender-billed race was described by George M. Sutton (*Auk,* 68:27, 1951). Its range was then thought to be mainly restricted to the Choctawhatchee Bay area of northwest Florida. Since, this range has been extended to as far east and south as Gulf Hammock (Levy County) on the peninsula. The behavior, nesting and food are the same as *D. d. dominica.* It is altogether likely that this race will be found to occur further west than is now known. The outstanding character is the very slender bill, definitely longer than the typical Yellow-throated. *Winter* range not known.

ALEXANDER SPRUNT, JR.

34

SUTTON'S WARBLER*

Parula americana x Dendroica dominica

FOR the discovery of Sutton's warbler much of the credit must be given to the singing of a winter wren. Lloyd Poland and I were making our way along an old road not far from Opequon Creek, a dozen miles south of Martinsburg, West Virginia; the date was 30 May, 1939. As we approached a fallen tree, we were pleasantly surprised to hear the full song of a winter wren. The end of May was an unusually late date for a winter wren in this area; he should have been in the cool forests of the mountains or the northland. Over and over this diminutive fellow sang his beautiful song while foraging about for food among the tangles of roots and limbs of the fallen tree. It was difficult to break

away from this late morning concert but there was work to be done.

We slowly walked along the old road and as the winter wren's song faded into the background the woods once again became quiet. We were near our destination, when suddenly the quietness was broken by the song of a parula warbler. Ordinarily, this would not have caused us to take notice. But this song was not ordinary; it resembled that of the parula, but was repeated twice in rapid succession. It was an unusual double buzzy trill. We stopped to investigate. I "squeaked" a few times and promptly a yellow-throated bird appeared. "A yellow-throated warbler," we exclaimed almost in unison as we gazed at the bird through our binoculars. A new bird for the area, we thought. But almost immediately our bird sang the double buzzy trill that

* Most ornithologists, including the Check-list Committee of the A.O.U., regard this as a hybrid of the Parula W. and the Yellow-throated W. The scientific name, *Dendroica potomac* Haller has been given to it.

Male

Immature

Female

Male

John H. Dick
'55

had first attracted our attention. Were we observing a yellow-throated or a rather large and unusual looking parula warbler? Our excitement ran high, but was soon relieved somewhat when I promptly collected the bird. Upon examining it, however, we became more excited and confused than ever! The bright yellow throat had a streak of tawny across it and the greenish-yellow back patch of the parula was prominent. It resembled the yellow-throated warbler but lacked the white facial patches and black streaked sides and flanks. Here was a bird that resembled two rather unrelated species of different genera!

Two days later a second specimen, a female, was taken along the Potomac River in a low, open sycamore association, almost 20 miles north of the first. Both specimens were nearly identical except for the amount of black in the facial patches.

A full description and account was subsequently published in *The Cardinal* (January 1940). Additional notes have appeared in ornithological journals in the nearly two decades that have passed since the discovery. A good account will be found in the chapter on "Fugitive Warblers" in Roger Tory Peterson's *Birds Over America*.

There are several West Virginia records. Maurice Brooks and the late Bayard Christy observed a Sutton's Warbler on 21 May, 1942 in possibly the same spot as the original discovery. But perhaps the most interesting and certainly the most recent for this area is that recorded by Harold D. Mitchell and a group of Buffalo Ornithological Society members. The entire group of eight had under observation for several

minutes a Sutton's Warbler along Opequon Creek south of Martinsburg, on 29 May, 1950.

There are no fall records for West Virginia although there are several for other states including Florida and South Carolina. I would certainly, but reluctantly, question these fall observations. However competent and careful an observer may be, fall warblers are especially difficult, particularly so in the case of one where no fall specimen exists. It should be pointed out that even a yellow-throated warbler in fall plumage might not clearly show the black side and flank streakings if the feathers had unusually heavy edgings of grayish, as is often the case. Several descriptions of Sutton's Warbler sent to me suggesting fall birds have been nothing more than those of immature Parula Warblers.

Spring birds are an entirely different matter. The lack of side and flank streakings is diagnostic as well as the absence of white facial patches so prominent in the Yellow-throated Warbler. In good light the greenish-yellow patch on the grayish back can also be seen. This would be particularly true of early spring birds before too much wear dulls the plumage. There is less reason to doubt the sight records of Sutton's Warbler for spring and summer.

Although the A.O.U. committee on nomenclature has suppressed Sutton's Warbler by placing it on the hypothetical list, it is hoped this will not deter further investigations, as there seems to persist a genuine interest in the bird.

In the nearly two decades that have passed since the finding of Sutton's Warbler little knowledge has been gained concerning it. But there has been no lack of interest and it is unfortunate that some-one has not been able to uncover its secret. Is it a true species or a hybrid? This question may not be answered accurately for years.

KARL W. HALLER

[*Comment:*   Much uncertainty about this bird still exists and only a few additional individuals have been reported seen since Haller took his specimens. Maurice Brooks and Bayard Christy have been mentioned. George H. Breiding and Laurence Hicks observed the bird some 18 miles west of the type locality on June 21, 1944.

Since then the bird has been reported from Florida and South Carolina. Mrs. E. G. Brownsey observed one at Tampa September 28, 1944, the first reported outside West Virginia. Another was reported by Mrs. Talbot Brewer from Anna Maria Island (Florida west coast) April 23, 1954

and still another from Stock Island, immediately east of Key West, by Margaret Hundley on September 25, 1954.

The South Carolina observation is from McClellanville, Charleston County, August 16, 1952 by Mr. and Mrs. Robert Edwards.

This bird resembles the yellow-throated warbler except for lack of streaks on the sides, and the parula warbler in having a faint yellow tinge on the back. The male has a "hint" of brownish on the upper breast. I can hardly do better than to quote Dr. George M. Sutton for whom the bird was named, in his comments accompanying Haller's description—"Is it," he asks, "perhaps, an interspecific or an intergeneric hybrid?" That question remains unanswered and the Committee on Nomenclature of the American Ornithologists' Union continues to place the bird on its Hypothetical List.

(ALEXANDER SPRUNT, JR.)]

35

GRACE'S WARBLER

Dendroica graciae

THIS tiny, dainty mite of a bird is one of the smallest of the warblers and one of the most attractive. Definitely of the west, Grace's Warbler is to the towering pines of southwestern plateaus what the Yellow-throated is to southeastern cypress swamps.

I first became acquainted with it along the south rim of Arizona's Grand Canyon, where the tiny bird offered an amazing contrast to the colossal immensity of its environment. Later, in company with the artist, John Henry Dick, more were studied amid the spectacular desert ranges of the Huachuca and Chiricahua Mountains. This is a bird of the pines, usually of the upper portions of these great trees. Now and then it descends to lower levels such as bush growth, and in this case shows little fear of observers.

Active and vivacious much of the time, it can be deliberate in movement as it searches out cracks and crannies with methodical earnestness. It "fly-catches" in the open air and also hovers, chickadee-like, about heavy clusters of needles or cones, where it seeks out small insects from the bases of the needles.

The song is often delivered from near the tops of tall trees and while clear enough, the tiny size of the bird militates against volume and it is often the case that difficulty is experienced in both hearing and seeing the performer. The usual inadequacy of words in describing bird song applies in the case of this bird. It has been given as "chip-chip-chip," "tseet-tseet-tseet" and "tsip-tsip-tsip." Wetmore (1920) compares it with that of the Chipping Sparrow, a more widely known song.

Though strongly reminiscent of a Yellow-throated Warbler in appearance, Grace's recalls to my mind, the Parula as well. It differs from the former in being decidedly smaller with no black in the cheeks, and having a yellow line under the eye. This warbler was discovered in 1878 by Dr. Elliott Coues and named by him for his sister Grace. The term seems eminently fitting for such a daintily petite form. Another race of Grace's Warbler, slightly differentiated, occurs in Central America, south to Nicaragua.

Dendroica graciae graciae Baird
    (Lat., *graciae,* for Grace Coues)

Type Locality Fort Whipple, Arizona

LOCAL NAMES: Northern Grace's Warbler, Grace Warbler

FIELD CHARACTERS: *Male,* upperparts light blue-gray, with black spots on the head and back; throat bright yellow; wings with two white bars; tail black, two outer feathers heavily marked with white.
    Female and Immature, similar in pattern but browner. The absence of yellow except on the throat, breast and in front of the eye and the gray back distinguish this bird from female and young Townsend's Warblers.
    Length, 4.50 inches.

NESTING DATA: In coniferous trees, of pine-oak forests, usually at some elevation (20 to 60 ft.). Nest of vegetable fibers and plant down, cobwebs, string and hair, lined with the latter and/or feathers.
    Eggs—3 or 4, usually 3. White or creamy, finely spotted with shades of brown and drab, concentrated in wreath about large end, though occasionally speckled all over.

VOICE: Song like that of Chipping Sparrow, the notes even and not slurred, the concluding syllable the same as the others. Has been compared to that of the Yellow Warbler. Words used vary from "chip," "tseet" and "zeet" to "tchew" and "tsip."

FOOD HABITS: Apparently entirely insectivorous.

GENERAL RANGE: *Breeds* from southern Utah and southern Colorado, south in mountains of New Mexico, Arizona and west Texas, at elevations between 6000–9000 ft., through western Mexico, south to northern Nicaragua. *Winters* from northern Mexico to Nicaragua.

ALEXANDER SPRUNT, JR.

John H. Dick
'55

PLATE 19
BAY-BREASTED WARBLER
Page 168

Blackpoll—Fall   Fall

Male

Female

BLACKPOLL WARBLER
Page 171

Male

Female

36

CHESTNUT-SIDED WARBLER

Dendroica pensylvanica

THIS pretty warbler is a striking example of the relation of wildlife to environment. Many present-day observers, familiar with its abundance, are surprised to learn that it was once rare or absent in the same areas. The early ornithologists barely knew it at all. Audubon saw only one bird, and Alexander Wilson but few. Ludlow Griscom has pointed out *(in litt.)* that this bird was unknown in Massachusetts in 1832 but that William Brewster reported it as common and generally distributed by the early 1860's. This increase was apparently the result of the regrowth of cut-over lands and abandoned fields following the cutting of the original forests and a period of agricultural occupation.

My acquaintance with it began in the southern mountain region, at altitudes between 3500 and 5000 feet, where it nests commonly as far south as northern Georgia. It apparently increased in the uplands following the death of the American Chestnut. The tameness of this bird is perhaps a good reason for its popularity, for it often allows close approach. Active and alert, one of its characteristic bits of behavior is the frequent elevation of the tail and drooping of the wings. Investigation of the nest will produce great concern, both birds fluttering almost within arm's reach on occasion.

The typical song of the Chestnut-sided, which is persistently delivered early in the season, has often been rendered into such words as "I wish to see Miss *Beecher*," and as words go these are rather well chosen. The emphatic "Beecher" ending is the diagnostic part. This bird has two songs, however, the first as rendered; and a late-season one which is much less regular and correspondingly difficult to notate. A. R. Brand (1938) found that the average number of vibrations per second was 5125, well over the mean of 4000 for perching birds as a whole.

The spring migration route of this warbler avoids the Atlantic Coastal Plain and centers between the Blue Ridge Mountains and the Mississippi Valley. There are indications that numbers of this species pass over the open Gulf of Mexico, and they are common on the Texas coast and eastward to western Florida. The fall flight appears to reverse that of spring.

This is one of the more easily recognized warblers. As adults, both sexes show chestnut flanks and a yellow crown; in immature plumage, the bright greenish-yellow back and white belly (plus eye-ring and wing-bars) are diagnostic. Because of its abundance it is frequently victimized by the cowbird, and it sometimes responds by covering the intruding egg with an additional nest flooring.

Dendroica pensylvanica (Linnaeus)
(Lat., *pensylvanica,* of Pennsylvania)

Type Locality Philadelphia, Pa.

FIELD CHARACTERS: *Male,* upperparts black with white streaks; crown yellow, bordered with black stripes from bill through eye; sides of head and underparts white; a wide chestnut band on each side of body; two yellow wing-bars; three outer tail feathers with white terminal spots.
Female, similar in pattern but duller.
Immature, similar to female but uniform bright olive-green above and white below, with yellow wing-bars.
Length, 4.60 to 5.25 inches.

NESTING DATA: At low elevations, often no higher than 3 feet, in brushy second growth, bushes, thickets and tangled vines. Nest a compact cup of grasses, leaves and weeds, lined with hair or fine grass.
Eggs—4 to 5. White, speckled with dots and splashes of gray, brownish and lilac.

VOICE: Two songs, "territorial" and "nesting." Former heard when bird arrives on nesting area, both heard during nesting season. Loud, musical and pleasing. Resembles that of Yellow Warbler. Territory song often rendered as "very, very pleased to *meetcha*" or "I wish to see Miss *Beecher.*" (4 to 9 notes.) Nesting song very variable, lasting longer than territory delivery. (*See Chapter 5*)

FOOD HABITS: Almost wholly insects, occasionally seeds and berries. A very useful bird in controlling insect pests of shrubs, shade-trees and forests. A good flycatcher.

GENERAL RANGE: *Breeds* from south central Saskatchewan, Manitoba, Ontario, Quebec, Nova Scotia, south to North Dakota, Nebraska, Wisconsin, northern Ohio, western Maryland, New York, Massachusetts and Maine south through mountainous uplands to eastern Tennessee and northern Georgia. *Winters* from Nicaragua to Panama. Abundant in Costa Rica.

ALEXANDER SPRUNT, JR.

37

BAY-BREASTED WARBLER

Dendroica castanea

AMONG the warblers of the northern woodlands a few are in some respect unusually conspicuous. The male Bay-breasted Warbler attracts attention by reason of its rather large size and distinguished garb of gray, buff, and reddish brown. It is one of the less common members of its clan, which circumstance of course adds interest for the human observer. However, notwithstanding this usual relative rarity, it at times becomes locally abundant. In the United States it is one of the latest warblers to appear in spring.

During migration it frequents all kinds of woodland, but with an apparent preference for coniferous trees, whether on mountain slopes, swampy land, or elsewhere. It is to be found also in the timber bordering streams, trees along fence rows and highways, mixed woods about ponds and lakes, the shrubbery and ornamental trees about houses and plantations in the country, and even the dooryards and the trees along the streets of many towns and cities.

It visits all parts of the trees and bushes, and occasionally descends to the ground. During the breeding season it ranges from the ground to the tops of tall trees; but at other seasons it is to be found more on the lower branches.

[W. W. H. Gunn comments: "This is quite contrary to my experience with them in Ontario where, on breeding territory, those I have seen remain for the most part at midlevel in the conifers and conspicuously avoid the treetops. Dr. J. M. Speirs, who is familiar with these birds on their breeding grounds in Ontario, agrees with me on this observation."]

When feeding in trees or bushes it normally moves rather deliberately, passing from branch to branch by hops or short flights; and it searches each leaf and flower for insects. At times, however, it is more active, and flits about the terminal twigs, sometimes hanging to them like a titmouse or chickadee, or even flying out to catch prey on the wing. Particularly in autumn it gathers into loose flocks, and then it often associates with other warblers, especially the Blackpoll, or joins the bands of other small birds that rove the countryside. Its flight from tree to tree is rather jerky. On longer stretches it is steadier, but even so, is somewhat erratic.

This bird sings at times rather persistently, and under some circumstances continuously from the same perch for as much as 15 minutes. Also the female while on the nest will sing her weaker song in answer to the love song of her mate.

[*Comment:* Few people have had the opportunity to study nesting female Baybreasts, but if it is established that they do sing, this would be an important exception to the general practice with female warblers. (W. W. H. GUNN)]

Incubation lasts about 12 days, and the female alone performs this duty. During this period the sitting bird is very fearless, or tame, whichever it may be, and it is difficult to induce her to leave the nest. Pounding on the tree or shaking the branch on which the nest rests have usually no effect, nor has thrusting a stick close to her; only pushing aside the twigs above the nest and practically touching the bird causes her to depart. Under such circumstances the female performs as though wounded, and remains in the close vicinity for some time, endeavoring to attract the attention of the intruder to herself and thus away from the nest. If this fails she will then sometimes fly close to the intruder's head and scold vociferously, which alarm notes bring the male to the scene to join in the protest.

While the female is incubating she is fed much by the male, either on her rest periods off the nest or when sitting on the eggs. These rest periods occur every 15 or 20 minutes during parts of the day, and last approximately 5 minutes. When the young are hatched they are attended by both parents, and the male does his share for the 11 days that the young remain in the nest. The female has been observed during a thundershower protecting the young birds in the nest by standing over them with her wings spread. She also performed the same service to shield the young from the too intense heat of the sun's rays. Then for a short time after the young have left the nest the parents continue their watchful care, until their offspring are able to fend for themselves.

Dendroica castanea (Wilson)
    (Lat., *castanea*, the chestnut tree)

Type Locality Pennsylvania

LOCAL NAMES: Autumnal Warbler; Bay-breast; Little Chocolate-breasted Titmouse.

FIELD CHARACTERS: One of the larger warblers, about 5½ inches long. *Male* with crown chestnut; rest of upper surface gray, streaked with black; a buff patch on sides of neck; wings with two broad white bars; three outer tail feathers terminally spotted with white; chin, throat and sides russet, and rest of lower surface buff to cream white. *Female* duller. *Young of the year* olive green above, buffy white below, the lower tail coverts buff, and the sides of body sometimes with a trace of russet. In autumn most like the Black-poll Warbler, but lower parts buffy instead of yellowish white or greenish yellow; under tail coverts pale buff instead of white or very pale yellow;

legs and feet darker, sometimes plumbeous instead of flesh color.

NESTING DATA: The nest is situated in evergreen or mixed forest on a mountain slope or on lower ground. It occupies a place on a horizontal branch of a spruce, hemlock, birch, or other tree, even on a shrub, usually 5 to 20, occasionally 50 feet up. It is bulky and rather large for the bird, sometimes nearly 6 inches in diameter, and composed of bark strips, twigs, roots, moss, grasses, and lichens; and lined with rootlets, moss, pine needles, and hair of such animals as the northern hare.

The eggs vary from 3 to 7, usually 4 or 5; are white, bluish or greenish white or pale gray, heavily or finely marked with dull or reddish brown, drab, and lilac.

The breeding season lasts from May to July.

VOICE: The common call is a rather sharp "tsip." The song has been variously compared with that of the Blackpoll, Blackburnian, Black-and-White, Cape May Warbler, and American Redstart, particularly in quality. It is composed of a repetition, sometimes in couplets, of high-pitched, thin, sibilant, often feeble, notes, and in the breeding season is considerably varied; but the quality persists, and this song is probably somewhat more liquid than that of any of the five birds above mentioned. (*See Chapter 5*)

FOOD HABITS: The Bay-breasted Warbler's food consists largely of insects, a few spiders, and a small amount of vegetable matter. The insects include click, ladybird, leaf-eating, June, and other beetles; house flies, gall flies, Mayflies, ants, lace-winged flies, ichneumon flies; moths and their cocoons; canker-worms, measuring-worms, and other caterpillars, hairy and smooth; locusts, grasshoppers, leaf hoppers, and dragonflies with their eggs and larvae. In the autumn it occasionally eats such berries as those of the Virginia creeper and mulberry.

GENERAL RANGE: *Breeds* from central Manitoba, northern Ontario, central Quebec, New Brunswick and Nova Scotia south to southern Manitoba, northern Minnesota and Wisconsin, southern Ontario and Quebec, northeastern New York, central Vermont and New Hampshire and southern Maine. Has been recorded in British Columbia, Alberta, Saskatchewan and southwestern Mackenzie. *Winters* from central and eastern Panama to northern Colombia and western Venezuela.

HARRY C. OBERHOLSER

38

BLACKPOLL WARBLER

Dendroica striata

THE male of this species, so like the Black-and-White Warbler in general coloration, possesses an entirely black cap which is responsible for the common name. Despite its plain plumage this bird has much of unusual interest about it.

The spring migration brings it up from South America across the West Indies into Florida, from which it fans out to its far northern breeding grounds. As W. W. Cooke (in Chapman, 1907) points out, no Blackpoll Warbler can have a migration route less than 3500 miles in length and the extremes of the range—Alaska and Brazil—are twice that distance apart. Even if the migratory flights were performed in a perfectly straight line, which of course they are not, many of these birds would travel 10,000 miles annually. Actually, the deviations from a straight course add greatly to

the distance covered, and no one can say what the real mileage amounts to. The Blackpoll is thus the "Arctic Tern" of the warbler tribe. The fall flight is a reversal of the spring journey, the birds funneling down through Florida, which now becomes their exit to the tropics. At this season the Blackpoll is of strikingly different appearance, a streaked yellowish-green bird difficult to distinguish from the fall Bay-breasted Warbler.

In summer the Blackpoll is a dweller of the spruce forests of northern Canada and of the higher mountains of the northeastern United States, and occurs as far south in the Rockies as Manitou, Colorado. It is a deliberate bird with almost vireo-like movements, though vigorous in defending its nesting territory. It is adept at fly-catching and often indulges in this aerial ma-

the East, and stragglers from the main host wander widely. In spring it is one of the latest of the army of migrant warblers and the characteristic crescendo of its soft sibilant call is heard well into June in our large northern cities. In fall the swollen population sends great numbers flitting across the whole countryside. Being a night migrant it is susceptible to attraction by lights and many perish at these man-made structures. Its long over-water migrations claim their percentage, but nesting success is obviously high enough to compensate for the many hazards these long travels impose.

Dendroica striata (Forster)
(Lat., *striata*, streaked)

Type Locality Fort Severn, Hudson Bay

FIELD CHARACTERS: *Male,* crown black; upperparts pale olive-green, streaked with black; underparts white, streaked on sides of neck and body with black; two white wing bars; two or three outer tail feathers marked with black.
Female, upperparts olive-green or gray with narrow streaks of black; underparts whitish or pale yellow, slightly streaked on breast and sides.
Immature, similar to female but with more yellowish underneath. Under tail coverts white to pale yellow.
Length, 5.00 to 5.50 inches.

[One of the most challenging field problems is to distinguish the fall Black-poll from the fall Bay-breast: (1) Black-poll is tinged with greenish-yellow below and is noticeably streaked. (Bay-breast is buffier with breast streakings very indistinct or wanting); (2) Black-poll has *white* under tail-coverts (Bay-breast, *buff*); (3) some Bay-breasts have a touch of bay on flanks—these individuals are easy; (4) Black-poll has *pale yellowish legs* (Bay-breast, *blackish*). This is the most useful field mark of all (ROGER TORY PETERSON)]

NESTING DATA: Usually low in a spruce, from 1 to 10 ft., up. Rarely on the ground. In far north, on the ground or low in alders. Nest of small twigs, weed-stalks, grasses and *usnea* lichen; lined with hair, fine rootlets or feathers, the latter characteristic.

neuver. The Blackpoll seems to exhibit rather more tendency toward albinism than other warblers, a phenomenon which has frequently been noted in both partial and total states.

The voice is very high-pitched, weak and insect-like. It resembles that of both the Black-and-White and the Bay-breasted, but is actually the highest pitched song of any passerine bird. The average frequency per second, as determined by A. R. Brand (1938) was 8900, "over an octave above the highest tone on the piano." Highest frequency was 10,225; lowest 8050. As a result, the Blackpoll's song is often inaudible to many people; they can *see* the bird sing but cannot hear it.

The vast range traversed by this species causes it to be seen in numbers over much of

Eggs—4 or 5. Creamy white, spotted and speckled with shades of brown, gray and lilac, often in a wreath about large end.

VOICE: Thin, wiry and very high-pitched, inaudible to some ears. 6 to 12 short, sibilant notes. [In lowlands of eastern Canada a very rapid "shivering" trill. (Bond)] Rises to increased volume then falls smoothly off. Much variation. Average vibrations per second 8900, extremes being 10,225 and 8050; highest of recorded passerine bird songs. (*See Chapter 5*)

FOOD HABITS: Mainly insects, including mosquitoes and termites, but sometimes seeds and berries.

GENERAL RANGE: *Breeds* at edge of timber from northwestern and southern Alaska across to Newfoundland, south to southern Nova Scotia, and islands off eastern Maine; New England mountains, and the Catskills. *Winters* from northern South America to eastern Brazil; accidental in Chile. Migrates through the West Indies.

ALEXANDER SPRUNT, JR.

39

PINE WARBLER

Dendroica pinus

THE male Pine Warbler is one of the few truly yellow birds of the eastern United States. His mate is duller colored but is easily identifiable, especially in the nesting season when few Pine Warblers are found away from pine areas. Young birds of the year, however, are a sore trial to observers—nondescript, brownish birds, showing little if any yellow coloration. Fortunately, they are usually found in family groups with one or both of the well-marked parents, when they can be recognized by inference even when orthodox methods of identification fail.

The Pine Warbler, when it settles down for the summer or the winter, is strictly a bird of pine areas and is hardly ever seen far from pine trees. In migration, of course, it may turn up anywhere—just as we sometimes find the marsh-loving Yellowthroat in our gardens far from any swamp or marsh. Nesting begins early, as early as mid-March in the South, not until May or June in the northern parts of the range. The compact and well-made nest is often saddled in plain sight on a horizontal limb well out from the trunk of the tree. In the South, where pine needles are long and grow in dense clusters, the nest is usually concealed among the needles—and then the finding of a nest is a real triumph for even a keen observer. It is completely hidden from below and can be located only by patient watching of the parent birds. Two broods are often reared in a season except in the northernmost parts of the bird's range. In the deep South, the occasional sighting of young birds still being fed by their parents late in June or even in July suggests that three broods may sometimes be reared.

Most of the insect hunting done by the

174

Pine Warbler is carried on high among the terminal tufts of pine needles, but much food is also gleaned from the bark crevices of the larger branches and even from the trunks of the trees. The bird's actions then, although unlike the systematic search by the Brown Creeper and the nuthatches, gave rise to the appropriate older name for the species, "Pine Creeping Warbler." In winter, in the South, the Pine Warbler is often a ground feeder, associating at such times with the drifting flocks of Bluebirds, Palm Warblers and Chipping Sparrows. When one of these flocks is flushed from its feeding, the Pine Warblers almost invariably stop for an instant to cling sidewise to the trunk of a tree before flying higher to the safety of the branches.

Although a Pine Warbler may be difficult to see in the tops of the tall trees, there is never any trouble in hearing it. It is a persistent singer except for a short period during molt and migration. Resident and wintering birds in the South sing throughout the winter. The song is often called a trill, but it is really a series of separate notes uttered in rapid succession. It is much more musical than the song of the Chipping Sparrow with which it is often compared, and the notes are sweeter, slower, softer and more pleasing. But there is more to be said of this song than mere description. Its charm gains much from the setting in which it is heard: a bright December day in the pineries of the deep South, a faint tang of wood smoke in the cool air, the almost imperceptible whispering of a breeze in the canopy of shining needles—then the pure tones of a Pine Warbler from far overhead bring true enchantment to the listener.

Dendroica pinus pinus (Wilson)
(Lat., *pinus,* pine)

Type Locality Georgia

LOCAL NAME: Northern Pine Warbler

OLD NAME: Pine Creeping Warbler.

FIELD CHARACTERS: *Adult male in spring,* greenish olive upperparts, unstreaked; bright greenish yellow breast, usually with obscure dusky streaks; a yellowish line over the eye; two whitish wing bars; white patches at the ends of the two outer tail feathers; under tail-coverts white.
Adult female in spring, duller throughout than the male, with less yellow on the breast.
Both sexes in winter, duller and more brownish than in spring.
Immature birds, very plain, with no bright colors, decidedly brownish above. The wing bars, tail patches and unstreaked back are the only good field marks.
Length, 4.95 to 5.75 inches.

NESTING DATA: Nest usually in pines of any species within the breeding range of the bird, rarely in cedars and cypresses. Sometimes saddled on a horizontal branch from 15 to 80 feet from the ground, but often concealed in a cluster of needles at the tip of a branch (this is particularly true in the south, where the pines are longer-leaved than elsewhere). Nests are compact and well-made of weed stems, bark strips or pine needles, lined with pine needles, fern-down, hair or feathers.
Eggs are usually four in number, sometimes three or five; white, grayish or greenish, spotted with various shades of brown or red, often in a wreath around the larger end.

VOICE: Forbush (*Birds of Massachusetts*) characterizes the song as "a slow, monotonous succession of soft sweet notes, given like the song of a Chipping Sparrow but slower, with longer intervals between the notes, and much softer." There is no variation in the tone of the song, except as the whole is given in a higher or lower key. The call note is a simple *chirp*. (See Chapter 5)

FOOD HABITS: The food consists largely of insects (grasshoppers, moths, larvae, beetles, ants, bugs, flies, scale insects) and spiders. In winter, the food includes many vegetable items: pine seeds, many kinds of wild fruits and berries and some weed and grass seeds.

GENERAL RANGE: *Breeds* in pine forests from southern Manitoba, western Ontario, northeastern Minnesota, northern Wisconsin, northern Michigan, central Ontario, southern Quebec, and central Maine south to southeastern Texas, south-central Louisiana, southern Mississippi, and northern Florida; local and rare from southern Minnesota, southern Wisconsin, southern Michigan, Ohio, and western Pennsylvania south to southern Missouri, Kentucky, and West Virginia. *Winters* in the southern one-third of its breeding range, though strays may be found in winter as far north as Massachusetts.

Dendroica pinus florida (Maynard)

Type Locality Deep Creek, Florida

LOCAL NAME: Florida Pine Warbler

The Florida race has a longer bill and the upper parts are slightly more yellowish (Bent).

RANGE: Resident and non-migratory in the southern two-thirds of the Florida peninsula, from Gainesville south to Everglade National Park.

FRANCIS M. WESTON

THE PINE WARBLER IN MICHIGAN

The Pine Warbler, local in northern Michigan during the summer, is generally found in three types of areas: In the upper peninsula it occurs chiefly in the Seney area including the great Seney National Wildlife Refuge. Here it prefers the ridges covered with scattered red pines. On June 28, 1948, we were listening to a Pine Warbler singing at the Seney Refuge headquarters when the bird flew into the tree above us and immediately went to the nest near the tip of one of the branches. The nest was tucked into a group of 'needle bunches' where these were thickest. It was 38 feet from the ground and contained three young Pine Warblers and one young Cowbird. The female was very mouselike when she approached, actually crawling up the branch to the nest. This site was apparently typical of the area.

A. Northern Pine. B. Florida Pine.

I found nests on two occasions along the dunes of Lake Michigan in the mixed oak-white pine areas of Muskegon County. Adults were feeding young at nests June 24, and July 2, 1950 here. Both were located in white pines, one 75 feet, the other 54 feet from the ground. Both nests were hidden far from the trunk in thick bunches of needles. Again both birds were watched bringing food to the young. The male always came back singing from tree to tree and continued to sing almost to the edge of the nest.

In the third area, throughout the northern portion of the lower peninsula, Jack Pine is the predominant tree. Groups of oaks are also found on these areas but the Pine Warblers seem to prefer Jack Pine stands where the pines are over 25 feet in height. The nests which we have found in this area were usually out near the tips of the branches and were found by watching the singing males.

The birds are very aggressive when any other birds appear near the nest and I have watched them chase Bronzed Grackles, Red-wings, Black-capped Chickadees, Hairy Woodpeckers, Nashville and Myrtle Warblers from the area.

Often, Pine Warblers come to a bird bath for water and are then very tame. I watched one during early July, 1933 at Spooner, Wisconsin, drink from puddles around a pump in a tourist park while I was getting water only a few feet away.

The song of the Pine Warbler is one of the most distinctive songs of the pine woods areas. It has much more pep and zest than the songs of such closely associated species as the Chipping Sparrow, Kingbird, Hermit Thrush, Slate-colored Junco, Myrtle Warbler and Black-throated Green Warbler. In some of its nesting territories in Oscoda and Crawford Counties, Michigan, where small Jack Pine abound, the lively song of Kirtland's Warbler can also be heard.

As soon as the species arrives in the spring the male begins to sing. Unlike many other species, he will sing from the top of one pine, then suddenly from some distance away, then farther away until he disappears in the distance. However, in a few minutes back he will come and repeat the same performance, singing as he goes from tree to tree.

The song is an energetic *Zip-zip-zip-zip-zip-zip* often given by the same male rapidly, then repeated later much more slowly,

the different syllables much more pronounced. Even after nesting is completed, this warbler will sing for some time during the early morning or late evening.

LAWRENCE H. WALKINSHAW

[*Comment:* The Pine Warbler is ideally adapted to a group of pine trees that are noted for the production of pitch, and the needles of which are gathered together into bundles of two and three. At least fifteen species of the genus *Pinus* are involved, and as is well known, they are dominant and form extensive stands in the southeastern states. In such country the Pine Warbler might be described as abundant and widely distributed. The northern limit of this group of pine trees in extensive stands is reached in the pine barrens of New Jersey, the eastward end of Long Island, and the whole southeastern coastal plain of Massachusetts, including Cape Cod and the eastern half of Plymouth County, in all of which habitats the Pine Warbler can be termed an abundant summer resident.

The effect of clearing and human disturbance has been the steady elimination of local pitch pine groves outside the above-mentioned coastal plain, and the Pine Warbler has been steadily decreasing in the Northeast in recent years. Its effort to push north and establish itself in other types of pine woods has not been conspicuously successful. But over sixty years ago it was reported as a rare, local and sporadic summer resident in high stands of white pine, which have also been steadily decreasing by lumbering, and by hurricane damage since 1938. (LUDLOW GRISCOM)]

40

KIRTLAND'S WARBLER

Dendroica kirtlandii

KIRTLAND'S Warbler is famous for its remarkably restricted nesting range—one of the smallest known for any mainland species of bird. Geographically it is confined to a nesting area about 60 by 80 miles in the central Michigan Jack Pine plains; ecologically it is restricted to dense stands of small pines, 3 to 18 feet tall. Formerly the nesting Kirtland was found only in the thick stands of young Jack Pine (*Pinus banksiana*) which spring up after a fire or after the destruction of full-grown pines by tornadic winds, but now foresters plant great stands of jack pine in rows, which are quickly occupied by the warblers when the new trees are big enough. Even plantings of red pine are now used by Kirtland's Warbler, though the natural stands of this tree are never dense enough for this fastidious bird.

Kirtland's Warbler is a very frequent singer while nesting, and its loud song is almost always the clue which enables us first to make the bird's acquaintance and later to study it as intimately as our time will allow. Many hundreds of bird students have been guided to this beautiful bird by the constant singing of the males, but very few indeed have seen a Kirtland's Warbler after the season of song is over. Though the song is nearly always of an easily recognizable general pattern, individuals have their own special way of rendering it, and one can use distinctive songs to search out some banded male as it returns year after year to the same nesting territory.

The nest is built entirely by the female, the male singing steadily as she works, stopping when work stops and resuming instantly when she starts gathering nest material again. In one observed instance the female built a nest in four days, but actually did much of the work the first day, making on that day 131 trips with nest material; on the fifth day she laid the first egg.

Kirtland's Warbler feeds mainly on the insects which it finds on the pines and on the oaks that are scattered among them, but often it hunts briefly along the ground, always progressing by hopping or flying. Sometimes, too, it will fly out from a branch to catch a moth on the wing or hover before a pine twig, picking small caterpillars from between the sprouting young needles. The male brings food regularly to the female while she is incubating the eggs, offering it to her near or even at the nest; he takes his full share of feeding the nestling young.

Kirtland's Warblers usually nest in loose colonies, though some isolated nests have been found. Anyone searching for this famous warbler can usually count on finding it between mid-May and the first week of July if he seeks out areas of 80 acres or more of young pine plantations or natural stands of young pines that have come up after a forest fire. The singing males can be heard a quarter-mile or more and are not often silent as long as 10 minutes, especially before the heat of the day.

Kirtland's Warblers are rather easily marked with leg bands, and many score have been so identified and studied year after year. More than half of those marked as adults have been found in subsequent years—always in the same general vicinity, and often in exactly the same grove. Males return to the old territory somewhat more consistently than females, but both members of one pair returned and nested together for three consecutive summers in the same territory. Individual birds have been followed much longer: a male for nine successive summers and a female for eight. In Oscoda County in 1947 we found one male that had two nests at once—in adjoining territories. One of his mates was a yearling female which we had banded as a nestling the year before in a colony 19 miles away; the other was a female we had followed since 1944, and which had always nested nearby.

[*Comment:* "The Kirtland's Warbler . . . was first discovered on May 13, 1851, when a migrant was taken at Cleveland, Ohio (by Charles Pease, who presented it to his father-in-law, Jared P. Kirtland, a well known naturalist of the day for whom the bird was named). The first nest was located on July 8, 1903, in Crawford County, Michigan. Every nest found subsequently has been within 60 miles of the first. In winter, the bird is known only in the Bahama Islands." This succinct statement by Harold Mayfield (*Auk* 70:17, 1953) indicates the limited distribution of this rare warbler. He and his associates made a survey of the singing males in the Jack Pine country of the Lower Peninsula of Michigan. During June, 1951, this species was found in only eight counties. Four hundred and thirty-two singing males were counted and an equal number of females estimated. Thus, allowing for possible sources of error, the total population of Kirtland's Warbler is believed to be less than a thousand. (A. R. FAVER in *The Chat*)]

PLATE 20
CHESTNUT-SIDED WARBLER
Page 166

Immature

Female

Male

Dendroica kirtlandii (Baird)
   (Lat., *kirtlandii*, for Jared P. Kirtland)

Type Locality Near Cleveland, Ohio

LOCAL NAME: Jack Pine Warbler.

FIELD CHARACTERS: *Adult male,* upperparts blue-gray (slate), with black streaks on back and narrow black facial mask. Yellow (pale to bright) below, with black streaks along sides and sometimes spotting on breast.
   Adult female, less blue above, duller yellow below; lacks the mask. In fall, both sexes are washed with brown on sides and upper parts, making them difficult to identify in the field. Both sexes habitually jerk tail up and down (like the Palm Warbler).
   Length, 5.75 inches.

NESTING DATA: Nest a closely-woven cup of dry grasses or similar plant material, lined with finer grasses or with deer hair or delicate red stalks from moss. Placed directly on ground, usually beneath overarching plants which allow access from only one side; in dense stand of young pine. Often parasitized by the Cowbird.
   Eggs—4 to 5. Creamy or slightly pinkish-white, blotched and speckled with fawn and brown (uniformly or in wreath at blunt end).

VOICE: Low-pitched for this genus, but very loud and emphatic. A "liquid bubbling" song, somewhat like that of the Northern Water-thrush or the House Wren. *Chip-chip-che-chee-chee-r-r-r* (Chapman); or *wichi chee chee-cheer-r-r* (Forbush). Call note a *tsip*. (*See Chapter 5*)

FOOD HABITS: Insects and their larvae; berries.

RANGE: *Breeds* in small area in northern half of the Lower Peninsula of Michigan (north to edge of Presque Isle County, south to Ogemaw County; east to Iosco County, west to Kalkaska County, and there limited to dense stands of young pines, usually Jack Pines. *Winters* in the Bahamas.
   JOSSELYN VAN TYNE

41

PRAIRIE WARBLER

Dendroica discolor

SHOULD common names of birds undergo any drastic alteration this warbler ought to be among them. "Prairie" is misleading; Scrub Warbler would be better, for such habitat is the home of this exquisite little bird. I have long thought it one of the most appealing of the family, a close view of a high-plumaged male being as lovely a picture of animated nature as one could see.

Open brushy lands, often of mixed pine and scrub oak, appeal to it, and the disappearance of heavy woodlands and the subsequent scrubby growth in the clearings, have brought this warbler into areas it did not formerly inhabit. Even now it is rather spotty in occurrence; for a certain locality may harbor numbers of the birds and another not far off be almost lacking. The Prairie is another easy warbler to see on account of its low ranging tendencies. From practically ground level in a ditch full of small willows, to small saplings and trees fifteen to twenty-five feet high, is the usual zone in which it forages. Now and then it will resort to higher perches to sing. Scattered pines, patches of hickory, dogwood and blackjack oak are frequented as well as low bushes. It is an essentially eastern warbler. From the Jack Pine country of Michigan and central New England, it ranges to the bayous of Louisiana and the flatwoods of Florida.

During winter it can be met with in the southeastern part of the country north to lower South Carolina; it winters in some numbers in Florida where it is easy to find in the mixed "hammocks" of the south-central portion of that State. The southern (Florida) race of this warbler is mainly a coastal bird and lives among the mangroves of both sides of Florida and in the Keys. To many who know the bird in its northern summer home it doubtless appears an incongruous place to find it but *paludicola* could almost be termed aquatic, so fond is it of watery situations.

The song of the Prairie Warbler is one of the most distinct of the entire family. The notes are uttered on a steadily ascending scale, not in a trill but separate and distinct. They carry well even though not particularly loud. It is frequently possible to hear them as one travels along in an automobile. *Zee-zee-zee-zee-zeét* is about as good a rendition into words as any.

Field recognition of the Prairie Warbler is as easy as any representative of the family can be. The brilliant yellow underparts "from stem to stern" together with the black striped sides, very heavily so at times, are at once diagnostic. The Prairie is a tail-wagging warbler but the habit is not as pronounced as in the Palm Warblers. It sometimes flutters like a hummingbird in feeding and also secures insects in the air like the flycatchers.

The northern bird is often victimized by the cowbird but although the latter is lacking in the south, raccoons and snakes sometimes take a toll in that region. Where the warbler is imposed upon by the cowbird, it sometimes constructs a false bottom to the nest to isolate the intruded egg.

Migrant Prairies, like other warblers, appear almost anywhere but in rather sporadic occurrence. In former years they were occasionally lighthouse victims along the Florida reef and elsewhere, but with the rise of radio beacons and the steady diminu-

tion of lighthouses, such hazards have decreased in recent years. It is one of the commonest warblers at the Dry Tortugas in both migrations. I have seen them there in numbers at times; in the period of September 3 through 9, 1949, they were present every day and as tame as I have seen them anywhere.

Dendroica discolor discolor (Vieillot)
(Lat., *discolor*, different colors)

Type Locality New York

LOCAL NAME: Northern Prairie Warbler

FIELD CHARACTERS: *Male*, upperparts olive-green, back spotted with chestnut to greater or less degree; line over eye and entire underparts bright yellow; two yellowish-white wing bars; sides of neck and body heavily streaked with black; tail with large white patches on three outer feathers.
Female, similar in pattern to male but colors duller; chestnut back markings largely lacking.
Length, 4.25 to 5.20 inches.

NESTING DATA: In bushes or saplings at low elevations, 1 to 10 feet from ground, averaging about 4 ft. The southern bird nests mainly in red mangroves at 6 to 10 ft., usually over water. Nest a compact cup of weed stalks and leaves, plant down, bits of bark etc., lined with feathers, hair or fine grass.
Eggs—3 to 5, usually 4. White or greenish-white, marked with spots and splashes of chestnut, umber and grayish-lavender. Either scattered over shell or in a wreath around large end, occasionally the small end.

VOICE: Very distinctive and easy to remember. A series of ascending notes like "zee-zee-zee-zeet." Persistently uttered, with the head held vertically, sometimes from quite an elevated perch. Though not loud, the notes have a penetrating quality. Song period very long in parts of the range, as much as five months. (*See Chapter 5*)

FOOD HABITS: Very largely insects and spiders.

GENERAL RANGE: *Breeds* from South Dakota, eastern Nebraska across to southern New Hampshire; south to east Texas, eastern Oklahoma, southeastern Louisiana and southeastern Georgia and the

Carolinas. *Winters* throughout the West Indies, to Martinique and the Dutch West Indies (Windward Group). Also on islands off eastern Mexico, Honduras and Nicaragua.

Dendroica discolor paludicola Howell
(Lat., paludicola, a swamp dweller)

Type Locality Anclote Key, Florida

LOCAL NAME: Florida Prairie Warbler

This southern race differs from *D. d. discolor* in having a lighter yellow breast, grayish back with few if any chestnut markings and less heavily streaked sides. It is largely coastal in distribution and very partial to the red mangrove (*Rhiziphora mangle*) amid which it lives and nests. The eggs are like those of the northern bird. It is quite common and as persistent a singer as *discolor*.

RANGE: Eastern Georgia, southeastern South Carolina, south to the Florida Keys. *Breeds* on both coasts of Florida. *Winters* in central and southern Florida and the West Indies (Cuba and St. Croix).
ALEXANDER SPRUNT, JR.

A. Northern Prairie. B. Florida Prairie.

[*Comment:* In Michigan the Prairie Warbler nests in two types of areas. One is the sandy dunes along the Great Lakes where the birds actually nest in small junipers, or even under the canopy of bracken ferns for protection against the hot sun, or in small shrubs in areas little inhabited by other birds. The nests are from a few inches to about three feet from the ground and are well constructed of plant fibres lined with cottony materials. The second type of area where the birds are found is the Jack Pine plains and the oak plains of northern Michigan—often where the Clay-colored Sparrow is found—in the oaks, small maples, shadbush, beaked hazel and similar bushes, or in the Jack Pine areas, where we have found a number of nests in pines a few feet above ground. Often these latter areas are the same as those used by Kirtland's Warbler.

In two nests in Muskegon County, Michigan, incubation required 12 days; the young have remained in one nest for eight days, in another, 10 days, and eight days in a third. The female did all the work of nest building and incubating of eggs but the male helped considerably in feeding the young. (LAWRENCE H. WALKINSHAW)]

John H. Dick
'55

PLATE 21
PRAIRIE WARBLER
Page 182
Adult Male

Immature

KIRTLAND'S WARBLER
Page 178
Male

Female

42

PALM WARBLER

Dendroica palmarum

THIS dull and relatively uninteresting warbler was described by pure chance from Santo Domingo, and it took some time to discover that it was really a North American bird, wintering in the West Indies. There was the usual presumption that it remained to breed in the high mountains of the island, and it took over one hundred years for this rumor finally to be put to sleep.

The common name Palm Warbler was a literal translation of the scientific name, and has turned out to be most inappropriate. For years I have amused myself keeping an informal life list of the people who have actually seen a Palm Warbler in a palm tree. To be fair, if the scrub palmetto (*Serenoa*) is allowed to count, the inappropriateness of the name could be reduced.

Actually, the Western race of this bird is a common and conspicuous winter visitant to all the islands of the Greater Antilles, but relatively rare in Puerto Rico, and unknown east of the Islands of St. Croix in the Virgin Islands.

This is possibly the commonest winter land bird in Florida, where it is primarily a dooryard, open field and pasture bird; but it becomes increasingly rare along the Gulf Coast of Louisiana, where there are very few authentic winter records.

As early as 1880 it became known as relatively rare or casual as a fall migrant on the Atlantic slope. It has been steadily increasing, apparently, and it is occasionally common—up to 69 birds in a day in southeastern Massachusetts. In the recent cycle of mild winter climates, it has tended to winter further and further northward, and it is now of regular occurrence in early winter north to northern Massachusetts and even southeastern New Hampshire and east on Cape Cod.

Western Palm Warblers start their northward migration in early March. The last migrants in Florida remain until late April, with an extreme date for May 2, and casually in June in coastal South Carolina. The birds cross the Allegheny Mountains at some undetermined point, and move northward through the Mississippi Valley to Canada. It is apparently relatively uncommon eastward in western Pennsylvania and extreme western New York, but often abundant in marked flights in southern Michigan west to Minnesota (earliest April 11) where at times as many as 50 birds may be seen in a day.

The Western Palm Warbler nests in the high Canadian zone in Canada. It is believed, however, that the great horde of transients disappears more or less in the vast unexplored parts of subarctic Canada, where the bird is clearly partial to extensive areas of open muskegs, either wet or dry, among scattered spruces and tamaracks.

On migration this bird is primarily a bird of open or cleared country, but will occur in wooded areas. In October in southeastern Massachusetts it joins up with roving flocks of migrating kinglets and chickadees. It is consequently pure chance whether the birds are found in small trees or hopping on the ground in fields and pastures. The length of stay in fall is entirely dependent upon the weather, birds moving south rapidly before a severe or sudden cold wave.

Dendroica palmarum palmarum (Gmelin)

Type Locality Santo Domingo

LOCAL NAME: Western Palm Warbler

FIELD CHARACTERS: *Adults in spring,* crown chestnut; stripe over eye yellow; upperparts olive-brown with narrow dark streaking; rump greenish-yellow; throat, upper breast and under tail-coverts yellow, the breast finely streaked with chestnut; belly white, more or less tinged yellow; wings and tail dusky, the latter with white patches at tips. *Adults and immatures in fall and winter:* as above but colors much duller; line over eye whitish; underparts whitish and only the under tail-coverts yellow. This species is readily identified in all plumages by its habit of constantly wagging its tail up and down.
   Length, 5.00 to 5.75 inches.

NESTING DATA: On or near the ground, among hummocks or tufts of grass, concealed among small shrubby plants, compactly built of weed-stems, grasses, strips of bark, moss and hairs, and lined with fine grasses and rootlets.
   Eggs—4 or 5, creamy white, speckled on larger end with brown or lavender.

VOICE: Very similar to a Chipping Sparrow; *thi, thi, thi, thi, thi.* A simple, weak trill *"tsee tsee tsee tsee,* with a distinct swell" (Lynds Jones). Song described as "rich, soft and liquid—*hee''-u hee'' -u hee''-u hee''-u,* the first notes delivered slowly, the last two a little more rapidly" (Leonard W. King). (*See Chapter 5*)

FOOD HABITS: Beetles, ants, spiders, caterpillars, grasshoppers, etc. Forbush (*Birds of Massachusetts,* 1929) says "Probably this is one of the most useful warblers of the Mississippi Valley Region."

GENERAL RANGE: *Breeds* from southern Mackenzie, northeastern British Columbia, various parts of Alberta and northern Manitoba south to extreme northern Minnesota, and extreme northern Wisconsin, east to central Ontario. *Winters* from southern Florida, Louisiana, Mississippi, Alabama, Georgia and South Carolina, and the Bahamas to the Greater Antilles and Yucatan.

LUDLOW GRISCOM

[*Comment:* In Northern Michigan only one breeding record of the Western Palm Warbler had been found prior to

1955 and 1956. During these two years we found four nests. The species is not uncommon in the upper peninsula in the muskeg type marshes associated with Lincoln's Sparrow and the Sandhill Crane, at times with Brewer's Blackbird. Two nests were found set in the moss of the muskeg country. One was at the base of a small Jack Pine (*Pinus banksiana*); the other at the base of a small Black Spruce (*Picea mariana*). Both locations were semi-open. In another case a nest was found on the border of the muskeg but on a ridge resting on the dry sandy soil. Again it was in the semi-open. These nests were all in Schoolcraft County near Seney. The area where the Western Palm Warbler was found in 1931 was a dry sandy Jack Pine plains in the heart of a Kirtland's Warbler colony in Crawford County and the 1955 nest found by Mark Wolf in Iosco County was in a similar situation. This nest was resting in the ground between two small Jack Pines and Kirtland's Warblers sang all around. All five nests in Michigan produced young Palm Warblers. All five were made of dry grasses and lined with finer grasses and feathers. All were well hidden. Young left these nests June 16, 1931, June 16, 1955, June 18, 1955, June 24, 1956 and June 25, 1956.

Western Palm Warblers usually have been found while the male was giving his typical Chipping Sparrow-like song.

I found a nest with five eggs of this species at Fawcett, Alberta, May 25, 1942 which was also located in muskeg beneath small two-to-three foot dwarf birches and also set in the sphagnum moss. (LAWRENCE H. WALKINSHAW)]

Dendroica palmarum hypochrysea Ridgway
(Gr., *hypochrysea* gleaming with gold)

Type Locality Cambridge, Mass.

LOCAL NAME: Yellow Palm Warbler

This exceedingly well marked subspecies is the eastward nesting form of the species. It is characterized by being much brighter and more uniformly yellow on the underparts; it is larger in size, has a brighter rufous cap and more conspicuous rufous streaks on the chest.

On migration it is the prevailing form on the Atlantic coastal plain states, and is exceedingly rare at any locality west of the Alleghenies, if indeed an authentic specimen can be found. Curiously enough, the migration routes of the Yellow Palm and Western Palm Warbler cross in Florida, as the bulk of Yellow Palm Warblers turn westward and are the prevailing winter form across the Gulf Coast states of Louisiana and extreme eastern Texas.

Unfortunately we have here an ideal example of such exceptionally distinct subspecific variation that the idea has been sold to far too many amateur observers that the two subspecies are readily distinguishable in life. This is not the case, as intermediates do in fact occur, though none are as yet authentically reported from the breeding range. As the difference of size is rarely of any use in the field, there remains nothing but color, and confusion can occur in birds in the spring and in the fall plumage. In the fall, some specimens of the Yellow Palm are particularly dull below, and even in the spring plumage dull female Yellow Palms can be seen at the end of every normal spring migration which are often thought to be the rare Western Palm by enthusiastic observers. Every year in fall I personally see individuals which I am unable to identify with any definite confidence, and as my years of experience increase, I become more and more skeptical of those birds which I have seen in spring which I thought might be the rarer Western race.

By assuming that all records west of the Alleghenies apply to the Western Palm Warbler, it is easily apparent that this subspecies is southbound relatively early and that it appears with great regularity in the northern tier of states from late August to early September. As its late departure dates are almost entirely due to the variable local severity of the season, there is little point in tabulating extreme dates.

On the average the Western Palm arrives on the Atlantic Seaboard states at least two weeks ahead of the Yellow Palm.

The spring migration of the Yellow Palm Warbler on the Atlantic Seaboard states is approximately as follows, based on specimens. Last collected in Florida on March 15, six weeks before the Western Palm finally disappears. Migrants reach Washington, D.C. on the average of April 6, and occur around New York City and eastern Massachusetts in marked waves during the third week in April. The first arrivals are entirely according to the vagaries of the season, but in the recent warm cycles of climates the advance guard of Yellow Palms has reached both Boston and New York by the last days of March in a very advanced season. Stragglers are still passing through these areas by the middle of May, and consist almost wholly of dull-colored females. This is exactly when observers report sight records for the very rare Western Palm Warbler, and it is my suggestion that all alleged specimens should be critically examined, and if possible redetermined.

FIELD CHARACTERS: Similar to Western Palm but in spring *uniformly bright yellow underparts,* with a *bright yellow eye-stripe.* In fall and winter the yellow underparts less clear but much more yellow than in Western Palm Warbler which has pure yellow only on under tail-coverts. Bobs tail constantly, as in *p. palmarum.*

GENERAL RANGE: *Breeds* from eastern Ontario, central Quebec, and southern Newfoundland south to southern Nova Scotia, New Brunswick, Maine (Mt. Desert Island and Auburn) and New Hampshire.

A. Western Palm. B. Yellow Palm.

Winters from Louisiana to Florida, and casually up the Atlantic coast as far as New Jersey and Connecticut.

LUDLOW GRISCOM

43

OVENBIRD

Seiurus aurocapillus

SUPERFICIALLY, much more like a small thrush than a warbler, this little walker of the woodlands is a favorite with many bird-watchers. Perhaps its outstanding characteristic is its voice. Although not really difficult to see, the bird is known to many far better by vocal, rather than visual acquaintance. It is the familiar "teacher bird" of song and story and the rendition of the notes in louder and louder utterance has made the Ovenbird famous.

Hardly of lesser fame is the reason for its common name, the peculiar, arched-over nest so like a Dutch oven, set into the leafy ground. All in all, this warbler is so very different from most of the family that identification is easy.

Only on the migrations is the Ovenbird anything but a woodland species. Rather open forests with little underbrush but an abundance of fallen leaves, logs and rocks are its haunts, the same type of habitat that wood thrushes are fond of. It lives on or very close to the ground and blends into the surroundings well. The habit of walking is conspicuous and of course a variation from most other warblers.

If the Ovenbird is somewhat retiring in habits, it very definitely advertises its presence vocally. The sharp call note is persistently uttered if one is near the nest site, but it is the song that really claims attention; or we should say songs, for there is more than one rendition. The widely known "teacher" variety is transcended by the flight song which is much more musical and beautiful. It is given at varying altitudes, at times above treetop level and is certainly a wonderful performance.

[*Comment:* In our experience, the

flight song is given more frequently towards dusk than at any other time of day. It is sometimes given at night. It is also given more frequently towards the end of the breeding season than during the early part of it. In the summer of 1955, a friend and I obtained a series of recordings from a number of Ontario birds and found a surprising amount of variation. Some emphasized the first syllable, others the second; some sang very rapidly, some very slowly; some built successive phrases up to a crescendo, others sang them all at the same level. (W. W. H. GUNN)]

Now and then a female bird may have more than one mate, as many as three are on record (Bent). She is a close sitter and allows herself to be almost trodden upon before flushing or running off. The nest is usually quite invisible from above, only a rounded excrescence amid the leaves. Interference at the time of construction or early egg laying often results in nest abandonment, but once incubation is well along, she remains on the eggs closely and when flushed puts on a most convincing 'broken wing' act.

As might be expected with a ground nester, the Ovenbird is subject to predation by snakes, weasels, squirrels and others. It is also victimized by the cowbird. Harry W. Hann, in an entire issue of *The Wilson Bulletin* devoted to the Ovenbird (September 1937), describes this parasitism at great length. According to Hann's observations in Michigan, 52 per cent of all Ovenbirds' nests in which eggs were laid were parasitized by the Cowbirds, which laid from one to four eggs per nest. Female Cowbirds, he found, discovered the nest by observing the female Ovenbird building. This sight, according to Hann's theory, stimulated ovulation in the Cowbird who produced eggs in four or five days to coincide with the laying of the host, and laid them early in the morning before the Ovenbird laid. The laying time took only from 40–60 seconds and was often preceded by the removal of one or more Ovenbird eggs. This egg loss was estimated at 18 per cent of the total laid.

The incubation period of the Cowbird averaged 11.6 days, or 0.6 of a day less than the Ovenbird, giving the former an important headstart. However, the young Ovenbirds in the parasitized nests seemed to do as well as those in non-parasitized nests because of extra activity by both parents, the chief loss to the Ovenbird being in the removal of eggs. Furthermore, the survival rate of the Cowbirds was low, "Since out of 40 eggs laid only 22 hatched, ten birds left the nest and probably not more than five birds left the woods. In this light, the Ovenbird can not be considered a very favorable host."

Many of these warblers are killed by migration hazards. The Ovenbird is nevertheless one of the most abundant migrants on the Dry Tortugas. To see it there, on a September day, walking about by the dozen in the galleries and casemates of old Fort Jefferson, under the long vistas of arches, is as far a cry as one could imagine from the shade of northern woodlands, mossy logs and lichen-clad rocks.

Aside from its habit of walking, the Ovenbird may be known at once by the golden brown crown and streaked underparts. There are three races:

PLATE 22
PALM WARBLER
Page 186

Western Palm in flight

Adult Western

Yellow Palm

Immature

John H. Dick
'55

Seiurus aurocapillus aurocapillus (Linnaeus)
    (Gr., *seiurus,* tail-waving; Lat., *aurocapillus,* golden-haired).

> Type Locality "in Pennsylvania-at sea, apparently off Haiti" (A.O.U. Check-list)

LOCAL NAMES: Eastern Ovenbird, Golden-crowned Thrush, Teacher Bird.

FIELD CHARACTERS: Center of crown and nape ochraceous tawny, bordered on each side with blackish; upperparts greenish-olive; underparts white, chest and sides streaked and spotted with brownish-black.
    Length, 5.40 to 6.50 inches.

NESTING DATA: On the ground in woodlands. Sunk in slight depression and arched over in shape of a Dutch oven. Invisible from above except as rounded protuberance amid leaves. Nest of grasses, fibers, leaves, weed stems, rootlets and moss. Lined with hair or fine rootlets.
    Eggs—3 to 6, usually 4 or 5. White, speckled and spotted with reddish-brown, lilac and hazel often in a wreath about large end.

VOICE: Best-known song is the "teacher-teacher-TEACHER" rendition, given in crescendo delivery, varying in accent to one and the other syllable. Also a flight song described as "a wild outpouring of intricate and melodious song." (Bicknell, 1884). Given at varying elevations from 10 to 15 feet to above treetop level. (*See Chapter 5*)
    A call note like "zick" is often uttered about the nest.

FOOD HABITS: Largely insects but also ground life, such as snails, slugs and earthworms. A few seeds and wild fruits taken at times.

GENERAL RANGE: *Breeds* from southeastern Mackenzie and southern Quebec, south to northern Louisiana and northwestern South Carolina. *Winters* from southern Louisiana and southeastern South Carolina south to Mexico, Central America, the West Indies and northern South America.

Seiurus aurocapillus furvior Batchelder
    (Lat., *furvior,* swarthy)

> Type Locality Deer Pond, Newfoundland

A. Eastern. B. Newfoundland. C. Gray.

LOCAL NAME: Newfoundland Ovenbird

This race differs from *S. a. aurocapillus* in being generally darker.

RANGE: Breeds in Newfoundland. Winters from Guatemala, Cuba and Bahamas south to Costa Rica and Panama.

Seiurus aurocapillus cinereus A. H. Miller
    (Lat., *cinereus,* gray)

> Type Locality Powder River County, Montana

LOCAL NAME: Gray Ovenbird

A paler race than the eastern bird.

RANGE: *Breeds* from southern Alberta and southeastern Montana south to the Arkansas River (Colorado) and central Nebraska. *Winters* in Mexico and Central America.

ALEXANDER SPRUNT, JR.

44

NORTHERN WATERTHRUSH

Seiurus noveboracensis

THE Waterthrushes, like the Ovenbird, seem somewhat incongruous as warblers. Forbush (1929) says that "Though not really a thrush, the Waterthrush is well named. It is a large wood warbler disguised as a thrush and exhibiting an extreme fondness for water." Exactly!

A walker like the Ovenbird, it is also a teeterer. The body goes up and down almost constantly and the tail wags continuously. It is fond of walking along old, slanting logs which disappear into mud or water, and is a frequenter of wooded streams, pond edges and swamps where down timber occurs in profusion.

During the migrations it is sometimes possible to see waterthrushes in astonishing numbers. Arthur T. Wayne, my ornithological mentor for many years, once saw what he called "vast hosts" of the birds in mid-September in the coast country of South Carolina. In a swamp near his plantation home he saw hundreds at once in a space of a hundred square feet and estimated that, in the area of the swamp he covered, there were as many as 25,000 individuals! At such seasons the birds may appear anywhere, even in towns and cities. I have seen as many as 15 at a time on the Tortugas in September and the surroundings there seem very out of line for these woodland birds.

Even on those bits of land where many other migrants are amazingly tame, the Waterthrushes are shy and elusive and one must follow them about carefully to be sure of their identity. Though a few winter in Florida, I have never found them in the Okeechobee-Kissimmee Prairie region at that season.

The bird is not hard to recognize despite

being sometimes hard to find. The constant habit of tilting the body combined with the conspicuous eye-stripe (buffy in *noveboracensis* and white in *motacilla*) and the streaked underparts are a sure trio of field marks. The very distinctive, sharply enunciated "clink" call note is also diagnostic.

Seiurus noveboracensis noveboracensis (Gmelin)
(Lat., *noveboracensis,* of New York)

Type Locality New York

LOCAL NAME: Northern Small-billed Waterthrush

FIELD CHARACTERS: Upperparts olive; eye-stripe buff; underparts pale yellow, streaked and spotted with blackish.
Length, 5 to 6 inches.

NESTING DATA: On ground among roots of fallen trees or bases of living ones; stump cavities; sides of banks or cuts. Nest material largely mosses, leaves, pieces of bark and small twigs, lined with blossom stalks of moss.
  Eggs—4 or 5. Creamy white, marked with spots of hazel, grayish-lavender and reddish-brown tending to wreath about large end.

VOICE: Notable among the warblers for excellence. *twit twit twit—twee twee twee-chew chew chew*. There is a perch and flight song hard to render into words, but a very ringing musical warble ending in a lower "chew-chew-chew," and the flight song punctuated by "chippering" notes. The call note, rendered as "clink" is distinctive, sharply delivered and easily recognized. (*See Chapter 5*)

FOOD HABITS: Aquatic insects such as beetle larvae and moths, small crustacea and mollusks, with some minnows and worms.

GENERAL RANGE: *Breeds* from northern New York, southern Quebec, Labrador, and Newfoundland, south to West Virginia and Pennsylvania (in Appalachians) Massachusetts, Maine and Nova Scotia. *Winters* mainly from Mexico and the West Indies south to northern South America (British Guiana, Curaçao, Colombia, Ecuador, Peru and Vene-

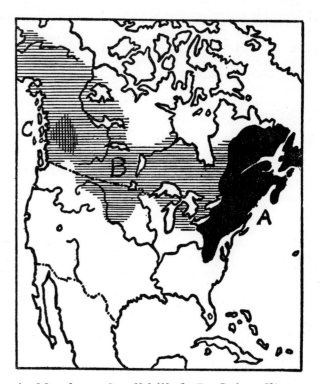

A. Northern Small-billed. B. Grinnell's. C. British Columbia.

zuela). Has been recorded from northeastern Siberia and France.

Seiurus noveboracensis notabilis Ridgway
  (Lat., *notabilis,* noteworthy)

Type Locality Carbon County, Wyoming

LOCAL NAME: Grinnell's Water-thrush

This is a northwestern race of the above bird, differing from it in being larger, with less olive above, less yellow below, usually white. It is similar to the eastern bird in habits and nesting but seems to sing from more elevated perches. The migration is to the eastward of the Rocky Mountains and reaches the south Atlantic coast (South Carolina) and Florida en route to the Bahamas, Cuba and South America, a diagonal cross-continental flight, or approximately so. This is the race that Wayne found in such abundance in September in coastal South Carolina. I have found it only once at the Tortugas, but more study is needed there.

RANGE: *Breeds* from north-central Alaska, northern Yukon, northwestern and central southern Mackenzie, northeastern Saskatchewan, northern Manitoba, northern Ontario, and north-central Quebec south to southern continental Alaska, northern British Columbia, and from Alberta to northern Idaho, western Montana, central Saskatchewan, central northern North Dakota, southeastern Manitoba, northeastern Minnesota, northern Wisconsin, southeastern Michigan, northeastern Ohio, extreme northwestern Pennsylvania, southeastern Ontario and southwestern Quebec. *Winters* from the Bahamas, Cuba, Mexico and Baja California, south to northern South America.

Seiurus noveboracensis limnaeus McCabe and Miller
(Gr., *limnaeus*, marsh or pond)

Type Locality Indian Point Lake, B. C.

LOCAL NAME: British Columbia Water-thrush

This is the race which breeds in British Columbia and appears to be intermediate between *noveboracensis* and *notabilis,* though its range is an enclave in that of *notabilis.*

RANGE: Central and northern British Columbia. *Winters* from Baja California south to Panama and Colombia.

ALEXANDER SPRUNT, JR.

[*Comment:* Stephen W. Eaton in a discussion of variation in the Northern Waterthrush (*Auk.* 74, 229–239) tells of a fourth race, *S. n. uliginosus* described by Burleigh and Peters (1948) as the breeding bird of Newfoundland, and of the temptation to name several additional races. But his own examination of 504 specimens taken throughout the bird's entire range leads him to conclude that despite great individual variation, the geographic variation is so slight that "it would seem best to treat the species as monotypic." (D. A. G.)]

[*Comment:* The Northern Waterthrush is a common bird in suitable habitats of southern Ontario where its loud, explosive, uninhibited song may be expected during the last few days of April or the first days of May. North of Lake Superior it is much less common since conditions as a whole are less suited to this species. Here it is not expected until after the middle of the month. Although it has been described as one of the more elusive species we have found it relatively easy to approach and observe while it feeds and sings near its nest.

The species is one of our earliest nesters and full complements of eggs may be found before other warblers of the area have started nest-building. Sometimes this will be under an upturned root along the shady rocky shore lines of a northern lake; again it may be under the overhanging bank of a meandering stream. At other times it is found in loosely knit colonies, particularly where a storm of recent years has uprooted many trees in a flooded area. Here the nests will be found in the upturned roots, almost always over the water-filled hole from which the roots had been wrenched. Sometimes in these areas the birds are very abundant—three of us once found 22 such nests in a week of birding north of Lake Ontario. Again, two occupied nests were found under a single stump, one placed two feet above the other. A nest of the Winter Wren was built in the same stump. Scarcely 50 feet away, three nests were found in the roots of another upturned tree.

Elsewhere in its range the Cowbird is said to be an unimportant factor in the nesting of this species, but such is not the case here; in our series of 40 nests, twenty percent were parasitized. (A. E. ALLIN AND PAUL HARRINGTON)]

John H. DICK
'55

PLATE 23
OVENBIRD
Page 190

NORTHERN WATERTHRUSH
Page 194

LOUISIANA WATERTHRUSH
Page 198

45

LOUISIANA WATERTHRUSH

Seiurus motacilla

THOUGH similar in behavior and habits to the other waterthrushes, this species differs in definite respects both as to details of plumage and habitat. While the Northern Waterthrushes seem to prefer pond edges or slow moving watercourses, bogs and swamps, the Louisiana prefers rapidly running water. Richard C. Harlow writes of the two birds in Bent's *Life Histories* as follows: "In the Pocono Mountains of Pennsylvania, where the Northern Waterthrush is very common and the Louisiana a common breeder, the normal nesting habitat of the northern species is in Rhododendron bogs amid damp surroundings, where water is slow-moving or stagnant, and where upturned roots of fallen, moss-covered trees abound. The Louisiana is here normally a bird of the fast-flowing trout streams, nesting in the banks or gullies near by. Both species may nest in overlapping zones, but they are much more frequent in the respective habitats indicated above."

The song is thought by many to be the finest of the group and has a more pronounced quality of wildness, a feature enhanced by its dark haunts. Though long known to have nested from Nebraska and southern New England to as far south as Piedmont (upper) South Carolina and adjacent mountains, it has recently been found breeding below the central part of that State and to within about 75 miles of the coast. It breeds also in mid-eastern Georgia and almost to the Florida line below Thomasville. There are indications that it may even breed in northern Florida, so that it occurs practically over the whole central midwest, east and southeast.

Any good look at the bird will reveal the perfectly *white* eye-stripe and practically immaculate throat. The underparts are much lighter (white) than the yellowish shade of the other waterthrushes. Constant teetering is of course, indulged in. One is reminded of the Spotted Sandpiper.

Heavy woodland swamps, with running brooks or full ditches, where underbrush, old logs and other debris choke the banks, are places to look for this rather elusive forest sprite. Where the song rings out amid such surroundings it imparts an impression of eeriness that few avian vocalists can, or do produce. Even the dainty motions of its walking over rocks, logs or the stones of a running stream seem somewhat unreal. As with others of its tribe, it appears in the most non-typical localities during migration, a town garden, city cemetery or park, and even sparsely grown barrier beaches off the coast.

Seiurus motacilla (Vieillot)
(Lat., *motacilla*, tail-waver)

Type Locality Kentucky

FIELD CHARACTERS: Upperparts grayish-olive; line over eye white; underparts buffy white or white, streaked on breast and sides with olive. Throat usually without markings. Sexes alike.
Length, 5.75 to 6.40 inches.

NESTING DATA: Much like the other waterthrushes in being situated in roots of windfalls, niches of cliffs and ravines or mossy logs. Nest of leaves, grasses and rootlets, lined with moss stems.
Eggs—4 to 6. Creamy white, speckled, spotted and splashed with chestnut, purplish gray and brown shades. Occasional eggs are sparingly spotted or immaculate.

VOICE: Of very high order, thought by some to exceed all of the group, particularly in the wild quality. The song is loud, high-pitched and musical

with three loud introductory whistles and a jumble of descending notes. (*cf. Chapter 5*)

FOOD HABITS: Mainly insects and spiders but also small minnows, snails and crustaceans.

GENERAL RANGE: *Breeds* from central Nebraska east to southern Ontario, Vermont and New Hampshire, south to eastern Oklahoma, eastern Texas, Louisiana, across to northeastern North Carolina. *Winters* from southern Sonora, Mexico, Cuba, Bahamas and Bermuda, south to Panama, Trinidad, Colombia and Venezuela.

ALEXANDER SPRUNT, JR.

[*Comment:* In southern Michigan the Louisiana Waterthrush frequents the banks of shaded rivers. Arriving in late April or early May the wild rambling song of this species indicates the presence of the bird. Soon thereafter the females arrive and nesting begins. These are very large, clumsy, yet well insulated structures built in a hole on a steep river bank or in the dirt of the overturned roots of some fallen tree close to the river bank. Often the Prothonotary and Golden-winged Warblers frequent the same areas. The outside of the nest is made of dead leaves packed closely together and lined with fine dead grasses. The four or five eggs are whitish spotted with brown. The young usually hatch in June or July and remain a few weeks along the same rivers, but by mid-August none or very few birds can be found. Michigan is the northern-most part of the species range and I have found them as far north as Oceana County along the White River. The exact division boundary of this species and the Northern Waterthrushes is not known in Michigan but in several areas both species are found in summer. (LAWRENCE H. WALKINSHAW)]

46

KENTUCKY WARBLER

Oporornis formosus

ALEXANDER WILSON named this warbler for the state where he found it. Bent (1953) says that the name "is not inappropriate, for Kentucky is not far from the center of abundance in the breeding season." Wherever seen, it is a handsome and attractive bird.

The species lives in rather heavy woodlands, undergrowth and fern tangles, often near water and at very low elevations. It is essentially a ground warbler and seldom forages more than a few feet above it. It is a walker and bobs its tail occasionally in the manner of the Waterthrushes.

["The Kentucky is a woodland bird, a lover of deep shade and dense damp thickets. Ridgway (1889) says that it is one of the most abundant of birds in the rich woods of southern Illinois. The main migration route of the great bulk of these birds is through Texas to the Mississippi Valley, where its center of abundance in summer is in the bottomland forests of the great rivers, mainly west of the Alleghenies and east of the great plains." (A. C. BENT)]

It is an industrious, methodical searcher, poking about among leaves and debris, creeping over roots and logs looking for its food. The song might be referred to as unwarblerlike and has often been compared to that of the Carolina Wren, a very apt comparison. To some hearers, it sounds like the song of the cardinal and titmouse. At any rate, it is loud and clear, carries well and is not hard to trace, for it is uttered persistently. Dr. Frank Chapman (1912) once counted 875 songs from a bird in New Jersey in three hours. It was singing before he began his count and continued to do so when he left off.

Being on the ground, the nest is hard to find, both because it resembles nothing so much as a bunch of leaves, and for the reason that the bird is inclined to sneak away from it on the ground for some distance before flushing. When actually encountered, on the nest or when feeding young, it indulges the usual warbler trait of feigning injury, in the attempt to lead the intruder away. It is also a common victim of the cowbird.

This is a comparatively easy warbler to recognize by reason of the black "whisker" mark running in front of and behind the eye, widening behind; plus of course, the olive-green back, wholly yellow underparts and lack of wing bars. It should not be confused with others of the family that range at ground level, or close to it, such as the Waterthrushes, Ovenbirds or Worm-eating Warbler, none of which it remotely resembles. The Kentucky Warbler is uncommon at the Tortugas, the bulk of the migration being well to the westward.

Oporornis formosus (Wilson)
(Gr., *Oporornis*, autumn bird; Lat., *formosus*, beautiful)

Type Locality Kentucky

FIELD CHARACTERS: Crown black, bordered with gray; eye-ring and a line to bill yellow, a wide black stripe under the eye. Upperparts dark olive; no white in wings or tail; underparts bright yellow. *Female* similar but duller.
Length, 5.00 to 5.85 inches.

NESTING DATA: On the ground at the foot of a bush or tree among plants of bushes or very low limbs of trees. Well concealed and rather bulkily constructed of dead leaves of various sorts forming the outside walls. Inner layer of weed stalks and grasses, lined with rootlets.

Eggs—4 or 5. White, speckled and spotted with dark brown, reddish and lilac, either over whole shell or wreathed about large end.

VOICE: A clear whistle of from five to seven notes, loud and carrying in quality, as well as musical. Resembles certain phrases of Carolina Wren and Cardinal: *tory-tory-tory-tory* or *tur-dle tur-dle tur-dle*. Call note a "chuck" uttered persistently when alarmed. *(See Chapter 5)*

FOOD HABITS: Very largely insects and spiders but occasional vegetable items.

GENERAL RANGE: *Breeds* from southeast Nebraska and central Iowa east as far as southern Connecticut; south to east Texas, northwestern Florida and South Carolina. *Winters* from Vera Cruz, Mexico, south to northern Colombia and Venezuela.

ALEXANDER SPRUNT, JR.

47

CONNECTICUT WARBLER

Oporornis agilis

THE Connecticut Warbler is one of the rarer and more elusive of the wood warblers. Discovered in 1812, in Connecticut, by Alexander Wilson it has subsequently received only sporadic study. Ernest Thompson Seton discovered the first nest at Carberry, Manitoba, June 21, 1883, and John Macoun located a nest in the same swamp in 1896. T. and A. Shortt collected a juvenile at Vivian, Manitoba, in 1932. Richard Harlow found eight nests near Belvedere, Alberta, between 1923 and 1926. A pair was observed feeding a young bird, by M. J. Magee, on August 17, 1918, at Agawa, Algoma District, Ontario and there are two breeding records on Royal Ontario Museum maps from Cochrane District. N. L. Huff discovered a nest in Minnesota on June 25, 1929 and a second nest, which contained young, was found in the same area five days later, by W. J. Breckenridge and William Kilgore. Since young birds have been collected on several occasions in northern Michigan, it may be assumed it breeds in that State. It has also been observed during the breeding season in Wisconsin as well as in northeastern British Columbia.

From its winter home in northern South America, the Connecticut Warbler reaches the southeastern United States probably by way of the West Indies in early May. The main movement is then up the Mississippi Valley to fan out across a narrow strip of the Canadian zone along the southern edge of the coniferous forests from northeastern British Columbia to northeastern Ontario. During spring migration only occasional birds are seen east of the Alleghenies. Travelling singly or in small groups they seldom mingle with the mixed flocks of other warblers. They feed on the ground or at low levels, and keep to the shelter of dense tangles of vines, brush and shrubbery of low lying ground, rarely travelling in the trees. Under such conditions, they are readily overlooked even along their main migration route, and even at the borders of their breeding grounds in Minnesota, Ontario and Manitoba it is probably one of our rarest warblers.

At the extremes of its long narrow breeding range, it prefers well-drained ridges and open poplar woods but elsewhere it is a bird of cold, damp, Black Spruce and Tamarack swamps. Most of these areas are large and dense but throughout them there are openings where only the occasional Spruce or Tamarack rises from the swamp floor of Labrador Tea, Pitcher-plant and thick layers of Sphagnum. Here, earlier in the year, Canada Jays have raised their young, and family groups still wander through the forest clearings. Today the swamp rings with the songs of Tennessee and Nashville Warblers, Solitary Vireos and Ruby-crowned Kinglets. An Olive-sided Fly-catcher calls from a dead stub and the plaintive note of a Yellow-bellied Fly-catcher accentuates the immense solitude.

In one of these clearings we hear a far-carrying, loud, ringing song which is distinctive of these swamps and rarely heard elsewhere. It comes from some low elevation but so well does the coloration of the bird blend with its surroundings that we fail to find the singer after minutes of searching. Suddenly the song bursts forth anew but this time from a tree a hundred feet away. Again a stealthy stalk, and this

time, if we are fortunate, we see the songster sitting motionless on a branch before it dodges behind a main trunk to once more elude our observations. Possibly it was behavior such as this which caused Wilson to name this woodland sprite *agilis*, the nimble, or freely-moving. The Connecticut Warbler feeds on the ground or at low elevations, walking deliberately along the branches picking its food from cracks and crevices in the bark or snapping at a passing insect but so secretive are its habits that were it not for its song it might be completely overlooked. Capable observers in areas where it is relatively common admit to having found it on only a few occasions.

In such a habitat, this warbler builds its nest of grasses sunken in the deep moss in a fashion similar to that of the Nashville and Tennessee Warblers which nest in the same area. By lucky chance a nest may be found by observing the building or watching the parents carrying food to their young. More likely, it will be found, if perchance one steps near the nest when the adult will be seen running or half-fluttering from the hollow in the moss well protected by Labrador Tea. So well is it hidden that only a few such nests have been found. Nor were the nests located in its poplar woods habitat much easier to locate although such areas are more readily travelled than are the Spruce and Tamarack swamps.

By late August, the Connecticut Warbler is commencing its long southern migration and by mid-September its breeding grounds are deserted. Moving eastward to the Atlantic Coast, it then flies south to

Florida, where it arrives in early October, thence through the West Indies to its winter home. In the autumn it is very uncommon in the Mississippi Valley although at this season the occasional bird has been found in Colorado, Utah, and Kansas. These birds probably originated in the northwestern portion of its range. Others may be confused with the races of the Mac-Gillivray's Warbler, *Oporornis tolmiei*, which should be distinguished by an incomplete eye-ring and a darker throat. In its more leisurely southward movement, the Connecticut is seen more frequently than in the spring but it still travels alone, keeps close to the ground, and must be sought out in dense weed patches and vines of the damper areas.

Oporornis agilis (Wilson)
   (Gr., *opor*, autumn, plus *ornis*, bird; Lat., *agilis*, from *ago*, to move; agile)

Type Locality Connecticut

FIELD CHARACTERS: A large greenish-yellow warbler with hood and white eye-ring; no wing or tail patches. It walks rather than hops. May be confused with Mourning Warbler which lacks complete eye-ring; in this species the yellow under tail-coverts reach nearly to the end of the tail but only halfway in the Mourning. It is sometimes mistaken for the Nashville but the latter is smaller and its throat is yellow rather than gray.
   Adult male, white eye-ring, slate-grey hood contrasting sharply with lemon-yellow belly and under tail-coverts. Sides dark olive; upperparts olive-green.
   Adult female, similar but hood paler and slightly tinged with brown.
   Immatures, eye-ring buffy; hood brownish; back darker. *Nestlings,* upper parts dark olive-brown; breast and sides snuff-brown merging into buffy-yellow on the belly. (Kilgore, William and Breckenridge, W. J. *Auk,* 46:551–552, 1929)
   Length, 5.25 to 6.00 inches.

NESTING: Nest usually sunken in moss on the ground.
   Generally composed of fine grasses but occasionally a few leaves may be used in the outer nest and fine rootlets or hairs included in the lining.
   Eggs—3 to 5. Ovate in shape measuring .77 x .56 inches. Creamy-white ground color, speckled and blotched with lilac, brown and black. The markings are generally distributed but tend to be more prominent at larger end without forming a definite wreath.

VOICE: The call note is a distinctive sharp metallic "peenk" or "plink." The song is a two- or three-note phrase repeated five or six times a minute. Usually compared with the songs of the Maryland Yellow-throat and Ovenbird, it has been variously written as "beecher-beecher-beecher-beecher" or "freecher-here, freecher-here, freecher-here" and also as "fru-chapple, fru-chapple, fru-chapple whoit." W. J. Breckenridge, however, interprets this song as "chap-el-free chap-el-free chapel-free-chap" and comments on the emphasis building up from weaker first notes to more emphatic ones at the middle and end. The songs heard in the bogs north of Lake Superior are loud, ringing and musical and remind me of those of the Mourning though not so rich. I have written it in my notebook as "chuckety chuckety chuckety chuck" which is close to Harlow's description, "chipety chipety chip," of the birds he heard in the poplar woods at Belvedere, Alberta. Murray Speirs described phonetically the songs of two birds singing north of

Lake Superior in 1956 as "tŭ chíbee-too, chíbee too, chíbee-too" and "sss tŭ chíbee tŭ chíbee tŭ chíbee." (*See Chapter 5*)

FOOD HABITS: Spiders are said to form a considerable part of its diet. They also consume small insects including their larvae and probably their eggs.

GENERAL RANGE: *Breeds* in a narrow east-west strip of Canadian Zone in northeastern Brit-ish Columbia, Alberta, southern Manitoba, northern Ontario, northwestern Quebec, and the northern portions of Wisconsin, Michigan and Minnesota. Spring migration is across the West Indies to southeastern United States, thence up the Mississippi Valley to its breeding grounds. In the fall, the birds move eastward to the Atlantic Coast and then southward to their winter home. *Winters* in Venezuela and Brazil after passing through Colombia.

A. E. ALLIN

48

MOURNING WARBLER

Oporornis philadelphia

ALEXANDER WILSON, the first ornithologist to discover this secretive bird gave it the specific name *Philadelphia,* because he had found it "within a few miles of Philadelphia." For its common name he chose "mourning warbler," which was suggested by the patch of black, rather like crape, on its breast. Wilson, during all his wanderings, never saw another individual. Audubon saw very few. Could this little bird, like the Chestnut-sided Warbler, be one of those species which has benefitted by the cutting down of the ancient timber? Shrubby second growth is certainly much more suited to its needs than mature forest. There is no question that the Chestnut-sided has vastly increased since Audubon's day (he found it but once) but, on the other hand, the Mourning could have merely escaped observation. Even today many bird students regard this as a *rara avis,* seldom seen.

And still, the northwoods country is full of these furtive sprites. In June, go through any slashing in Vermont, any burn in northern Ontario, any briary ravine in the Adirondacks, and you will be almost certain to hear the lively song that gives its presence away, a cheerful song, not at all consistent with the bird's sombre name. I have rendered it *chirry chirry, chorry chorry,* the last two notes falling slightly in pitch and accelerating in tempo. There is quite a variation in the songs of individuals, but the Carolina Wren-like "turtling," typical of the genus *Oporornis* is usually evident.

In its winter range in Costa Rica, Alexander Skutch actually finds the bird abundant. This is not surprising, for the very considerable numbers in the north country have to be accounted for somehow in the tropics. But how do most of the Mourning Warblers in migration slip by the army of bird watchers undetected? There is some evidence that they may hop from Yucatan across the Gulf of Mexico, but very few are spotted during the early stages of their journey either in Mexico or in the Gulf states. The bulk must go northward through the Mississippi Valley and up the Appalachians. Rarely is one seen in spring along the Atlantic coastal plain south of New York. Their arrival in the northern states is late. Although an occasional individual might appear by the first or second week of May, most of them come through during the closing days of that month (and even the first week of June), after the peak of warbler migration has passed, at the time when the average bird watcher regards the fun as over. Skulking and hiding in the rankest herbage, they keep well out of sight. Occasionally one might test its vocal chords in song thereby betraying its presence deep in a thicket, but I have always found the call note, a strong almost bisyllabic *tchip,* a bit sharper than a yellowthroat's, the best indicator. One cannot convey the quality of any sound as subtle as a "chip" on paper (thank Heaven we now have tape-recorders), but once learned, the note of the Mourning Warbler is quite distinctive.

Once on its breeding grounds in the northern Appalachians and in Canada, the bird is easier to find. It sings freely and even hops to the lower branches of the saplings where one can get a good look at its gray hood and dark breast smudge. But most of its time is spent close to the ground where it plays a good game of hide and seek.

Mourning Warblers seem to have two preferred habitats in which to nest—dry slashings and ravine slopes choked with brambles and other scrubby vegetation, and also the bushy edges of swamps and bogs. I have found nests in a blackberry thicket on a dry slope, and also in the heart of a skunk cabbage in a swamp.

It seems as though the Mourning Warbler prefers to spend two-thirds of the year in the tropics. Singing stops in July and the birds move out during August and early September. Rare as they appear to be in the spring, they are seen even less frequently in late summer passage, for by this time the weedy undergrowth has become a jungle. Occasionally one is recorded in late September or early October. These tardy individuals might be confused with Connecticut warblers, for juvenile Mournings in autumn have white eye-rings, but these rings are broken in front of the eye, not complete as in the Connecticut.

Oporornis philadelphia (Wilson)
   (Gr., *oporornis,* autumn bird; Lat., *philadelphia,* city of Philadelphia)

Type Locality within a few miles of Philadelphia, Penn.

FIELD CHARACTERS: Olive above, yellow below, with a *gray hood* completely encircling the head and neck; *male* with an apron of *black crape* on the upper breast where the hood meets the yellow. *Female* lacks the black crape on the hood. *Juvenile* in fall has a white eye-ring, broken before the eye, not complete as in the Connecticut warbler. The yellow under tail-coverts reach nearly to the end of the tail in the Connecticut, about halfway in the Mourning. Skulks in thickets.
   Length, 5.00 to 5.75 inches.

Nesting Data: Nest on or near the ground (up to 2 feet), at the base of a plant. Rather bulky with a foundation of dead leaves and grass, lined with finer grasses, rootlets and sometimes a few hairs.

Eggs—3–5 (usually 4), whitish, speckled or blotched with brown and gray, occasionally dotted with black, evenly marked or with a tendency for the spots to concentrate in a wreath toward the larger end.

Voice: Song, a cheerful chant, lower in pitch than most other warbler songs, variable: *chirry chirry, chorry chorry,* the last two notes falling slightly in pitch and slightly faster (R.T. Peterson); *yeee, yeee, churr churr* (Harrison Lewis); *wee suree surree surree surree* with a falling inflection (Francis H. Allen). Also *trué-trué-trué-teu too too.* (J. Bond). Its call note is a *tchip,* sharper than note of a Yellowthroat, slightly bisyllabic. (*See Chapter 5*)

Food Habits: Little known; beetles and spiders (B. H. Warren); and, in winter, protein bodies from the leaf bases of young Cecropia trees (Alexander Skutch).

General Range: *Breeds* from Newfoundland and Nova Scotia west to central Manitoba, central Saskatchewan and east-central Alberta and south to North Dakota, central Minnesota, Michigan, southern Ontario, southeastern New York, central Massachusetts and New Hampshire, southern Maine, and in the Appalachians to Pennsylvania and West Virginia. *Winters.* Migrates through the Mississippi

Valley and Appalachians (rare on coastal plain and in Gulf States) to Central America and northern South America (Nicaragua and Costa Rica to Venezuela, Colombia and Ecuador).

Roger Tory Peterson

49

MacGILLIVRAY'S WARBLER

Oporornis tolmiei

VERY similar in plumage and in habits to the Mourning Warbler of eastern North America, the MacGillivray's or Tolmie's Warbler is distinguished from it chiefly by the fact that the male has white markings on the eyelids, blacker lores, and more uniform gray tips on the black upper-breast feathers. Females and young of the two species would be scarcely distinguishable in the field, but both kinds are not normally found together in North America, except rarely on migration in the Mississippi Valley. Both species show a great tendency to forage close to the ground in dense, soft-leaved shrubbery or understory herbs and brush, where they are very reticent to expose themselves to view. Only when singing is the male apt to mount to a perch more than 6 feet above ground. Then, if he is singing in earnest, he may even sit quite exposed atop a sapling as much as 20 feet or more above his lower thicket domain. He may even sing from such a perch for 15 minutes or more at a time, rather unlike the "sing-while-eating" behavior of many warblers. If one learns to recognize the song variations, MacGillivray's Warblers are found to be quite common through most of their range.

The low moist thickets which this species selects as breeding habitat almost always include as major components various thin-leaved shrubs or vines such as blackberry, salmonberry, cherry, currant, serviceberry, snowberry, poison-oak, nine-bark, or *Spiraea*, and sometimes small areas of willow or alder. This sort of vegetation is found chiefly on forest areas burned or logged some years previously, or about the edges of meadows or in springy places surrounded by drier hill or mountainsides. As associates in such thickets, the Nashville Warbler and Fox Sparrow may both be common, although these species also live in drier places than the MacGillivray's Warbler does. However, it is not particularly a riparian species like the Yellow Warbler, but seems to prefer moist, shady thickets on a slope. The small trees or lower branches of scattered larger ones that may be used as song perches are not an absolute necessity, apparently, for in the hills near Oakland, California, the species is found in purely shrub areas on certain moist, northerly slopes. The dense growth of harsher, thick-leaved shrubs (chaparral) on drier slopes is, however, not occupied.

Other than when in song, MacGillivray's Warblers are among the most elusive of warblers. If approached too rapidly, they slip silently along through dense twigs or ferns close to the ground; and only a distant harsh *tchek* gives a clue to the route they have taken. A quiet observer is soon forgotten, however, and if he is in a favorable position and coaxes them out by squeaking, brief views at close range are likely. Their nests, however, are usually too well hidden in the dense tangles to be found easily.

Even when in migration this species shows partiality for any close-to-the-ground thickets, where it skulks in typical fashion. On the southward movement, which takes place from late July to late September, this is especially true in the more arid Southwest, where it occurs chiefly in the mountains. In spring, however, the foothill chaparral areas and intermingled live-oaks in southern California are considerably greener and more moist, and the birds forage more widely and farther from the ground. In late April along the base of the San Gabriel Mountains northeast of Los Angeles, California, I have several times encountered waves of migrant warblers, downed by showery weather. MacGillivrays are moderately common in such waves, even in the smaller canyons with not a particle of surface water available except during the showers. Arrival of the breeding males in the Pacific states in general, even north to Washington, may take place by mid-April, while migrants continue to pass through these same areas, and along the Rocky Mountains as well, nearly through May. Apparently it is the more northerly breeding populations which enter the United States last, and it is these that may be concentrated in waves by suitable weather along their flight lines.

Oporornis tolmiei tolmiei (Townsend)
   (Gr., *opor,* autumn, and *ornis,* bird; *tolmiei,* after W. T. Tolmie, a surgeon of early Fort Vancouver)

Type Locality Columbia River

LOCAL NAME: Tolmie's Warbler

FIELD CHARACTERS: *Adult male,* a somewhat bluish-tinged, slate gray "hood" over the whole head and extending onto upper breast, where it ends abruptly. Lores black, and area of hood on throat and especially on upper breast with broad blackish spots and intervening light gray feather tips. Eyelids white, but not forming a complete eye-ring. Crown-feathers brown-tipped in fall. Back, wings and tail smooth olive green. Bend of wing and all of underparts below hood bright yellow. Bill dark above, flesh-color below; feet light brown.

Adult female, hood brownish slate above, to light brownish-gray below, or even nearly white on throat, without dark markings. Otherwise much like the male, but white of eyelids less prominent and colors of back and underparts duller.

Immature female in fall, similar to adult female, but usually more yellowish brown about the head. Can be confused with female Yellowthroat.

Length, 5.00 to 5.50 inches.

PLATE 24
KENTUCKY WARBLER
Page 201

Male

Female

HOODED WARBLER
Page 233

Female

Male

Immature

John H. Dick
'55

NESTING DATA: A small, compactly made cup of dried grasses, lined with fine grass, horsehair, and/or a few rootlets. Usually within 2 feet of the ground, occasionally to as high as 6 feet, in dense, moist brushy places or amid tall weeds or ferns.

Eggs—3 to 5, usually 4. Dull white to light cream color, with dark brown, gray, or lavender spots often chiefly about the larger end.

VOICE: Song relatively loud, composed of 3 or 4 even notes, usually doubled and of rough quality, followed by one to three shorter ones of different quality on a slightly lower pitch: *zweedle, zweedle, zweedle, zidl, zidl;* or a softer version, *tswee-it, tswee-it, tswee-it, tswee-it, wik, wik.* Among the other warblers breeding within its range it most closely resembles the song of the Nashville Warbler, which, however, has a more prominent "see-saw" swing in the introductory notes and is in general less harsh. The ordinary call note is a heavy *tchek,* similar to that of a Yellow-throat, but not quite so husky.

FOOD HABITS: Mostly or entirely insects, so far as known.

GENERAL RANGE: *Breeds* in the more humid locations through most of western North America from southeastern Alaska, southwestern Yukon, central British Columbia, central Alberta and southwestern Saskatchewan, south through most of Oregon to central California, through Idaho and Montana to central Wyoming and southwestern South Dakota; occurring chiefly in mountain areas toward the south, except along the Pacific coast. *Winters* from northern Mexico to Panama. In migration occurs casually eastward to the upper Mississippi Valley and central Texas.

Oporornis tolmiei monticola Phillips
  (Lat., *monticola,* of the mountains)

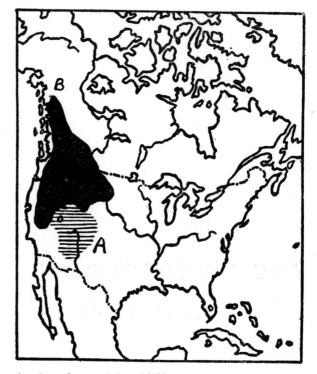

A. Southern MacGillivray's. B. Tolmie's.

Type Locality San Francisco Mountain, Arizona

LOCAL NAME: Southern MacGillivray's Warbler

A relatively longer tail than *Oporornis tolmiei tolmiei.* Also duller coloration.

RANGE: *Breeds* chiefly in mountains from southeastern Oregon, southern Idaho and Wyoming south to Nevada, central Arizona and central New Mexico. *Winters* from Colima, Mexico, south to Guatemala. East in migration to south Texas.

HOWARD L. COGSWELL

50

THE YELLOWTHROAT

Geothlypis trichas

IN any account of this widespread and familiar warbler one could hardly do better than to quote Alfred O. Gross, who prepared its life history for Bent's *Life Histories of North American Wood Warblers* (1953). Here is what he says:

The species of *Geothlypis* respond more readily to the influences of the environment than do other American warblers. As a result 12 subspecies of *trichas* have been recognized by the 1931 (*and 1957*) A.O.U. Check-list and subsequent supplements. . . . The color pattern of the 12 subspecies is similar; and they vary chiefly in minor differences of size and intensity of color. In a number of instances, the great individual variation which characterizes these birds so obscures their subspecific differences that *determination of skins is often difficult* and positive identification in the field, especially where the ranges overlap, *is impossible. (Italics supplied.)*

No statement could be clearer. Yellowthroats are probably known to more people in this country than any other warbler. The great range inhabited, the unsuspecting nature and general abundance of the birds, together with the tendency of living at low elevations, render them observationally available on almost any field trip in suitable environment. In the case of the male we have another "unmistakable." The black mask gives it away at once. The very different female is another matter, as she could be confused with other plainly colored species; but a little practice, with attention paid to habitat and behavior, can rectify this.

Not a garden or yard bird very often, the Yellowthroat is a dweller of both wet and dry situations and always requires considerable cover close at hand. Edges of woodlands, hedgerows, marshes, swamps and watercourses, where tangles of vines, briars, bushes and weeds abound, are chosen haunts. Not unlike the wrens in excited behavior, they come and go with quick movement, and though one might think them shy birds, actually they are not. By sitting or standing quietly and using the "squeak," it is often possible to attract them to within a few feet.

The song is one of the most distinctive and readily recognized of the warbler tribe. The usual verbal rendition is "witchity-witchity-witchity," with many variations, depending on the locale.

[*Comment:* Yellowthroat songs in northern and central Ontario seldom adhere to the classic "witchity witchity." There is much variation and some are scarcely recognizable as Yellowthroat songs. Some are quite complex. Commonly, syllables are added to a phrase and notes in a phrase are repeated. (W. W. H. GUNN)]

Coming from a grass clump, bushes or weeds along a ditch-bank or marsh, it is indeed a characteristic sound of such surroundings. I have had a Yellowthroat come into a duck-blind where I was sitting quietly, using the squeak and alight on my outstretched boot.

This warbler is often a heavy loser to migration hazards. Its abundance throughout the country is doubtless one reason. Tall structures like the Washington Monument and Empire State Building take a truly enormous toll.

Nesting so near the ground as they do invites attack by snakes and small mammals. Gross mentions A. L. Rand's experience of finding a Yellowthroat in the stomach of a Large-mouth Black Bass. The northern form of the Yellowthroat is parasitized by the cowbird and, like some others, occasionally seals off the intruding egg by making a false bottom to the nest, or even two or more of such. Dr. Herbert Friedmann, our authority on the cowbird, lists the Yellowthroat as seventh in order of species most frequently victimized. The form nesting in the southern states is of course not subject to such parasitism. The following grouping of races follows the 1957 A.O.U. Check-list.

Geothlypis trichas trichas (Linnaeus)
(Gr., *geothlypis*, a ground finch; *trichas*, a thrush)

Type Locality Maryland

LOCAL NAME: Maryland Yellowthroat

FIELD CHARACTERS: *Male,* upperparts olive-green; bend of wing yellow but no bars. Throat and breast yellow, belly whitish, sides brownish. A broad black band across forehead and sides of head, bordered behind by bluish gray.

Female, lacks mask. Upperparts olive-green washed with gray or brown, rump and upper tail greener. Eye-ring whitish; throat and breast yellow in varying degree, belly whitish tinged with buff.

Length, 4.50 to 5.65 inches (including *G. t. brachidactyla*).

NESTING DATA: At low elevations on the ground or a little above it, in sloughs, islands, along edges of swamps and creeks. Sometimes in dry situations such as fence rows, briar tangles and brushy roads. Nest rather large and bulky, of leaves, weed stalks, grasses and fern strips, lined with hair or fine grass and usually well concealed. Rarely more than 3 feet from ground.

Eggs—3 to 5. White, speckled and spotted with reddish-brown and gray, often about large end but variable in arrangement of markings.

VOICE: A rather loud, clear repetition of two to six notes with one accented. "Witchity-witchity" are words used to describe it. Variation exists but general effect distinctive and recognizable. A flight song exists also, a rather jumbled series of short notes uttered as the bird ascends to a height of about 20 feet (occasionally higher), ending at summit of flight.

Call notes are much like those of the wrens in quality. (*See Chapter 5*)

FOOD HABITS: Largely insects. Gypsy moth larvae eaten in parts of range. Numbers of species are represented in insect content.

GENERAL RANGE: *Breeds* from southeastern Oklahoma, northern Arkansas east to Pennsylvania and New Jersey; south to east Texas and northern portions of Alabama and Georgia. *Winters* from southern Texas and Louisiana east to Florida, the Bahamas and Haiti, south through Mexico and Central America. One record for Lundy Island, England.

Geothlypis trichas brachidactylus (Swainson)
(Gr., *brachidactyla*, short-digited)

Type Locality Northern North America

LOCAL NAME: Northern Yellowthroat

This form differs from *G. t. trichas* in being larger, with more green on the upperparts and more yellow in posterior areas, with browner flanks.

RANGE: *Breeds* from Labrador, southwestern Newfoundland, Quebec, and northeastern Ontario, south to New Jersey, northern Pennsylvania southeastern New York and Connecticut and West Virginia, west to Minnesota and Nebraska, Oklahoma and Missouri. *Winters* from the southern U.S. to Bahamas, Greater Antilles, eastern Mexico to Costa Rica and Panama.

Geothlypis trichas ignota Chapman
(Lat., *ignota*, unknown)

Type Locality Tarpon Springs, Fla.

LOCAL NAME: Florida Yellowthroat

This race described by Frank M. Chapman (1890) is the breeding yellowthroat of the lower Atlantic coast and Florida, though it was once thought to extend north to the Dismal Swamp of Virginia. Its habits, behavior and nesting are very similar to the other eastern forms and it is not pronouncedly migratory. Its main difference is a longer bill and tail, deeper yellow and darker flanks.

RANGE: Largely resident from southeastern South Carolina, Southern Mississippi and Louisiana southward through southern Florida.

Geothlypis trichas typhicola Burleigh
(Lat., *typhicola*, cat-tail dweller)

Type Locality Athens, Ga.

LOCAL NAME: Athens Yellowthroat

Much like *ignota* but differing in having a much smaller bill and less brownish underparts and flanks. Burleigh (1937) who described it says that "it is one of the most characteristic birds of Georgia." Apparently all wintering Yellowthroats of that State (based on specimens) are of this race but it is not confined to Georgia as a nester. In all respects of general habit and habitat it is like *ignota*.

RANGE: *Breeds* from southeastern Virginia and central Alabama, northeastern Georgia, central South Carolina, eastern North Carolina, south to southern Georgia and southeastern Alabama. *Winters* in southern half of breeding range south to Vera Cruz.

Geothlypis trichas occidentalis Brewster
(Lat., *occidentalis*, of the west)

Type Locality Truckee River, Nev.

LOCAL NAME: Western Yellowthroat

This is the Yellowthroat of the far west. It is larger than *t. trichas* with a longer tail, paler upperparts and richer yellow beneath, this color extending further on the abdomen. The edging of the mask is white. It lives in the tule growth and in fresh and brackish marshes.

RANGE: *Breeds* from Oregon, southern Idaho and western part of the Great Plains south to central eastern California, southern Utah, northeastern Arizona and northern New Mexico to Texas. *Winters* from central valleys of California to southern extreme of that State, through Baja California and western Mexico to Cape San Lucas, southern Texas and Arizona south through Mexico to Guatemala.

Geothlypis trichas campicola Behle and Aldrich
(Lat., *campicola*, plains dweller)

Type Locality Rosebud County, Mont.

LOCAL NAME: Northern Plains Yellowthroat

The breeding form of the northern Great Plains and Rockies. Varies from *occidentalis* in grayer upperparts, less yellow below and grayer flanks and belly.

John H. Dick
'55

PLATE 25
CONNECTICUT WARBLER
Page 203

Male

MacGILLIVRAY'S WARBLER
Page 210
Female

Female

Male

MOURNING WARBLER
Page 207
Male-Female

Fall Male

RANGE: *Breeds* from southern Yukon, Alaska, British Columbia, Oregon and Washington, east to Saskatchewan, northern Wyoming and North Dakota, as far as western Ontario. *Winter* range unknown, but extends to Sonora, Mexico.

Geothlypis trichas sinuosa Grinnell
(Lat., *sinuosa,* full of curves)

Type Locality Palo Alto, Calif.

LOCAL NAME: Salt Marsh Yellowthroat

This race lives mainly about San Francisco Bay but is not confined to salt marsh, despite the common name. It seems to be even more common along freshwater streams, about lake shores and wet meadows. A flight song is indulged, not unlike that of a chat, both in vocal behavior and quality. It is a smaller bird than *occidentalis* and darker on the back and sides.

RANGE: *Breeds* and is resident in marshes of the San Francisco Bay region. *Winters* scatteringly as far south as southern California (San Diego).

Geothlypis trichas chryseola van Rossem
(Lat., *chryseola,* golden)

Type Locality Sonora, Mexico

LOCAL NAME: Sonora Golden Yellowthroat

This race though living mainly in Mexico, penetrates Arizona and has been taken in west Texas. Yellowthroats about Tucson and Bisbee, Arizona are referable to it. It is more yellowish above than *scirpicola,* brighter yellow below and with little if any gray on the flanks.

RANGE: *Breeds* and partly resident from southeastern Arizona, New Mexico, and western Texas south to north central Sonora to Durango. *Winters* from southern Arizona south to central Sonora.

Geothlypis trichas scirpicola Grinnell
(Lat., *scirpicola,* rush-dwelling)

Type Locality El Monte, Calif.

LOCAL NAME: Tule Yellowthroat

Living in southern California, this form differs from *occidentalis* in being larger, having a longer tail and brighter colors.

RANGE: Resident along Pacific slope of Baja California to Santa Barbara, California, southern San Joaquin Valley and south fork of Kern River; southeastern Nevada, southwestern Utah and western Arizona, south to northwestern Sonora.

Geothlypis trichas arizela Oberholser
(Gr., *arizela,* distinct)

Type Locality Fort Steilacoom, Wash.

LOCAL NAME: Pacific Yellowthroat

This race of the Pacific slope differs from *occidentalis* in being smaller and with narrower white frontal band.

RANGE: *Breeds* Pacific Coast from southeastern Alaska, southern British Columbia, south through western Washington and western Oregon to south central California. *Winters* from northern California to southern Baja California.

Geothlypis trichas insperata Van Tyne
(Lat., *insperata,* unexpected)

Type Locality Rio Grande Delta, Tex.

LOCAL NAME: Brownsville Yellowthroat

This is a little understood form as it has not yet been found in winter and nothing is known about its nesting. The general appearance is like that of the other Yellowthroats but it differs from *t. trichas* in having a distinctly larger bill, more white in the forehead and uniformly paler coloration.

RANGE: Known only in the Lower Rio Grande Valley delta region near Brownsville, Texas.

Geothlypis trichas modesta Nelson
(Lat., *modesta,* plain)

Type Locality San Blas, (Nayarit), Mexico

LOCAL NAME: San Blas Yellowthroat

This Yellowthroat is resident in a strip of tropical salt water situations in western Mexico, being accidental in Baja California. Very similar to *sinuosa,* it is slightly grayer and has a longer tail and bill.

RANGE: Resident from central western Sonora south to Colima, western Mexico. Accidental in Baja California.

ALEXANDER SPRUNT, JR.

51

BELDING'S YELLOWTHROAT

Geothlypis beldingi

BELDING'S, or the Peninsular Yellowthroat, is restricted to the southern half of the Baja California Peninsula, Mexico, having been reported only south of 28° N. Latitude. There is no United States record. A close ally of the Common Yellowthroats of the G. *trichas* group, it differs in its distinctly larger size (averaging about a half inch longer), more extensive yellow on the underparts, and with the black mask of the adult males bordered by yellow (instead of whitish). On migration or in winter common Yellowthroats of various subspecies may occur in suitable habitats anywhere in Baja California, and one subspecies (*G.t. scirpicola*) breeds south to about 30° N. Latitude, but there appears to be a substantial gap between the known breeding ranges of G. *trichas* and G. *beldingi*.

Judging by what little has been published, in habitat and general behavior Belding's Yellowthroat does not differ materially from the more northern yellowthroats. It has been found in the lowlands along marshy borders of rivers and canyons, particularly where there is a heavy growth of cattails or rushes (tule). At San José del Cabo, near the tip of the peninsula, it has been reported to be one of the commonest land birds. Its song is said to be sufficiently different from the northern races of G. *trichas* to be readily distinguished, but no comparison has been published with the Mexican races of that species. As is generally true with tropical representatives of temperate zone birds, the egg clutch is smaller (two to four) than is usual for G. *trichas* in the United States (three to five).

Geothlypis beldingi beldingi Ridgway
(Lat., *beldingi* for L. Belding)

Type Locality San José del Cabo,
Baja California

LOCAL NAME: Belding's Peninsular Yellowthroat

CHARACTERS: Larger in all dimensions than Common Yellowthroat; entire underparts yellow, with buffy tinge usually restricted to sides and flanks. *Adult males* with black mask bordered above and behind by yellow (instead of whitish). Immature males have the mask border less yellow, more grayish, and are duller above and below. *Females* (apart from size) are much like Common Yellowthroats in equivalent plumage but have the area about the eye paler and more yellowish. Measurements: Length about 5½ in. Wing, 65 mm.; tail, 63 mm.; culmen, 13 mm. (measurements rounded to nearest millimeter); weight, 15 gr. (compared with 9–10 gr. for certain northern races of *G. trichas*) (W. H. Behle, *Condor*, 52; 213–218, 1950). Females are somewhat smaller.

NESTING DATA: Egg dates—March 25 (partly incubated) to May 17. Clutches—2 to 4, most often 3. Nests at Comondú in cat-tail clumps 1½–4½ ft. above ground or over water, resembled some Song Sparrow nests, measured 115 mm. external diameter, 150 mm. height, 50 mm. internal diameter of cup, 55 mm. inner depth. Made of dry cat-tail leaves, thinly lined with fine fibers and a few horsehairs or mostly with scanty horsehairs. (W. E. Bryant, *Proc. Calif. Acad. Sci., ser. 2, 2: 20, 311, 1889*). At San Ignacio nests were in heavy tule patches, made of dry tule strips, tied to living tule stalks, well-woven and lined usually with palm fiber (G. Bancroft, *Condor, 32: 42, f. 18, 1930*). Eggs—white or creamy-white, very sparingly speckled, spotted or blotched with vinaceous, lilac, gray, brown or black, mainly about larger end, sometimes forming a wreath of fine dense speckling, with overwritings of black (Bryant, 1889; Bancroft, 1930, A. C. Bent, 1953).

VOICE: A loud chip reported by L. Belding; a song described by Frazar as resembling "that of the Maryland Yellowthroat [*G. trichas*], but it is so much heavier and fuller that it can be easily recognized"; it is also said to give a flight song mounting in the air (W. Brewster, Bull. Mus. Comp. Zool., 41: 188–190, 1902). W. E. Bryant (1889) reports singing sometimes from low trees; he characterizes the notes as loud and clear, interspersed with low short buzzes, writing the song as follows, the asterisks indicating the buzz: *Sweet, sweet * * * ear * * * sweet, sweet, ear * * * sweet, sweet, ear,* lasting about five seconds; a shorter version was *sweet, sweet, ear * * * sweet, sweet, ear * * *,* sometimes with the last buzzing omitted.

RANGE: Cape district of Baja California.

Geothlypis beldingi goldmani Oberholser
(Lat., *goldmani* for E. A. Goldman)

Type Locality San Ignacio,
Baja California

LOCAL NAME: Goldman's Peninsular Yellowthroat

CHARACTERS: Said to be duller above and below than *beldingi,* with the border of the mask pale grayish or whitish. W. H. Behle (*Condor,* 52: 214–215, 1950) contends that *goldmani* represents merely the immature male plumage of *beldingi.*

RANGE: Baja California between 28°–26° N. Lat.
EUGENE EISENMANN

A. Yellowthroats.
B. Belding's Yellowthroat.

52

GROUND-CHAT

Chamaethlypis poliocephala

THE Ground-chat, or Gray-crowned Yellowthroat, differs from the Yellowthroats of the genus *Geothlypis* chiefly in its heavier bill, which approaches that of the Yellow-breasted Chat in thickness. Otherwise this species, now recognized as the single representative of its genus, bears considerable resemblance, in size, appearance and habits, to the more widespread and familiar Yellowthroats. The crown is slaty gray and the remainder of the upper plumage, including the wings and tail, are shades of olive-green. The underparts are canary yellow, fading to whitish on the abdomen. In the male the lores are black, which on some individuals extends also to the forehead and the upper part of the cheeks. In the northern races there is a conspicuous white or pale yellow spot on each eyelid, but this is mostly lacking in the Central American representatives of the species. The female resembles the male except for the smaller amount of black on the lores, which in some individuals are devoid of black. The bill is dark on the upper mandible and light on the lower, and the long, conspicuous legs are pale flesh-color. Although in the plumage of the body the Ground-chat so closely resembles the common Yellowthroat, the pattern on the male's head offers an adequate recognition mark. The black on the Ground-chat's head is much more restricted, not extending to the ear-coverts nor to the forepart of the crown as on the North American Yellowthroats; and there is no sharply contrasting band of white or light gray crossing the head transversely behind the black. The females of the two groups are, however, sometimes confusingly similar in appearance.

The Ground-chat ranges from the Río

Grande valley in the extreme south of Texas through Mexico and Central America to Chiriquí in western Panama, and from sea level up to about 5000 feet, and exceptionally even higher, in the Central American mountains. Although abundant in suitable localities throughout this extended range, its peculiar habitat requirements prevent its being as uniformly distributed as many other birds. It avoids the low, tangled thickets, hardly penetrable by a man without a machete to open a path, which in humid tropical regions quickly cover over resting croplands, and this prevents its occurrence in large areas of the Caribbean lowlands. It is equally averse to wide expanses uniformly covered with grasses. It prefers grassy areas diversified by scattered low trees and bushes or clumps of coarse bracken fern, or, in the highlands, somewhat open thickets broken by patches of grass. In more arid regions I have found it on sterile hillsides sparingly covered with bushes. But it always requires enough cover to keep itself well concealed, so that one hears the Ground-chat a dozen times for every time he glimpses it. But if fortunate, the diligent bird-watcher will at last espy the elusive warbler, perhaps clinging to a nearly upright stem, where despite the perpendicularity of his perch he manages, with his conspicuously long legs, to hold his body nearly level.

The Ground-chat has a delightfully full and mellow voice. Even its calls are musical. One consists of two notes uttered with a rising inflection, another of three notes in falling cadence. This longer call is so beautifully modulated that one might mistake it for the bird's song if he had never had the good fortune to hear the far longer and richer song itself. Over the years I have listened to the Ground-chat's music at points scattered from the Isthmus of Tehuantepec in Mexico to southern Costa Rica, and I have been impressed again and again with its outstanding beauty. Its mellowness, variety and length make it one of the finest wood warbler's songs I know. It is delivered from a bush or low tree rising above or beside the herbage where the songster usually lurks, or from a taller stem of grass.

The nests of the Ground-chat are well concealed amid low vegetation and have rarely been found by ornithologists. One which I discovered in the Motagua Valley in Guatemala on June 21, 1932, was six inches above the ground in a clump of grass in a bushy pasture. The open cup, composed largely of dry grass blades and dead leaves, had substantial walls and a very thick bottom. It was lined with fine fibers and some horsehairs, and it resembled some nests of the Yellowthroats. It contained two eggs, which were white with umber markings that were crowded on the thick end but sparingly scattered elsewhere. One had also a few black spots on the thick end. In southern Texas, however, nests with four eggs have been found. Such an increase in the size of the set with increasing latitude is common among birds. Apparently no one has yet studied the nest life of this attractive warbler.

Chamaethlypis poliocephala (Baird)
(Gr., *chamaethlypis*, on the ground; a kind of finch: *poliocephala*, gray head)

Type Locality Mazatlan, Sinaloa, Mexico

LOCAL NAME: Gray-crowned or Thick-billed Yellow-throat

FIELD CHARACTERS: *Adult male,* top of head grayish; lores black, this color extending below eye; a white or yellowish spot on each eyelid (in the northern forms); back, wings and tail olive-green, without wing bars or tail patches; below bright yellow, becoming paler on abdomen and with sides and flanks tinged with olive; bill rather thick, with upper mandible dark and lower light; legs pale flesh-color.

Female, similar but duller, with little or no black on lores.

Length, 5 to 5½ inches.

NESTING DATA: Nest an open cup, substantially built of grasses and leaves, lined with fine fibers or horsehair, near ground, often in a clump of grass.

Eggs—2 to 4, white or creamy, speckled with shades of brown and drab, chiefly on the thick end.

VOICE: The beautiful song is long-continued and mellow.

FOOD HABITS: Probably largely insectivorous, but eats some berries.

GENERAL RANGE: From extreme southern Texas south through Mexico and Central America to western Panama.

Chamaethlypis poliocephala ralphi (Ridgway)

Type Locality Brownsville, Texas

LOCAL NAME: Rio Grande Ground-chat

FIELD CHARACTERS: Paler yellow particularly on the lower surfaces than the above. Tail and upperparts grayer.

RANGE: A resident of southern Texas and Tamaulipas, Mexico.

ALEXANDER F. SKUTCH

PLATE 26
YELLOWTHROAT
Page 214

Eastern Male

BELDING'S YELLOWTHROAT
Page 219

Female

Male

Eastern Female

John H. Dick
'55

53

YELLOW-BREASTED CHAT

Icteria virens

SOME birds have been described as acrobats, others as animated gems, still others as butterflies but here indeed, is the clown! Anyone who has watched the Chat to any extent cannot help but agree that the bird is a comedian if we insist on ascribing human attributes to lower animals.

That the bird is a warbler may seem strange to the novice student, for superficially it is unlike others of that family. However, structurally and otherwise, it falls into the warblers logically enough, and is the largest of the group. And, one might well add, though common throughout its range, it is one of the hardest to see. The Chat is adept at making itself inconspicuous much of the time. The thicker the tangle of vines, the sharper the briars, the stiffer the twigs of sapling and brush,

the better from the bird's standpoint.

Immersed and submerged in such forbidding greenery, it is more often heard than seen. Indeed, no trouble is experienced in hearing the chat—the question is not whether it is here, but where, and from what quarter those astonishing calls, squawks and gurgles are coming. The chat is a ventriloquist of no mean ability and seems present one moment, gone the next. Even while one is wondering where to look, the bird itself may appear in the air above the tangle and go through a series of incredible contortions while dropping back into obscurity. The loosely flopping wings, pumping tail and dangling legs are hardly more surprising than the vocal accompaniment of whistles, clucks and grunts.

Occasionally, it may sit quietly on a perfectly exposed perch and one can then see it to advantage and realize that it is as handsome as it is unpredictable.

The nest is very hard to find, in my experience, as might be supposed from the haunts frequented. The veteran ornithologist of South Carolina, Arthur T. Wayne, who was in the field almost continuously for forty years, discovered but two. The dense, thorny fastnesses amid which the Chat dwells are practically impenetrable without armor. Audubon's plate of the species shows it in a Cherokee Rose vine which is a typical location, and about as difficult to investigate as any growth I know, except perhaps some of the cacti.

The Chat is not a woodland bird. Field edges, hedgerows, overgrown pastures and scrub country compose its home and it may and often does, live close to human habitation. The queer notes can frequently be heard at night and, throughout the wide range, the bird is far better known to many by its voice than by the occasional glimpses it allows.

Icteria virens virens (Linnaeus)
(Gr., *icteria*, yellow; Lat., *virens*, green)

Type Locality South Carolina

LOCAL NAME: Eastern Yellow-breasted Chat

FIELD CHARACTERS: About the size of a Catbird. Upperparts and sides of head gray olive-green; lores black, a white line to and over the eye; throat and breast bright yellow; lower abdomen white. Bill black; eye-ring white.
Length, 6.75 to 7.50 inches.

NESTING DATA: Composed of grasses and leaves, lined with finer grass, at low elevations, occasionally on the ground, more often from 2 to 8 feet above it. In dense thickets and tangles of vines, briars and brush, frequently impossible to investigate.
Eggs—3 to 5. White, marked with spots of reddish brown and lilac.

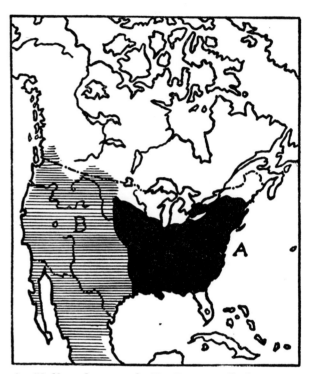

A. Yellow-breasted. B. Long-tailed.

VOICE: A strange medley of varied notes, whistles, clucks, and gurgles, sometimes heard at night. Definitely ventriloquial in character. Referred to as a mimic by some writers but such seems open to question. (*See Chapter 5*)

FOOD HABITS: Principally insects such as weevils, beetles, ants, moths and caterpillars. Also a considerable variety of berries, among which are wild strawberries, grapes and blackberries.

GENERAL RANGE: *Breeds* from northeastern Dakota, across to southern Ontario, on to southern Vermont and New Hampshire, south to southeastern Texas, the Gulf States and northern Florida. *Winters* from Mexico and Central America to Panama.

[*Comment:* The Yellow-breasted Chat has been recorded at St. John's, Newfoundland, for four consecutive winters: 1950–51, 1951–52, 1952–53, and 1953–54. Observations were usually of single individuals in the vicinity of feeders. None was noted to survive the January cold storms and after two such storms frozen carcasses were found. These have been examined by W. Earl Godfrey, who determined that the specimens were of the Eastern nominate race. (LESLIE TUCK)]

Icteria virens auricollis (Deppe)
(Lat., *auricollis*, golden neck)

Type Locality Mexico City

LOCAL NAMES: Long-tailed Chat, Western Yellow-
breasted Chat

This is the western race of the Yellow-breasted Chat and differs from it only slightly. The wings, tail and bill are longer (tail longer than wings), there is more white in the malar region and the yellow of the under-parts is deeper. This is the race formerly known as the Long-tailed Chat. It is a common bird throughout its range and, in some areas is abundant. Nesting habits and behavior are like those of the eastern bird.

RANGE: *Breeds.* The Great Plains west to the Pacific Coast, from British Columbia and south-western Saskatchewan south to the tableland of Mexico and Baja California. *Winters* from southern Baja California, southern Texas south to Colima, Oaxaca and central Guatemala.

ALEXANDER SPRUNT, JR.

54

FAN-TAILED WARBLER

Euthlypis lachrymosa

YEARS ago, while collecting plants in the dark undergrowth of the woodland on the outskirts of a great coffee plantation on the Pacific slope of Guatemala, I met a bird new to me. Its head was largely black, with a yellow stripe along the center of the crown and a conspicuous white spot above, below, and in front of each eye. The rest of the upper plumage was dark grayish-olive, with no markings on the dark wings, but with conspicuous white tips on the outer feathers of the broad tail. The under plumage was yellow, very bright on the throat, but tinged with olive on the sides and flanks. There was a small party of these birds, whose number I could not count in the dense vegetation, and they were following a swarm of army ants, in the fashion of so many birds that live in the undergrowth of the tropical forest. One of them *walked* on prominent, flesh-colored legs along a slanting, mossy trunk. These birds resembled none that I had ever seen before, and I was undecided whether they belonged to the wood warbler or to the antbird family. Later, from the description I then wrote, I identified them as Fan-tailed Warblers. I have never again met these strange warblers which so aroused my interest.

The Fan-tailed Warbler is found locally in much of Mexico, except the extreme north, and along the Pacific slope of Central America as far south as Nicaragua. A single straggler was once found in Baja California, thereby earning for the species a nominal place in the American Ornithologists' Union's list of North American birds. In the more southerly parts of its range it occurs from near sea level up to

John H. Dick
'55

PLATE 27
YELLOW-BREASTED CHAT
Page 225

Adult Male

Immature

about 4500 feet in the mountains. It spends most of its time on or near the ground in heavily shaded undergrowth and has often been met in rocky places; but whether the rocks themselves contribute anything to its welfare, or whether it is associated with them simply because the unsuitability of stony outcrops for agriculture causes such situations to be left in a fairly natural state, appears not to be known. Others beside myself have noticed that these warblers walk like water-thrushes and ovenbirds rather than hop in the manner of nearly all other wood warblers; that they travel in small parties; and that they sometimes follow army ants. As they work over the ground, rocks and fallen logs, they are constantly fanning out and contracting their tails, somewhat in the fashion of redstarts, thereby revealing the white tips of the feathers which, more than all else, serve to draw attention to their presence in the dimly lighted undergrowth. Their song is long-continued, rich and varied, and has been assigned a high place among the musical performances of the wood warblers. Apparently nothing has been recorded about the Fan-tailed Warblers' nesting and the intimate details of their lives, a circumstance for which some enterprising young bird-watcher, sighing for new worlds to conquer, may some day be thankful.

Euthlypis lachrymosa (Bonaparte)
(Gr., *Euthlypis,* an agreeable finch; Lat., *lachrymosa,* tearful)

Type Locality Vera Cruz, Mexico

FIELD CHARACTERS: *Adult male,* head largely black, with center of crown yellow, a white spot on each eyelid and one on either side of forehead; hindhead and remaining upperparts blackish slate-color, sometimes tinged with olive on back; tail slate-black, all the feathers (except sometimes the middle pair) tipped with white; rest of under plumage yellow, becoming olive on sides and flanks and whitish on under tail-coverts; bill black; legs flesh-color.
Adult female, not always distinguishable from male, but sometimes paler.
Length, 5½ to 6 inches.

NESTING DATA: Nidification unknown. [*Comment:* W. L. Dawson told me of a set of eggs taken. Perhaps these are in some California museum. (J. BOND)]

VOICE: Song mellow, sustained and varied.

FOOD HABITS: Insectivorous.

GENERAL RANGE: Southern Sonora, southern Chihuahua and southern Tamaulipas south to the Isthmus of Tehuantepec and along Pacific side of Central America to Nicaragua. Recorded once in Baja California (December 31, 1925).

ALEXANDER F. SKUTCH

55

RED-FACED WARBLER

Cardellina rubrifrons

PERHAPS no other bird is so indelibly associated with the matchless mountain forests of Arizona and New Mexico as the Red-faced Warbler. I cherish the memory of the first one I saw, in the Graham Mountains of southeastern Arizona, late in April when Gambel oaks were yet leafless, and melted snow was tumbling down Noon Creek. It flew out of a pine to the topmost twig of a big-tooth maple, there delivered its bright song just once, then flew on. My delight in seeing this beautiful tropical warbler for the first time, even so briefly, has stayed with me ever since.

It was in these same Graham Mountains that Henry W. Henshaw, the first ornithologist to find the Red-faced Warbler within the boundaries of the United States, became familiar with it in long-ago 1874.

Since then it has been seen by many others; yet, because of the remoteness and circumscription of its range, it remains one of the least-known warblers; and to see it in its fabled canyons must be the wish of many a naturalist.

Its preferred habitat is among the dark Douglas fir and Engelmann spruce at elevations of 6500 to 9000 feet, and it often may be seen in pines and oaks. George Sutton has noted a definite affinity for aspen groves in the Santa Rita Mountains. It builds its nest always on the ground, usually concealed by overhanging vegetation, sometimes under a log or rock, and ordinarily on a well-drained bank or hillside. It is very secretive in the nest vicinity, and its eggs may be found only as the reward of much care and patience.

Early April to about April 20th, depending on the earliness or lateness of the season, marks the arrival of the Red-faced Warbler on its breeding grounds. In the fall, some birds remain well into September, the latest record being for the 21st in the Chiricahua Mountains.

The Red-faced Warbler is small and quick, like many others of the wood warbler family. It feeds through the outer portions of the coniferous trees, with constant small jerks of the tail. Also like many other warblers, it is an adept at flycatching. Close examination will show the bill to be stout at the base, the upper mandible arched like a Titmouse's.

From Arizona and New Mexico its breeding distribution extends south along the Mexican cordillera into Central America. Although its territory nominally includes the higher mountains below the Mogollon Rim in Arizona, and the higher ranges of southwestern New Mexico, recent observations suggest it is extending its range. Nests have been found near Flagstaff and at Alpine in Arizona, both north of the Rim; and in New Mexico in 1942 I found it common in Water Canyon in the Magdalena Mountains.

Cardellina rubrifrons (Giraud)
(Lat., *cardellina,* a kind of finch; *rubifrons,* red-fronted)

Type Locality Mexico (locality not known, originally stated through error to be Texas).

FIELD CHARACTERS: An average-sized Warbler, of conspicuous red, black, white, and gray coloration. Face, throat, breast, and sides of neck a bright carmine red; a black hood covering the crown extends to behind and below the eyes; a narrow but conspicuous white patch on the nape; a white rump patch; a single white wing bar near the shoulder; rest of upperparts a pale gray; belly white, sides washed with gray. Sexes alike.
Length, 5.00 inches.

NESTING DATA: Nest always on ground, usually concealed beneath or alongside sheltering log, rock, sapling, or tuft of grass, built in a small scratched-out depression of loose plant fibers, grass, pine needles, etc., lined with finer material and a few hairs. Eggs usually 3 or 4, white, delicately marked with auburn with some concentration at large end.

VOICE: Song clear and penetrating, with considerable similarity to that of the Yellow Warbler: *a-tink a-tink a-tink tseee tseee tseee, tsweep* (Taylor). Usual call note a fairly loud "chip" similar to Myrtle or Audubon Warbler.

FOOD HABITS: Insectivorous; does considerable flycatching on the wing.

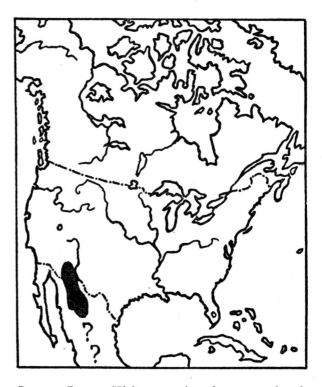

GENERAL RANGE: High mountains of east-central and southeastern Arizona, and southwestern New Mexico west of the Rio Grande, south through Mexico in the mountains at least as far as southwestern Chihuahua. Status further south uncertain. Migratory in northern part of range only. Winter range poorly known.

GALE MONSON

56

HOODED WARBLER

Wilsonia citrina

THIS really beautiful bird brings to mind again the comparison of the warblers with jewels. Aside from the beauty of its plumage, the habitat chosen by it lends to such likeness for much of it is dark swampland. Here, amid sometimes eerie gloom and heavy shadow, the Hooded Warbler glows with an intensity all but breathtaking. Olive-green, bright yellow, black and white, a color combination indeed, one to impress even the most casual observer.

Almost entirely eastern in range it lives in forested regions of mixed hardwoods, beech, maple, hickory and oak, often near water. In the southeast it is a bird of the cypress-gum swamplands where its brief but carrying song mingles with those of the Parula, Prothonotary and Yellow-throated Warblers. Though having seen it for many years in varying situations, it is always con-nected in my mind with the great cypress lagoons and bordering swamps of the Carolina Low Country, for it was there that I first became acquainted with it. To others, the mature woodlands of New England, the West Virginia mountains, the flat shores of Lake Erie, or the swamps of the Gulf Coast may come to mind. Wherever seen, it is memorable.

Lacking the brilliance of her mate, the female is rather hard to see for she is retiring and secretive as well. The typical call note is uttered by both sexes but no song emanates from the female. Only when flushed at close hand from eggs well along in the hatching can she be seen to any advantage in the summer home. One characteristic of the species which renders the male easy to watch is the tendency to live rather close to the ground. Tops of trees,

or even the mid-sections of them seem to hold little appeal for this warbler. At times it will sing from higher elevations, but it really finds its way of life amid thickety tangles, mazes of vines or dense swamp scrub. A very active warbler, it flits here and there, ever on the go and often indulging in aerial "flycatching" of insect prey. Like some others which share this habit, the Hooded Warbler frequently spreads its tail thus revealing the white markings thereon, a good field mark.

Recognition of the male is never any problem, even to beginners. The black hood and throat, framing the yellow cheeks, the olive-green back and bright yellow underparts stamp it apart from any other warbler. In migration females might easily be confused with female Pileolated Warblers; but the Hoodeds are larger and show white in the tail.

One would hardly connect belligerency with so lovely a bird but none the less, the males sometimes engage in violent conflict, though such encounters rarely if ever terminate fatally. On its trans-Gulf migrations this warbler appears occasionally on the Dry Tortugas. I have seen it there from September 4th–9th although only one or two at a time.

Wilsonia citrina (Boddaert)
(Lat., *Wilsonia,* for Alexander Wilson; *citrina,* lemon color)

Type Locality Louisiana

FIELD CHARACTERS: *Male,* forehead and sides of head bright yellow; a black hood encircles the crown and sides of neck, rest of upperparts olive-green; throat and chest black; underparts lemon yellow; three outer tail feathers with conspicuous white patches.
Female, similar but duller in color and without black hood, but showing more or less blackish on head and throat when fully mature.

Length, 5.00 to 5.75 inches.

NESTING DATA: At low elevations ranging from 1 to 6 feet. In small bushes, vines, palmetto and cane clumps or saplings. Nest of dead leaves, grasses, bark-strippings, plant down and weeds, lined with black rootlets or moss fibers. Sometimes attached to very slight supports.

Eggs—3 to 5, usually 4. White, wreathed and spotted with chestnut, purplish and lilac with some undershell markings of lavender.

VOICE: One of, if not the loudest of warbler songs with a clear, ringing quality often intensified by type of habitat. "Monte monte vid*e*o" or "weeta-weeta-wee-*tee*-o" is suggestive of usual song, though several more notes may be added. Song period covers as much as five months in the southern range. Call note a sharp, distinctive "chirp," easily learned, often with a ringing quality. (*See Chapter 5*)

FOOD HABITS: Largely, if not entirely insects. Wasps, beetles, plant lice, flies, ants, moths and caterpillars compose bulk of diet.

GENERAL RANGE: *Breeds* from Rhode Island across to southern Ontario, Michigan, southeastern Nebraska, south to east Texas and northern Florida. *Winters* from Mexico to Panama. Rare transient in West Indies.   ALEXANDER SPRUNT, JR.

57

WILSON'S WARBLER

Wilsonia pusilla

IT is fitting that Alexander Wilson, who first found and described several New World Warblers, should have had one named after him. Elliott Coues, writing in 1874 about a species Wilson had described more than sixty years before, termed it "Wilson's Black-capped Flycatching Warbler" or, more simply, "Wilson's Warbler"—a name that has been recognized for the species ever since.

Wilson's Warblers bear some resemblance to Yellow Warblers in appearance, but close inspection shows that they are a darker shade of green on the back and a more lemony yellow on the underparts. The shiny black cap worn by all adult males and, less prominently, by most adult females is diagnostic but not always easy to observe on these restless and rather secretive birds.

As Wilson noted, the bill of this warbler is broader at the base than it is high. This is an attribute of flycatching birds and so, too, are the prominent bristles about the base of the bill. Canada and Hooded Warblers share these characteristics with Wilson's and their close relationship has been given recognition by placing all three in the same genus—a genus of flycatching warblers. In keeping with these physical resemblances, it is also true that all three are exceptionally active, spending much time flitting about in low vegetation, catching insects on the wing.

For most of us, Wilson's Warblers are likely to be encountered only in spring and fall migration, because they breed well to the north and winter in Central America from Mexico through to Panama. In migration, members of the species regularly

235

reach all provinces and states excepting Florida and adjacent states in the southeast, where they are rare or absent.

In summer, they are to be found nesting all across the northern part of the continent from Alaska to Newfoundland in the regions of the northern boreal forest. They also extend sparingly into northern New England and the two western races nest south to New Mexico and southern California.

Although their summer range is largely associated with the northern coniferous forest, they do not actually live in the forest itself. Instead, they select a type of habitat similar to Yellowthroat country—except, of course, that the vegetation has a more northern or sub-alpine character.

Wet clearings in an early stage of regeneration, peat or laurel (*Kalmia*) bogs dotted with young or dwarf spruces and tamaracks, swales in which the willows and alders have not grown too high—these are the favorite nesting sites of the Wilson's. The general level of vegetation is seldom more than five or six feet high in the vicinity of the nest, which is placed on the ground, often at the base of a shrub or small tree. It is natural, therefore, for these birds to seem most at home within a very few feet of the ground, usually in fairly dense cover, but the males do seek out song perches that may be eight or ten feet high.

Wilson's Warbler songs fall somewhat in the pattern of Nashville songs in that they seem to consist of two parts, the second part being delivered more rapidly than the first. However, the song as a whole is briefer in duration and has a rough, chattery quality of its own. It contains variations in pitch, volume, and tempo. The pitch usually falls in the second half only to rise again near the end. The sound level is never particularly high but normally shows some increase as the song progresses.

Tape recordings of Wilson's songs replayed at lower speeds show that most of the song consists of a rapid repetition of the phrase "chewy" with a few additional phrases such as "wee-o" or "wit" added at the end. As the bird sings it, however, much of this detail is lost to human ears and the song becomes something like this:

chee chee chee chee chee *che-che-che*-ch-ch-wit-wit.

Wilsonia pusilla pusilla (Wilson)
(Lat., *Wilsonia,* for Alexander Wilson; *pusilla,* very small)

Type Locality Southern New Jersey

LOCAL NAMES: Pileolated Warbler, Black-capped Warbler, Wilson's Black-capped Warbler

FIELD CHARACTERS: *Male,* crown glossy black; upper parts olive-green; forehead, face and underparts, a bright lemony yellow. No streaking or wing-bars; no white in tail.
Female, similar but crown-patch more restricted and usually partially veiled by olive-green feather tips.
Immature, black crown-patch almost completely veiled or lacking; yellowish eye-stripe above black, beady eye.
Length, 4.5 to 5.0 inches.

NESTING DATA: Built on the ground; a relatively large nest of dried grasses and small leaves, hair sometimes being used in the lining. It is usually placed at the base of a small tree (*e.g.,* tamarack) or shrub (*e.g.,* alder), often well concealed in a grass hummock, in a swale or bog with such plants as Labrador tea, bog laurel, blueberry prominent in ground cover along with grasses.
Eggs—4 to 6, commonly 5. White or creamy white with fine reddish speckling often concentrated in the form of a wreath at the larger end.

VOICE: Song is a rapid, rather unmusical, two-parted chatter, the second part usually being at a lower pitch than the first. Delivered forcibly and with spirit, but not among the loud warbler songs. Sample interpretation:

chee chee chee chee chee chee tche-tche-tche-tche. Call note—a sharp *chip* difficult to distinguish from those of other warblers. (*See Chapter 5*)

FOOD HABITS: No detailed food study has been made, but believed to be almost entirely insectivorous; feeds in low vegetation, often catching insects on the wing.

GENERAL RANGE: *Breeds* north to the tree line, from northern Alaska, Mackenzie District, northeastern Manitoba, northern Ontario, northern Quebec, southern Labrador and Newfoundland, south to Maine, northern Vermont and New Hampshire, southern Quebec, central Ontario, northern Michigan and Minnesota, the northern portions of Saskatchewan and Alberta. It *winters* from Mexico south and east to Panama. In spring migration, it leaves wintering grounds in early to mid-April, reaches northern states in mid-May and breeding grounds by late May and early June. Fall migration begins in mid-August and is completed by late September or early October.

Wilsonia pusilla pileolata (Pallas)
(Lat., *pileolata*, black-capped)

Type Locality Kodiak Island, Alaska

LOCAL NAME: Northern Pileolated Warbler

Averages somewhat larger than *W. p. pusilla*. Plumage brighter—upperparts more yellowish-green and underparts a brighter yellow; however, not as bright as *W. p. chryseola* (see below).

Breeds from northern tree limit in Alaska southward along the coast to the Queen Charlotte Islands, extending in the interior to the eastern slopes of the Rocky Mountains and east to western Alberta, central Montana and eastern Wyoming, southward at high altitudes as far as New Mexico and western Texas. *Winters* southern Texas south to Panama.

A. Wilson's. B. Northern Pileolated.
C. Golden Pileolated.

Wilsonia pusilla chryseola Ridgway
(Lat., *chryseola*, golden)

Type Locality Red Bluff, Calif.

LOCAL NAME: Golden Pileolated Warbler

Averages somewhat smaller than *W. p. pusilla*. Coloration much brighter—upperparts much more yellowish, verging on olive-yellow; yellow of forehead nearly orange; yellow of underparts more intense.

Breeds along the Pacific coast, largely west of the mountain ranges, from southern British Columbia to southern California. *Winters* southern Baja California and Sonora south through western Mexico to western Panama.

W. W. H. GUNN

58

CANADA WARBLER

Wilsonia canadensis

THIS is another warbler with an inappropriate name. Though summering in parts of Canada it is equally at home at that season as far south as the mountains of Georgia and is common in the highlands between. I came to know it many years ago in the mountain ranges of the beautiful Blue Ridge. At this roof-top of the east, where Mount Mitchell rears its head 6684 feet above the sea, I spent more than twenty-five summers, in a paradise for warblers as well as humanity. Here, as in the Maritime Provinces, New England, the Adirondacks and the hills of Virginia, the Canada Warbler makes its nest and raises its young.

The Canada Warbler is a dweller in mixed coniferous and deciduous forests. In the north, it lives right in the forest rather than at the edge, but it usually selects some little glade into which the sun's rays penetrate to brighten the gloom of the more deeply shaded surroundings. (In New England it prefers either hurricane wrecked maple swamps or cedar bogs. L. G.) In the highlands of the south, rhododendron thickets, deep ravines, damp woodlands and spring-fed streams are its chosen home.

In either locale, amid a splash of sunlight filtering through the high growth, one may see it, glowing like a jewel, the black necklace standing out vividly against the brilliance of the yellow breast. Out it darts from a perch to snap up a passing insect, back it goes to await another. The Canada is an excellent flycatcher, clicking the beak audibly at times. Though very active in movement and always alert, it is not a shy bird and can frequently be approached to close range.

The spring migration is very largely eastern, most of the birds travelling north between the Ohio Valley and the Atlantic coast. The fall flight generally follows the mountains (Alleghenies) to the Gulf Coast, birds having summered in the northern midwest or central Canada, proceeding fairly straight to Texas. It is a definitely uncommon bird in Florida, passing mainly to the westward, and has not been recorded at the Tortugas. In twenty years of field work in that state I have not observed it once.

The Canada Warbler is one of the easy species to identify in the field. Its outstanding character is the bright yellow breast crossed with a necklace of black spots. The yellow eye-ring, gray back and lack of white in wings and tail are follow-up items. The female has a similar pattern but is generally duller.

Wilsonia canadensis (Linnaeus)
(Lat., *canadensis,* of Canada)

Type Locality in Canada

FIELD CHARACTERS: *Male,* forehead black, bordered with gray; upperparts gray; stripe from bill to eye, eye-ring and breast yellow, crossed with necklace of black spots. Under tail-coverts white.
Female, similar but duller.
Immature, like female but even more plainly grayish above and dull yellow below.
Length, 5.00 to 5.75 inches.

NESTING DATA: On or near the ground, atop mossy logs or stumps, cavities in banks or amid roots of windfalls. Constructed of leaves, bark strippings and weed stalks, lined with hair, fine bark fibers or fern rootlets.
Eggs—3 to 5, usually 4. White, spotted and sometimes splotched with chestnut, shades of brown and purplish-gray, such markings often concentrated in a wreath at large end.

VOICE: [A sharp, incisive 'chip' is used with great frequency as a call-note. It is often given

between songs and also goes to make up the beginning of the song which opens with the 'chip' and then, after a brief but measurable pause, suddenly explodes into a staccato burst of notes that usually ends with an emphatic 'swee-ditchety.' The whole song lasts more than 1¼ seconds. Sample interpretations:
  (a)   chip, chupety swee-ditchety
  (b)   chip, suey de swee-ditchety
(W. W. H. GUNN.)] (*See Chapter 5*)

FOOD HABITS: Apparently wholly insects and spiders. A finished flycatcher, much of its prey being taken on the wing.

GENERAL RANGE: *Breeds* from north-central Alberta, central Saskatchewan, central Manitoba, northern Ontario, and southern Quebec south to southern Manitoba, central Minnesota, northern Wisconsin, central Michigan, northern Ohio, through the Appalachian Mountains to eastern Tennessee, northwestern Georgia, western North Carolina, western Virginia, western Maryland, and central-eastern Pennsylvania, and to northern New Jersey, southeastern New York, Connecticut, Rhode Island, Massachusetts, Maine, and New Brunswick. *Winters* in Colombia and mountains of Venezuela, south to eastern Peru.
ALEXANDER SPRUNT, JR.

59

*AMERICAN REDSTART**

Setophaga ruticilla

THE American Redstart is probably the most abundant breeding warbler in the northeastern United States, and with the possible exceptions of the Blackpoll and Myrtle perhaps the most abundant warbler in North America. At present statements as to relative abundance of a species over a wide area must of necessity be subjective. Future research well may confirm my supposition.

The vivacious, and strikingly-patterned black and orange-red male fanning its tail,

* In using the term Redstart one must bear in mind that the word is commonly used to denote 3 different groups of birds. One group consists of 2 warblers breeding in the United States—the 2 *Setophaga* (*ruticilla* and *picta*) each represented by 2 recognized races. The second group is composed of the tropical Redstarts in the genus *Myioborus*. These are divided into 10 species with 21 named races. The third group, the Old World Redstarts, are not warblers but *Turdidae*.

Some taxonomists believe that the genus *Setophaga* should include all of the *Myioborus* or tropical Redstarts. Further study may well confirm this.

drooping its wings, whirling from limb to limb and fly-catching in skillful pursuit of insects demands attention wherever it appears. I have heard people from Maine to Florida refer to it as the butterfly-bird. Anyone who has seen a male Redstart in tropical jungles and hammocks flashing orange-red each time the sun strikes its plumage readily can understand why so many Latin Americans call it *Candelita* or little torch.

In spring the birds enter the United States on a broad front from Florida to Texas. The first flights, composed chiefly of males, reach Florida during the first week in April and New York the first week in May. At the peak of migration it is not unusual to see several hundred Redstarts in a day. As soon as the males reach their breeding grounds they establish territories by song, displays of intimidation and aggressive fighting with males of the same species. These territories average a little less than an acre.

This species prefers open deciduous woodlands with a good undergrowth of bushes and young trees, but it is very adaptable, frequently nesting in mixed coniferous-deciduous forests, shade trees and shrubbery around farms, orchards, and even in willow and alder thickets bordering ponds and streams. Although the nest ordinarily is placed in deciduous growth, twice when population pressure crowded a pair to the edge of a small birch grove, I have found nests in adjacent spruce. Singularly these nests, like many others in Maine, contained much of the so-called camouflage of white birch bark and stood out boldly against the dark spruce! The male never incubates, but frequently feeds the female as she sits on the eggs, and he often assumes the major responsibility in feeding the young. Several times as I climbed to nests I have seen both adults go through the injury feigning act, fluttering downward from limb to limb as though a wing were broken, at times as though in the last throes of death.

Southward migration starts as early as mid-July, some birds appearing in Florida by the end of this month. By mid-October most Redstarts have left the northern states and by the second week in November virtually all have gone south of the United States. Imagine my astonishment at Christmas time in 1931 to be shown a healthy-looking male in Inwood Park, New York City. This bird associated with White-throated Sparrows in a Forsythia thicket in a snow covered ravine from December 10

through 27. During migrations and on the tropical wintering grounds one is more impressed with the abundance of this tireless flash of color. At times Redstarts seem to be everywhere. During one flight in October, 15 landed on our fishing boat 20 miles east of Cocoa Beach, Florida. They perched on railings, on fishing poles and even on the heads of the startled fishermen! On this trip we twice saw Parasitic Jaegers attempt to catch a warbler as it flew over the open ocean and undoubtedly some Redstarts lose their lives in this manner.

Setophaga ruticilla ruticilla (Linnaeus)
(Gr., *setophaga,* insect-eating; Lat., *ruticilla,* red-tailed.)

Type Locality Virginia

LOCAL NAME: Southern American Redstart

FIELD CHARACTERS: Very animated, frequently fans tail and droops wings, often flycatches.
Adult male, only eastern warbler that appears mostly coal-black and bright orange-red. Most of bird black, belly white, orange-red on wings, sides, breast and sides of tail.
Adult female, same general pattern, but gray head, grayish-olive back, yellow instead of orange-red on wings, side, breast and sides of tail.
Immatures, resemble female. In first breeding season many males are somewhat mottled with black, the yellow areas show an orange wash. Full adult plumage comes at the end of the first breeding season.
Length, 4.50 to 5.75 inches, females average smaller than males.

NESTING DATA: Nest a firmly woven cup of plant down, grass, leaf stalks, strips of bark, tendrils, fine rootlets, feathers, spider webs and lichens with the outside diameter averaging 3 inches, the inside depth 1½ inches. It is usually placed in deciduous second growth in a crotch, or in a cluster of upright branches on a horizontal limb 10 to 20 feet above the ground, sometimes as low as a few inches, rarely as high as 70 feet.
Eggs—Usually 4, often 3, sometimes 5. They measure .68 x .50 inches and are grayish or bluish white, spotted and blotched with various shades of brown, chiefly at the larger end. Incubation takes 12 days,

sometimes 13. Normally one brood, sometimes two, egg dates concentrated between late May and early July. Young normally leave the nest in 8 to 10 days.

The Brown-headed Cowbird frequently deposits eggs in nests, chiefly those placed outside woodlands.

VOICE: Song a rather thin sibilant unexciting *see-see-see see sée* (rising inflection at end), *tsee tsee tsee tsee-o* (ending in downward slur) or *chewee chewee chewee*. Many birds alternate between two favorite songs, some indulge in unique individual renditions. The highest frequency is about 7,300 vibrations per second, the lowest 4,400. Collecting has proved that females sing. In most areas singing drops off abruptly in mid-July, and normally ceases by mid-August. After that typical songs seldom are heard, but there are often peculiar whispered, jumbled songs. Call note a sharp *chip* or *chick*. (See Chapter 5)

FOOD HABITS: Chiefly insectivorous, but I have seen some eat crushed nuts and grapes at a feeding station, and others have observed the species eating fruit of shadbush and magnolia. They devour quantities of eggs, larvae, pupae or adults of diptera, hymenoptera, lepidoptera, hemiptera, coleoptera and other insects as well as spiders and mites.

GENERAL RANGE: *Breeds* from North Dakota, Minnesota, Michigan, southern Ontario east to southern Maine; south to southeastern Oklahoma, northeastern Texas across to central Alabama, Georgia to southeastern Virginia. *Winters* in Mexico, Cuba and Puerto Rico south through Central America and West Indies to Ecuador, southern Venezuela and British Guiana.

Setophaga ruticilla tricolora (Müller)
   (Lat., *tricolora,* three-colored)

Type Locality Cayenne, French Guiana

LOCAL NAME: Northern American Redstart

This northern race is so similar in habits, song and appearance that it is indistinguishable from the American Redstart in the field. In fact, Dr. Wetmore (1949) could find no constant differences between adult males of the two forms. He found that females and immature males of *tricolora* are "somewhat darker above, washed with duller green in immature dress."

RANGE: *Breeds* from Alaska, Mackenzie and Saskatchewan east through central Ontario and Quebec to northern Maine and Newfoundland; south to central Washington, Idaho, Utah, Montana across to Nova Scotia. In *winter* from Baja California south to northern South America to British Guiana.

ALLAN D. CRUICKSHANK

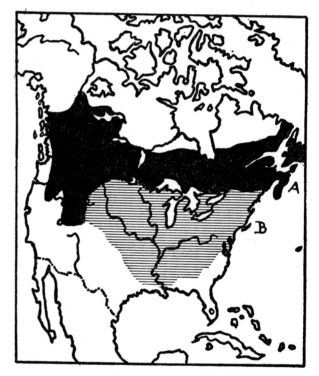

A. Northern. B. Southern.

60

PAINTED REDSTART

Setophaga picta

ANY account of this flashing avian jewel calls for superlatives. Certainly, those familiar with it could use no less, for successive observations of its brilliance cause almost as much enthusiasm as does first acquaintance. To see it, flitting among the oaks and pines of its canyon haunts, the blacks, whites and reds of its startling plumage glowing amid sunlight and shadow, constitutes one of the most striking sights of animated nature.

My first introduction to it was in the Apache National Forest of western New Mexico, followed by other sessions on lofty Mount Mingus in Arizona and later in the desert mountain ranges of the Santa Ritas, Huachucas and Chiricahuas and Dragoons. Each successive study proved more fascinating. Whether in Echo Canyon of the Chiricahuas in company with Red-faced War-blers and Arizona Juncos, or, on a rather birdless day in Cochise Stronghold of the Dragoon Mountains, where we ate lunch and wondered whether there were any birds about at all, suddenly to be surrounded by a half dozen of the flashing sprites; they proved a never-ending delight.

The Painted Redstart is an intermediate bird, so to speak, ranging between the tops of mountains and the lowlands of southwestern U.S. It is partial to oaks in the canyons from about 5000 to 7000 ft. and sometimes higher. A rather solitary bird in habit it does not mix with flocks of migrants, preferring a solitary existence. However, in spring and fall, numbers may be seen in a single day afield.

Actually a Central American and Mexican species, breeding as far south as Nicaragua, the northern race of two sub-species

PLATE 28
CANADA WARBLER
Page 238
Female

Male

WILSON'S WARBLER
Page 235
Female

Golden Pileolated

Male Wilson's

John H. Dick
'55

is the bird that extends into our borders, and is an early migrant, arriving in Arizona and New Mexico from mid-March to the end of the month. Shortly thereafter, they become settled for the breeding season which lasts from late March (New Mexico) to about a month later in Arizona up until July, with the height being from mid-May to early June.

In 1928 Josselyn Van Tyne added the Painted Redstart to the avifauna of Texas by finding it nesting in the Chisos Mountains of the Big Bend.

The general behavior of this redstart is very much like that of the eastern bird (American Redstart). Activity is, as the saying goes, "its middle name." It seems continually in motion, the drooping wings and fanning tail being as strikingly constant and the flitting to and fro, the flycatching habits, the meticulous search of crack and cranny, trunk of tree and lichen-covered rock all remind one of *S. ruticilla*. And as brightly plumaged as the latter is, there is something about the westerner as it appears, disappears, darts out into the air, spreads its tail and carries on its way of life which convinces one of the complete appropriateness of the name—painted!

Mrs. Florence M. Bailey (1928) gives a beautiful description of this redstart when she writes—"On the oaks, when the long black and white fan tail was outspread against the bark the suggestion was of a museum specimen, a pinned-out gorgeous butterfly." An additional characteristic is the tameness or, at least lack of shyness, for it is often possible to approach to very close range and sometimes, if the observer sits quietly, the Painted Redstart will all but alight on one's out-stretched arm or leg.

In the fall of 1947 a Painted Redstart made an unprecedented appearance in the Northeast, at Marblehead, Mass., the first instance of its occurrence outside the normal range (except for several California records). As may be imagined, the excitement among bird watchers was intense. Hundreds saw the bird and recognizable movies were secured. No explanation of such wandering presents itself.

This warbler must certainly be listed among the "unmistakables." One look is enough to identify it and it is one of the few warblers in which the young bird assumes practically adult plumage at the post-juvenal molt, and in which the sexes are indistinguishable in any plumage.

Setophaga picta picta Swainson
(Lat., *picta*, painted)

Type Locality Real del Monte
(Hidalgo) Mexico

LOCAL NAME: Northern Painted Redstart

FIELD CHARACTERS: Upperparts and tail black, latter with 3 outer feathers terminally white. Wings black, outer primary and secondary feathers edged with white, a large white patch on the coverts; throat and sides black; breast and belly scarlet; abdomen white.

Sexes alike; immature assumes adult plumage in first autumn.

Length, 5.25 inches.

NESTING DATA: Almost always on the ground, under a rock, tree-root or grass-tuft, usually on a sloping bank or rocky canyon wall, near water. Bent (1953) found a nest in vines growing over a cabin, about 10 ft., up, in Ramsey Canyon, Huachuca Mts., Arizona, a most unusual situation.

Nest of bark, weed-stalk fibers and grass, lined with hair or fine grasses. Rather large and shallow.

Eggs—3 or 4. Creamy white, finely speckled with chestnut and other shades of brown and drab. Markings either faint or sharply defined, more at large end but with no distinct wreath.

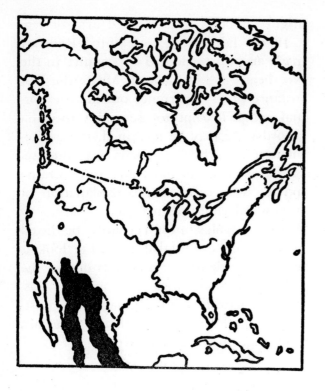

Song an "ordinary warbler *whee-tee, whee-tee . . .* having individual rich contralto quality" (Mrs. F. M. Bailey, 1928), otherwise rendered as *weecher weecher weecher*. Call-note compared to that of the peep of a young chicken (Swarth, 1904).

FOOD HABITS: Apparently entirely insects.

[*Comment:* Alexander Skutch writes of the Guatemalan race (*S. picta guatemalae*) in Bent: "It was keeping company with a Slate-throated Redstart in the lighter oak woods at an altitude of about 7000 feet. These two warblers are rather similar in color pattern; but the hues of the Painted Redstart were even more brilliant than those of its companion. . . . On the same morning I found a second bird in perfect plumage who was singing. His loud ringing *weecher, weecher, weecher* was wonderfully rich and mellow, surpassing in fullness of tone even the *ch'ree, ch'ree, ch'ree* of *Myioborus miniatus*."]

GENERAL RANGE: *Breeds* from northwestern Arizona, southwestern New Mexico and west Texas (Chisos Mts.) southward into Mexico and Central America as far as Nicaragua. *Winters* from central Sonora, central western Chihuahua, central Nuevo Leon and Tamaulipas and occasionally southern Arizona through southern part of breeding range.

ALEXANDER SPRUNT, JR.

Crescent-chested Warbler

CHAPTER 9

THE WARBLERS OF MEXICO

WARBLERS are so conspicuous an element of the migratory phenomenon in the United States and Canada that we customarily think of them as being essentially birds of the higher latitudes. This concept is further strengthened by their presence in all parts of temperate North America during the breeding season. Nevertheless, most warblers pass the greater part of their lives in warmer regions. In a very real sense, therefore, even those species that breed in the far north are no less a part of the southern fauna.

Mexico, by reason of its location, configuration, and diversity of terrain and habitat, is especially favored in the richness and abundance of its warbler population. The resident species include both northern and tropical representatives, the former in greatest variety, and at least seven species that do not occur elsewhere.

The annual influx of transient and wintering warblers from the north more than doubles the number of resident species, and of course enormously increases the number of individuals. Indeed, during the four seasons of a single year it might be possible, theoretically, to see in Mexico no fewer than sixty-six species, or considerably more kinds of warblers than occur in the United States and Canada. Only in the total extent of Central America can be found an equal or possibly greater variety than in Mexico.

TRANSIENTS AND WINTER VISITANTS

The resident bird fauna of Mexico is conspicuously enhanced by the arrival in late summer and fall of numerous migrants, many remaining until late spring.

Transient and wintering northern warblers together account for at least thirty-seven of the sixty-six species that have been recorded. A bird student familiar with this family in the United States or Canada can travel the length and breadth of Mexico during certain months (August–May) with the assurance of meeting numerous friends. Each has been discussed at length elsewhere in this book. It is our purpose here to relate the several categories of migrant warblers to the Mexican scene and to point out trends that are reflected in their seasonal movements.

Very few of the migrant warblers reported in Mexico are wholly transitory. Of the seven species that continue southward to winter deeper in the tropics all but the Blackpoll are essentially eastern birds. Chestnut-sided and Bay-breasted Warblers appear to be casual migrants in the extreme south (especially Quintana Roo), but are seldom reported. Canada Warblers are uncommon, but probably regular spring transients on the Caribbean slope. They have been observed in Veracruz from March 8 until May 28. One autumn record is of a specimen taken some miles off the Yucatán coast in late August. The only other autumn record was in Chiapas. Cerulean, Blackburnian and Mourning Warblers, all eastern species, regularly migrate through eastern Mexico and are especially conspicuous in spring.

About thirty northern warblers winter in Mexico, most regularly, and many in appreciable numbers. As with the transients, a majority (18) of the wintering species breed in eastern North America and, in Mexico, occur principally in the east and south. Black-and-White Warblers and Louisiana Waterthrushes are exceptions, in that both winter commonly in suitable habitat throughout the country.

For present purposes a list of eastern warblers that pass the winter in Mexico, with an indication of their status and distribution, will suffice. Northern species with transcontinental breeding ranges are not listed.

BLACK-AND-WHITE WARBLER Migratory on both coasts, wintering in southern Baja California, and from Colima and Nuevo León southward. Common.

PROTHONOTARY WARBLER Yucatán Peninsula and adjacent islands. Casual.

SWAINSON'S WARBLER Caribbean slope, including Campeche and Quintana Roo. Casual.

WORM-EATING WARBLER Migratory in the east, wintering in the Yucatán Peninsula and Chiapas. Uncommon.

GOLDEN-WINGED WARBLER Migratory on the Caribbean slope, wintering rarely in the Yucatán Peninsula.

BLUE-WINGED WARBLER Similar to preceding species.

TENNESSEE WARBLER Similar to preceding species.

AMERICAN PARULA WARBLER Tamaulipas southward on the Caribbean slope. Common.

MAGNOLIA WARBLER Migratory in the east (chiefly), wintering from Veracruz and Puebla southward. Common.

CAPE MAY WARBLER Yucatán Peninsula and adjacent islands. Accidental.

BLACK-THROATED BLUE WARBLER Cozumel Island, off Quintana Roo. Accidental or casual.

John H. Dick
'55

BLACK-THROATED GREEN WARBLER
Caribbean slope, including the Yucatán
Peninsula. Common.

YELLOW-THROATED WARBLER Southeast, especially the Yucatán Peninsula.
Common.

PINE WARBLER Tamaulipas.

PRAIRIE WARBLER Islands off Quintana
Roo. Common.

LOUISIANA WATERTHRUSH Countrywide
in suitable habitat. Common locally.

KENTUCKY WARBLER Migratory in the
east (chiefly), wintering from Veracruz
southward.

HOODED WARBLER Caribbean slope
from Veracruz southward. Abundant.

It is noteworthy that only six of the winter visitants are essentially western birds.
This circumstance is offset, however, by
the fact that a preponderance of resident
species, exclusive of essentially tropical
forms, have affinities in the Rocky Mountain and Pacific states.

The six western warblers visit Mexico
regularly, and none can be considered uncommon. Virginia's, Townsend's, and Hermit Warblers range over much of the western portion of the country, the first as far
south as Guerrero, the others south at least
to Nicaragua. Golden-cheeked Warblers
apparently migrate through eastern Mexico, wintering in the southern highlands.
The Western Palm Warbler (*palmarum*),
also essentially a western bird, virtually by-
passes Mexico in migration, but winters
sparingly in Yucatán, Quintana Roo, and
on adjacent islands. Only MacGillivray's is
widespread in winter, being found from
coast to coast, and southward to Colombia.

As might be expected, most warblers
that breed across North America have conspicuously extensive wintering grounds. Although the coastal slopes of Mexico are
especially important migratory avenues,
Nashville and Myrtle Warblers are widespread in winter, as are Northern Waterthrushes, Pileolated Warblers and American Redstarts. Ovenbirds occur only as
transients in western Mexico, but winter
commonly in the east and south, including
the Yucatán Peninsula.

Little is yet known in detail of the
habits, local distribution and relative abundance of northern warblers in their winter
homes. Nevertheless, several basic principles emerge from an analysis of the countless observations that have been made.

As a group, eastern warblers migrate
greater distances than do the essentially
western species. Most of the former winter
extensively in Central America as well as in
Mexico, and many range southward into
northern South America. In contrast are
the western warblers, two of which (Virginia's, Western Palm) do not winter south
of Mexico, and only one (MacGillivray's)
as far as Panama. The winter distribution
of the half dozen species that breed across
North America is varied, but as a group
the pattern is much like that of eastern
birds.

Much less is known of the arrival and
departure dates of migratory Mexican warblers than of their migration routes and
areas of winter occupancy. Evidence from
many sources suggests that even non-resident species occur in Mexico throughout
most of the year, being wholly absent—except for occasional individuals—perhaps
only in June. However, this is not to say

that non-resident warblers are numerous at all other times. In Mexico the rate of migration declines rapidly after the first week of May, and most northern species do not reappear until August or later.

A recent study of migration in Veracruz by Frederick Loetscher reveals a pattern of movement which, with some modifications, may well pertain elsewhere in the country. Considering Veracruz alone, and its total complement of migrants, Loetscher found that eastern species tend to arrive earlier in the fall (July 15) than do western birds, which seldom appear in numbers before early September. The eastern species also tend to remain later in the spring (May 1–15) than western birds, these rarely being found after April. It is noteworthy that the eastern, but not the western species are appreciably more abundant in spring than in winter. These trends, as they pertain to warblers, doubtless can be correlated in part with the seasonal pressures exerted on the Mexican population by the more numerous eastern species that winter also in Central and South America.

RESIDENT WARBLERS

Resident warblers comprise an interesting if not conspicuous element of the Mexican fauna, although far surpassed in variety by the hosts of northern migrants that flood the country each autumn and winter. As he travels about Mexico at any season a visitor from the north will notice with mixed emotions that many of the resident species breed also in the United States or Canada. Indeed, no fewer than fourteen of the twenty-nine resident warblers of Mexico are represented north of the border by the same or by closely related forms. It is noteworthy that all but three of the northern species are western birds, most found in mountainous areas. The sole exceptions (Yellow Warbler, Common Yellowthroat, Yellow-breasted Chat) are wide-ranging species that breed across the continent.

Of special interest to the student of Mexican birds and their faunal relationships are the seven warblers peculiar to Mexico. In a narrow sense these endemic species are the only "true" Mexican warblers, since found nowhere else. Their affinities as a group, however, are preponderantly northern, the Red-breasted Chat alone representing a genus (*Granatellus*) that is essentially tropical in origin and present distribution.

In addition to the diverse categories of resident warblers mentioned above is yet another group of eight species, unrepresented north of Mexico, but having southern affinities. As tropical elements in a largely temperate fauna they merit special attention. When finally known in sufficient detail, the distribution, ecological associations, and life histories of these and other tropical and semi-tropical birds may provide answers to many puzzling questions of fundamental importance.

An appreciation of the geography, topography, and climate of Mexico is requisite to an understanding of the distribution and affinities of its bird-life. Much of the interior of the country is a dry plateau or tableland, with a temperate climate, bounded on the west and east by forested mountain ranges that converge toward the south, where altitudes up to 18,000 feet are found. The coastal plains, narrowest in the west, vary from twenty-five miles to well over a hundred miles in width. The Pacific slope is essentially dry, and in part a desert; the Caribbean receives more rainfall, and in the south (except the Yucatán Peninsula) is decidedly humid.

The distribution of birds is directly related to the physical aspects of a region as reflected in its flora. Vegetation and, therefore birds, characteristic of the Temperate Zone are dominant in northern Mexico and persist southward in the mountains to Chiapas or beyond. Even boreal forests, inhabited by representative northern birds, exist in Mexico as more-or-less isolated "islands" at the highest altitudes. Tropical forests of several types clothe the southern lowlands, introducing into the Mexican fauna many birds with tropical affinities. Significant elements of the Tropical Zone have become established as far north as Sonora on the Pacific slope, and southern Tamaulipas on the Caribbean. Thus, in Mexico, resident birds characteristic of two faunal regions sometimes occur together, but generally they are separated in terms of altitude, this compensating for latitude. As applied to resident warblers, the ratio between species with northern affinities and those with tropical ties is approximately two to one.

The few comprehensive studies of tropical birds that have been made, chiefly in Central America by Alexander F. Skutch, reveal several fundamental differences between the northern and southern representatives of the same family. These relate especially to their behavior, social organization and breeding biology. The basic principles, as reflected in warblers, are discussed by Dr. Skutch in his chapter on the Warblers of Central America, and need not be repeated here.

Compared with northern warblers, the resident Mexican species are very poorly known. Our present knowledge of them relates chiefly to their affinities and to the broader aspects of their distribution. A brief review of the essential facts about each will serve to identify the larger areas of inquiry that merit special attention in the future.

As mentioned above, some twenty-nine warblers are resident in Mexico, one or more species being found in virtually every part of the country. The genus *Vermivora* alone is represented by four species, of which but one, the Crescent-chested Warbler (also known as Hartlaub's Warbler) (*V. superciliosa*), lacks close ties north of Mexico (Plate 31). A single race (*sordida*) of Orange-crowned Warbler breeds in Mexico (Todos Santos Islands, off Baja California) as well as in California, but in winter several other northern varieties occur extensively elsewhere, especially in the western highlands.

The Colima Warbler (*V. crissalis*) (Plate 5) is essentially a Mexican species, although represented in the United States by a small breeding population that is restricted to the Chisos Mountains, southwestern Texas. Much like Virginia's Warbler in general appearance and habits, it occurs locally in the mountains of northern Mexico (Coahuila, western Tamaulipas) south to Michoacán and Colima, where probably a winter visitant. Lucy's Warbler is resident both in extreme northern Baja California and in the lowlands of northern Sonora, but in winter ranges southward at least to Jalisco. The Crescent-chested Warbler (Plate 31) might be mistaken for either the American or the Tropical Parula (*pitiayumi*), being similar above, but differs from both in having conspicuous white superciliaries and a chestnut colored spot at the base of the throat. It lacks white on the wings and tail. The cup-shaped nest of green moss, lined with fibres, is placed on the ground. Two, but usually three eggs comprise a clutch. They are white, or faintly sprinkled with brown. The four resident Mexican races frequent pine and oak forests at high altitudes from southwestern Chihuahua, Nuevo León, and San Luis Potosí south to Honduras and El Salvador. A related form occurs in Nicaragua.

The Tropical Parula (now called Olive-backed Warbler) (*Parula pitiayumi*) (Plate 8) is essentially a southern species, represented in Mexico by several races of which one, known as Sennett's Warbler (*nigrilora*), occurs also in Texas. All resemble American Parulas superficially, but are easily distinguished by their clear yellow breasts. One variety, the Socorro (Parula) warbler of the Revilla Gigedo Islands (casual in Baja California) (Plate 8) is notably pale and may comprise a distinct endemic species (*graysoni*). Tropical Parulas are much like their northern relative in habits, and in Mexico occupy wooded areas on both coastal slopes. Feverishly active birds, they feed at all levels in shrubs and trees, but show a preference for those near water. The song is weak, and not especially musical.

Olive Warblers (*Peucedramus*) (Plate 9), and the four Dendroicas resident in Mex-

ico breed also in the western portion of the United States. Except for the widespread Yellow Warbler (*D. petechia*), all are virtually restricted to the highlands where climatic and ecological conditions are not unlike those of our western states. Some eight varieties of Yellow Warbler are resident in Mexico. Several, long considered representatives of a distinct species (Mangrove Warbler), have chestnut on their heads and are restricted to coastal mangrove swamps and brackish estuaries. Other Yellow Warblers occupy the interior, where they are often common locally in willows and cottonwoods bordering streams. Audubon's and Grace's Warblers breed south to northwestern Mexico; the Black-throated Gray only to northern Baja California. All three winter extensively in the highlands.

Common Yellowthroats (*Geothlypis trichas*) are widely distributed in Mexico, as in the United States. Five related species, all endemic, are distributed across the country, one or more occurring both in the lowlands and in the highlands. All resemble Common Yellowthroats superficially, and the females are virtually inseparable in the field. Male Peninsular (*G. beldingi*), Yellow-crowned (*G. flavovelata*) (Plate 31), and Chapala (*G. chapalensis*) Yellowthroats will be known by the yellow band behind the black facial mask. They differ especially in size, the Peninsular measuring about five and one-half inches in length, the Chapala almost an inch less, and the Yellow-crowned between the two. Since much alike, and occupying different areas (Baja California; coastal marshes of southern Tamaulipas and northern Veracruz; Jalisco), it is likely that all three are geographical representatives of a single species. Black-polled (*G. speciosa*) (Plate 31) and Hooded Yellowthroats (*G. nelsoni*) complete the Mexican assemblage of this genus. The former is black-crowned, and frequents highland marshes in the states of Michoacán, Mexico, Puebla, and Veracruz. The latter, distinguished by the broadness of its facial mask, occurs locally in the mountains of southern San Luis Potosí and Tamaulipas south to eastern Oaxaca. Like their northern relatives, the endemic Mexican Yellowthroats are furtive in habits, and frequent thickets or grassy areas near water where not easily observed.

The Red-breasted Chat (*Granatellus venustus*) (Plate 33) and Red Warbler (*Ergaticus ruber*) (Plate 31) are the only other warblers restricted to Mexico. The first is found on Maria Madre Island of the Tres Marias Group, and locally on the Pacific slope of the mainland from southern Sinaloa to Oaxaca. Males are brightly-colored birds, essentially bluish gray above and vermilion below, but with a white throat bordered with black. A conspicuous white stripe above and behind the eye, and white outer tail feathers insure the identification. Females are duller above and pale buffy white below. Alone, or in small bands of mixed sex, this rare warbler is usually found near the ground in thickets or forest undergrowth. Red Warblers (Plate 31) are rich red, brightest below, and have silvery cheeks. They resemble the Pink-headed Warbler (*E. versicolor*) (Plate 33) of Chiapas and Guatemala superficially, but are found only in mountain forests from southern Chihuahua and Durango to Oaxaca.

Other western warblers found more or less extensively in Mexico include the Gray-crowned or Thick-billed Yellowthroat (also known as Ground-chat) (*Chamaethlypis*) (Plate 8), Yellow-breasted Chat (*Icteria*) (Plate 27), Red-faced Warbler (*Cardellina*) (Plate 29), and Painted Redstart (*Setophaga*) (Plate 29). The first, essentially a lowland bird, breeds commonly in marshes and brushy meadows on both coastal slopes, and has a wide range through Central America. Yellow-breasted Chats breed in Baja California and western Mexico, but in winter are to be found in all parts of the country (Plate 27). Mountain forests, especially of pine or oak, are the preferred habitat of Red-faced Warblers and Painted Redstarts.

The remaining resident warblers all have southern affinities. Several are the northernmost representatives of essentially South American species or genera. Gray-throated Chats (*Granatellus sallaei*) occupy the Caribbean lowlands from Veracruz southward to Guatemala. Although much like the endemic Red-breasted Chat of the Pacific slope in habits and appearance, they differ in having slate-colored (not white) throats and wholly black tails. Slate-throated Redstarts (*Myioborus miniatus*) (Plate 32) resemble the more northern Painted Redstart, but will be known by their uniformly colored wings and chestnut crown-patch. Mountain forests are their home. Most of the Central and South American relatives have orange or yellow (not vermilion) underparts. Fan-tailed Warblers (*Euthlypis lachrymosa*) frequent undergrowth in wooded areas of both coastal slopes of Mexico. Their tawny underparts, expansive white-tipped tails, and bright yellow crown-patch are useful field marks (Plate 33).

The genus *Basileuterus* is perhaps the most characteristically tropical of any warbler group. Only seven of the twenty-two or so known species occur north of South America, and of these only three range north to Mexico. The Golden-crowned Warbler (*B. culicivorus*) (also called Yellow-crowned), yellow below and with a yellow (sometimes orange-tinged) median crown-stripe bordered with black, is common in the eastern lowlands and foothills where it seems to be equally at home in roadside thickets, open woodlands, and thick forests. It occurs also in Central and South America. The northeastern Mexican race (*brasheri*) is known as Brasher's Warbler. The Golden-browed or Bell's Warbler (*B. belli*) inhabits mountain forests from Tamaulipas and Jalisco southward (Plate 32); the Rufous-capped (*B. rufifrons*)

lowlands as well as mountains to an altitude of about 7,000 feet (Plate 32); both range south to Honduras. All members of the genus feed fairly near the ground and, so far as known, construct domed nests. The sexes are alike in plumage and most of the species are brightly colored, yellow or chestnut often being conspicuous.

Even a brief review of the warblers of Mexico suggests how superficial is our present knowledge of tropical American birds, whether of Mexico or of Central and South America. Museum specimens by the scores of thousands have been studied critically by generations of taxonomists, but further progress is most likely to be made in the field by the perseverance of disciplined observers. Important contributions to our knowledge will certainly be made by those who conduct their investigations in Mexico, where two great faunas meet.

EMMET R. BLAKE

PLATE 30
AMERICAN REDSTART
Page 240
Immature Male

Male

Female

J.H. Dick
'49

CHAPTER 10

NORTH AMERICAN WOOD WARBLERS
IN THE WEST INDIES

THE West Indies yearly receive a host of North American warblers. These comprise regular winter residents (19 species), transients (10 species) and vagrants (6 species). For the most part they frequent open settled districts in the lowlands and constitute an important and conspicuous element of the Antillean avifauna.

The term "winter resident" is rather misleading as applied to warblers, for many reach the islands from their northern breeding grounds in summer, those of the Austral Zone of southeastern North America as early as August or even July. This has given rise to the erroneous belief that some are native residents. June is the only month when all the species of migrant warblers may be said to be absent from the West Indies. Of the thousands of records, I know of only four in June and these pertain either to immature or to presumably sickly individuals. On the other hand, a few migrant shore-birds regularly pass the entire summer on the islands, foregoing their lengthy flights to their breeding grounds in the Arctic.

The virtual absence of North American warblers in June and July in the West Indies doubtless benefits the native species of this family, freeing them from competition for food at a period when the majority of these have young. Such competition at other times of the year must be severe, except in the Lesser Antilles where migrant warblers are scarce. It presumably accounts for resident Yellow Warblers having become largely confined to mangrove swamps in the Bahamas and Greater Antilles.

Among the earlier arrivals in summer are the Yellow-throated Warbler, Prairie

Warbler and Louisiana Waterthrush, but not before September do the bulk of the migrants reach the islands. The latest to appear is the Myrtle Warbler of which there are no West Indian records prior to October. From early autumn until early spring northern warblers abound in lowland areas in the Bahamas and Greater Antilles, and in more open, cultivated sections in the mountains. Many species are found only in low country, but none is confined to the mountains.

Migrant warblers move about singly or in groups composed of several species. They often respond to squeaking, particularly if one individual is induced to "chip." On such occasions I have had as many as six varieties in sight at the same time. Some show little preference in habitat. Among these I would include the Ovenbird and Redstart, which occur from arid coastal areas to humid mountain forest. The Cape May Warbler is also widespread during the winter, but apparently does not enter the rain forest, and is rare on islands east of Hispaniola. The Myrtle Warbler is found along the beaches, on the borders of mangrove swamps and in open farming country in the hills.

On the other hand, the Northern Waterthrush is chiefly confined to the coastal mangroves, the Louisiana Waterthrush to fresh-water streams. The Prairie Warbler prefers semi-arid scrub; the Palm Warbler, the borders of fields, parks and gardens, being frequently seen in Havana, Kingston, and Ciudad Trujillo. Yellowthroats occur in thickets at all elevations, but are most abundant in marshy places. Few migrant warblers are found in dense rain forest. Those most frequently observed in this environment are the Black-and-White, Parula, Black-throated Blue, Ovenbird and American Redstart, all of which are more numerous in lower, drier woods. The most widespread and as a whole the most abundant of the winter resident warblers in the West Indies is the American Redstart, but on some islands other species exceed it in numbers. The Prairie Warbler is the most abundant in the Bahamas, the Palm Warbler in Cuba, the Parula in Puerto Rico.

What has often caused astonishment to a northern ornithologist on his first visit to the West Indies is the abundance of the Cape May Warbler, considered one of the rarer species of North America. In its summer home, the Cape May inhabits the tall spruce forest of Canada and some of the border States. In the West Indies it is found chiefly in gardens and plantations, and occurs in mountains as well as lowlands, in low cover and in tall trees. It is most abundant in Hispaniola but occurs virtually throughout the West Indies. The two rarest North American warblers, the Kirtland's and the Bachman's, have very restricted winter ranges. The former occurs only in the Bahamas, the latter in Cuba, including the Isle of Pines. Formerly both were observed fairly frequently, but in recent years have seldom been reported. Kirtland's Warbler inhabits scrubby thickets, whereas Bachman's Warbler should be looked for among flowering Hibiscus trees, known in Cuba as *Majaguas*, where it searches for food among the blossoms. Swainson's Warbler, another of the rarer northern species, winters rather commonly in Jamaica, frequenting moist and relatively dry woodland undergrowth areas.

Three North American warblers, the Worm-eating, Magnolia, and Black-throated Green, winter regularly but sparingly in the West Indies; the vast majority are found during this season in Central America. Several species, notably the Cape May, Prairie and Palm, seem deliberately to seek islands on which to pass the winter months. These occur in some numbers on islands off the Caribbean coast of Central America, but are either absent or casual on the adjacent mainland.

By April most of the winter resident warblers are conditioned for their long and hazardous migrations to their breeding grounds in northern woodlands. As the time approaches for their departure they often associate in little flocks and move restlessly among the foliage. Occasionally one will sing, but the song is usually half-hearted, although readily recognizable. It is astonishing to hear a Northern Waterthrush singing in the depths of a tropical mangrove swamp! Apart from frequent chipping, northern warblers are usually silent at other times of the year in their winter ranges, although I have heard a Black-and-White Warbler in full song in Port-au-Prince in early January. By May, the majority have departed, but occasional individuals are seen during that month. In the case of Redstarts these are chiefly females and immature males.

The following list comprises warblers that are winter resident in the West Indies with inclusive known dates of their occurrence on these islands:

BLACK-AND-WHITE WARBLER:
    July 29–May 25

SWAINSON'S WARBLER:
    Sept. 25–April 14
WORM-EATING WARBLER:
    Aug. 18–May 5
BACHMAN'S WARBLER:
    Sept. 7–March 16
PARULA WARBLER: Aug. 4–May 14
MAGNOLIA WARBLER:
    Sept. 10–May 4
CAPE MAY WARBLER:
    Sept. 15–May 17
BLACK-THROATED BLUE WARBLER:
    Sept. 7–May 11
MYRTLE WARBLER: Oct. 1–April 28
BLACK-THROATED GREEN WARBLER:
    Sept. 30–May 6
YELLOW-THROATED WARBLER:
    July 11–April 29
PRAIRIE WARBLER: Aug. 1–May 8
KIRTLAND'S WARBLER:
    "October"–May 5
PALM WARBLER: Sept. 20–May 12
OVENBIRD: "August"–May 18
NORTHERN WATERTHRUSH:
    Aug. 20–May 20; casual early summer records
LOUISIANA WATERTHRUSH:
    July 14–April 22
COMMON YELLOWTHROAT:
    Sept. 7–May 11; 2 June records
AMERICAN REDSTART:
    July 28–May 25; 1 June record

Much less is known about the West Indian transients than of the winter residents, for these are on the islands for very limited periods en route to or from their wintering grounds in Central or South America. Most of the information we have on these is recent and has been acquired by resident naturalists. Many are not as rare among the islands as has been presumed. For my part, I have encountered only the Yellow, the Blackpoll and the Bay-breasted Warblers, although I have seen all of the winter resident species with the exception of Bachman's Warbler.

It appears that the principal migration route of the transients in the West Indies is by way of the Bahamas, Cuba and Jamaica. Apart from the Black-poll, there are not more than twelve records of the regular transient warblers east of Cuba. There is no evidence to substantiate the theory that the eastern islands form "stepping stones" for these birds or other migrants moving to or from South America.

The Blackpoll is the only one of the transients that occurs throughout the West Indies, but its occurrence is sporadic in the Lesser Antilles, where I have never seen it in April or May. This warbler was reported in great numbers on Grenada in late November, 1955, but apparently was not present at St. Lucia during this period. Blackpoll Warblers are apt to dawdle on autumnal migration, particularly as they approach their wintering grounds. On the other hand, they pass through the islands very rapidly in spring and are easily overlooked.

Other West Indian transients that winter in South America are the Cerulean, Blackburnian, Bay-breasted and Connecticut Warblers. There are no definite records of the Cerulean and Blackburnian east of Cuba, and only two of the Bay-breasted Warbler east of that island. The migration route taken by the Connecticut Warbler has still to be ascertained. Since there are no records of this species from Central America, it has been presumed that it migrates across the Caribbean Sea, but up to the present time there are only four records from the West Indies—three from the Bahamas, and one from Mona Island between Puerto Rico and Hispaniola.

The only other habitual transients of this family are the Prothonotary, Tennessee, Yellow, Chestnut-sided and Hooded Warblers, all of which winter for the most part in Central America. The Prothonotary and Hooded Warblers have been recorded with increasing frequency in recent years, the latter from as far east as Saba. North American Yellow Warblers migrate to some extent through western Cuba and a few individuals may winter on the southernmost Lesser Antilles, whence they have been recorded from late September to early December. The species is a common winter resident in Trinidad, presumably reaching that island from the west and by way of Central America.

Known dates of the regular transients in the West Indies are as follows:

PROTHONOTARY WARBLER:
    Sept. 14–Oct. 7; Feb. 28–April 7
TENNESSEE WARBLER:
    Sept. 28–Nov. 10; March 31–May 5
YELLOW WARBLER:
    Sept. 2–Sept. 10; April 21–May 8 (Cuban dates)
CERULEAN WARBLER:
    Aug. 7–Sept. 15; "April."
BLACKBURNIAN WARBLER:
    Aug. 9–Nov. 2; April 11–May 21
CHESTNUT-SIDED WARBLER:
    Sept. 11–Oct. 31; April 20–May 11
BAY-BREASTED WARBLER:
    Sept. 28–Oct. 31; April 7–May 7

John H. Dick.

John H. Dick

PLATE 31

(top row left to right)

Gray-throated Chat (*Granatellus sallaei*) Mexico
Yellow-headed Warbler (*Teretistris fernandinae*) Cuba
Crescent-chested (Hartlaub's) Warbler (*Vermivora superciliosa*) Mexico

(second row left to right)

Three-striped Warbler (*Basileuterus tristriatus*) Panama, Costa Rica, Colombia, Peru, Ecuador
Black-cheeked Warbler (*Basileuterus melanogenys*) Panama, Costa Rica
Red Warbler (*Ergaticus ruber*) Mexico

(third row left to right)

Green-tailed Ground Warbler (*Microligea palustris*) Beata Island
Yellow-crowned Yellowthroat (*Geothlypis flavovelata*) Mexico
Black-polled Yellowthroat (*Geothlypis speciosa*) Mexico

BLACKPOLL WARBLER:
Sept. 24–Dec. 9; April 1–May 24
CONNECTICUT WARBLER:
Oct. 6–Oct. 14; May 17
HOODED WARBLER:
Aug. 27–Oct. 15; February 19–April 16

Finally, there are six species of North American warblers that are so rare in the West Indies that they can hardly be considered more than vagrants to this region, and a record from any of the islands should be reported. These are the Golden-winged, Blue-winged, Kentucky, Mourning, Wilson's and Canada Warblers, which habitually migrate to or through Central America. All are probably very rare transients and some may winter sparingly. The very fact of locating even one of these warblers on a large island is an indication that others are present. This thought struck me forcibly when I collected a Lincoln's Sparrow in dense rain forest in Jamaica, the first definite record of the species from the West Indies. It seemed to me inconceivable that this was the only one of its kind on the island!

It will be noted that almost all of the warblers that breed in eastern North America have been reported from the West Indies. Those that are still unknown from the region are the Nashville Warbler and Yellow-breasted Chat. Both have been found on the Florida Keys and may occur as transients. In addition, the western Orange-crowned Warbler, which winters south to Key West, should be looked for during that season in western Cuba. Most surprising is the apparent absence in the West Indies of the distinct eastern race of the Palm Warbler (the "Yellow Palm Warbler"), in view of the abundance of the western race in Cuba. There have been sight identifications of this subspecies, but these are not acceptable since no authentic record based on a specimen has been obtained.

JAMES BOND

CHAPTER 11

Arrow-headed Warbler

THE RESIDENT WOOD WARBLERS
OF THE WEST INDIES

A VISITOR to the West Indies from the north may be impressed with the general similarity of the avifauna with that of North America. Although many of the birds will be strange to him, the majority are members of widespread North American families, and the songs he hears in fields or woodlands are apt to recall nostalgic memories of New England or other parts of eastern North America. True, there are a few exotic tropical birds in the West Indies, such as the todies and the two trogons, but these are rare exceptions.

The southernmost of the Antilles is Grenada, for the avifauna of Trinidad and Tobago is typically Neotropical, characterized by many South American families, many of which have worked their way northward into Central America since the formation of the Panama isthmus, but have failed to reach the West Indies because of water barriers. If Trinidad and Tobago were included as part of the West Indies the number of indigenous genera of land birds would be more than doubled and many families would be added to the region!

The fifteen resident species of West Indian wood warblers have North American affinities, at least for the most part. These comprise six species included in four endemic Antillean genera (*Catharopeza, Leucopeza, Microligea* and *Teretistris*), the Bahaman Yellowthroat (*Geothlypis*) and as many as eight species of the diversified northern genus *Dendroica*.

The most widespread and familiar warbler in the West Indies is the YELLOW WARBLER (*Dendroica petechia*), a species that exhibits much racial variation (Plates 10, 32). In the Bahamas and Greater Antilles, Yellow Warblers (sometimes called "Golden Warblers") resemble those of North America, but in the Lesser Antilles and elsewhere in the Caribbean area the adult males have more or less chestnut crowns. Those of Martinique have the entire head chestnut like the Mangrove Warblers of Central and northern South America. This is the only Antillean species of warbler that shows pronounced sexual dimorphism.

On the larger Greater Antilles, Yellow Warblers are almost entirely confined to the coastal mangroves, but on the smaller islands of the eastern Caribbean they are also found in gardens and shade trees in fairly open country at low elevations. Their songs resemble the more nondescript ones of North American forms, but are occasionally more melodious. Their nests and eggs are likewise characteristic of the species. Clutch size varies from two to three, three being the normal number in the Greater Antilles, two in the Lesser Antilles. The nesting season is remarkably prolonged, but is principally from April until July. I once found a nest with eggs on Grand Cayman as early as March 5.

The PINE WARBLER (D. pinus) is another North American species that is native to the West Indies, where it inhabits the pine forests of Hispaniola and northwestern Bahamas. Habits and songs are similar to those of North American forms. No nests have been reported from the West Indies, but individuals in breeding condition have been collected in May and early June in the mountains of Hispaniola.

A well-marked subspecies of the YELLOW-THROATED WARBLER (D. dominica) inhabits the pine barrens of Grand Bahama and Abaco. This differs from North American races principally by having the entire breast and abdomen yellow. In habits and in the quality of its song it resembles those that breed on the continent and occur as winter residents on these islands.

The Cayman and Swan Islands, in the heart of the Caribbean Sea, are inhabited by the VITELLINE WARBLER (D. vitellina), the West Indian representative of the Prairie Warbler, a common winter resident on the islands. It differs chiefly by lacking the bold black streaking on the underparts and sides of head (Plate 32). Like the Prairie Warbler it inhabits dense scrub, and its song, nest and eggs are not dissimilar; but an occasional song reminded me more of the Black-throated Blue Warbler. Nests found on Grand Cayman in April and May were well built cups composed largely of cottonlike fibers (Gossypium) with soft inner linings of feathers, situated from two to eight feet above the ground. As is the case with many other West Indian birds, the nest is sometimes finished a week or more before laying begins. As far as known, but two eggs comprise a clutch.

In the pine lands of western and eastern Cuba, and on the northernmost Bahama Islands (viz. Grand Bahama and Abaco) lives the OLIVE-CAPPED WARBLER (D. pityophila), a West Indian representative of Grace's Warbler, which inhabits western North America, Mexico and northern Central America. It differs from that species partly by having a yellowish olive-green crown and by lacking the conspicuous black streaking on the sides and flanks (Plate 32). Although found side by side with the Pine Warbler in its Bahaman range, the Olive-capped Warbler is more apt to be seen among the smaller trees. Its song is variable and difficult to describe. One rendering may be given as a rather shrill, rapidly uttered *wisi-wisi-wisi-wiseu-wiseu*. Some Pine Warbler songs are somewhat like it. Olive-capped Warblers breed in April and May. The only nest that has been recorded was situated well out on the horizontal limb of a pine about thirty feet above the ground, and was invisible from below. The frail cup contained two young almost ready to leave on June 13.

Another West Indian representative of Grace's Warbler is ADELAIDE'S WARBLER (*D. adelaidae*) of Puerto Rico, Vieques Island, Barbuda and St. Lucia (Plate 32). This species completely lacks the black streaking on both upperparts and underparts, and the entire breast and abdomen are yellow. Adelaide's Warbler mainly inhabits dense thickets and, except in St. Lucia, is found only at low elevations. The St. Lucian race, one of the most abundant and widespread birds of that island, is also found in mountain forest and is sometimes seen in trees high above the ground. The song is a variable trill, more melodious as sung by Lesser Antillean individuals in comparison with those of Puerto Rico. The frail, cup-shaped nest is situated in a bush from three to eight feet above the ground in Puerto Rico: one found in St. Lucia was ten feet up, well hidden among vines. The presence of a few feathers in the lining appears to be a characteristic feature. So far as known, this species lays three eggs in

Puerto Rico, two in St. Lucia. Apparently the female alone incubates, but the male takes part in the brooding and feeding of the young. The habit of "injury feigning" has been noted. As is the case with the Yellow Warbler, the breeding season extends over a considerable period, in Puerto Rico from March until June.

The two remaining resident West Indian *Dendroicae*, the ARROW-HEADED WARBLER (*D. pharetra*), and the PLUMBEOUS WARBLER (*D. plumbea*), are not closely related to any continental species, but similarities in their immature plumages suggest that they themselves may be allied.

The ARROW-HEADED WARBLER is confined to Jamaica, where it occurs chiefly at high elevations in mountain rain forest (Plate 33). It is found sparingly at much lower elevations in cool, well wooded ravines such as Fern Gully. The black and white streaked plumage is suggestive of a Black-and-White Warbler, but the Arrow-headed Warbler differs greatly from that species in behavior. It is less active than most warblers, and is usually seen moving leisurely through the forest undergrowth, occasionally foraging among the tall trees, with a constant flirting of the tail. The call-note is a soft *git*, quite different from the chip of a migrant warbler. Its regular song, heard during the breeding season in May and June, is a weak, very rapidly uttered trill that reminds one of the song of the Worm-eating Warbler. I once heard a male sing a prolonged and melodious "whisper song" just prior to copulation.

The cup-shaped nest of the Arrow-headed Warbler, although thin and in appearance frail, is in reality strongly built in order to withstand the torrential rains, for this warbler nests during the height of the first rainy season. The only occupied nest that has been recorded was situated in a sapling about seven feet above the ground, and contained two slightly incubated eggs on June 24. The construction of this nest was seemingly completed a week before an egg was laid, but this is not unusual among West Indian birds. Although mated pairs of these warblers are often seen during the winter months, this is not an indication that the breeding season is at hand.

The PLUMBEOUS WARBLER is a rather plain little bird, gray above and grayish white below, with two white wing-bars and a conspicuous white superciliary stripe (Plate 32). This species is confined to Guadeloupe, Marie Galante and Dominica, where it is most abundant in mountain forest. Occasionally one encounters an individual in the lowlands, near sea level. Its habits and habitat are like those of the Arrow-headed Warbler, and like that species, it twitches its tail continually as it moves among the undergrowth. The song may be described as a short, rather plaintive de-de-diu and is one of the few bird sounds heard in the rugged mountains of Guadeloupe. The nest is a roughly constructed cup, composed of leaves and rootlets with a soft lining of grass stems, and is situated in a bush or sapling. Occupied nests with clutches of two eggs have been found in April and May.

The humid, often cloud-covered, mountain forest of St. Vincent is inhabited by the WHISTLING WARBLER (Catharopeza bishopi), a colorless but most attractive little bird. Adults are blackish above, the underparts mostly whitish, the throat and a band across the upper breast black. There is a conspicuous white eye-ring. Immature individuals are entirely brownish (Plate 33).

In the field the Whistling Warbler sometimes appears wrenlike with tail cocked and wings drooping, although its habits in general are warblerlike. It is usually encountered in the undergrowth of the forest, but is occasionally seen high in the trees. The song is superlative and may be described as a rapid flow of short, rich notes, crescendo in effect. The call-note is a short tuck, reminiscent of that of the Olive-backed Thrush but much weaker. Nothing is definitely known of the nidification of this warbler, but it is said to build a cup-shaped nest in a sapling and to lay two eggs. The breeding season is in April and May, and I have noted young not long out of the nest in June.

On the neighboring island of St. Lucia is found the excessively rare SEMPER'S WARBLER (Leucopeza semperi), a very plain, nondescript species with dark gray upperparts and whitish underparts (Plate 33). During many weeks exploration of the island I have never seen, nor even heard, this bird, which is probably on the verge of extinction, although it was apparently not uncommon many years ago. Semper's Warbler is known to inhabit forest undergrowth and may nest on or very near the ground like the majority of tropical warblers, and consequently have suffered from the depredations of the mongoose. Nothing is known of its song, but it is said to chatter when alarmed.

The Whistling Warbler and Semper's Warbler represent monotypic Lesser Antillean genera. In the Greater Antilles there are likewise two endemic warbler genera, the Cuban *Teretistris* and the Hispaniolan *Microligea*, each comprising two species.

The two warblers of the genus *Teretistris* are allopatric, in other words, are not found side by side. The YELLOW-HEADED WARBLER (*T. fernandinae*) is confined to western Cuba and the Isle of Pines, the ORIENTE WARBLER (*T. fornsi*) to eastern Cuba. There is a considerable area in central Cuba where neither species occurs. Although distinctly different in coloration, these warblers are similar in other respects and are evidently very closely related. The Yellow-headed Warbler is mostly gray above and grayish white below; the head is strikingly yellow, but is darker, more greenish, on the crown and hind neck (Plate 31). The Oriente Warbler is entirely grayish above, and the yellow of the underparts extends to the breast and abdomen (Plate 33). Both species inhabit undergrowth and low woodland in both humid and arid districts, where they move about in a leisurely fashion like vireos. They seem equally at home in cool mountain forest as among xerophytic growth in hot, coastal areas. In winter they occasionally associate with winter resident North American warblers, in addition to Cuban Vireos, Stripe-headed Tanagers and other of the native passerines. The Yellow-headed Warbler and Oriente Warbler utter weak, rasping notes that can hardly be called songs. The nests of both are situated in shrubs, vines or saplings at low or moderate elevations above the ground. They are rather roughly con-structed little cups without soft inner linings. Two to three eggs are laid in April and May.

Unlike the two species of *Teretistris*, the GREEN-TAILED GROUND WARBLER (*Microligea palustris*), and the WHITE-WINGED GROUND WARBLER (*M. montana*) of Hispaniola are sympatric, for they are found side by side in the mountains. Both species are local in distribution, but the former is more widespread and occurs in mountain rain forest as well as in the lowlands, even in semi-arid districts.

The GREEN-TAILED GROUND WARBLER is rather nondescript. In the adult the crown and hind neck are gray, the remainder of the upperparts green. The underparts are mostly grayish white. There is an incomplete white eye-ring (Plate 31). I have encountered this warbler only in the mountains where it inhabits dense shrubbery and growths of bracken. In such lush thickets, the bird moves about in a leisurely manner, sometimes in pairs even during the winter months. Its behavior suggests that of a Yellowthroat, but it is much more deliberate in its actions. Its flight is short and tilting. The song, if "song" one may call it, is a curious weak rasping sound like that of a small bird in distress. A nest found in the Massif de la Selle in southeastern Haiti was situated in a dense, privetlike shrub, another in a blackberry bush; both were within four feet of the ground. The nests are cup-shaped and closely resemble those of Cuban warblers of the genus *Teretistris*. The eggs, two in number, differ from those of other West Indian warblers in having a pale greenish ground-color. The breeding season in the mountains is at its height in late May and early June, but it may be much earlier in the lowlands, for such is the case with other birds of Hispaniola.

The WHITE-WINGED GROUND WARBLER is confined to the higher mountains, and is one of the few birds restricted to the Subtropical Zone of Hispaniola. It somewhat resembles the preceding species, but the underparts are white and there is a prominent white wing-patch, an excellent field character (Plate 33). Moreover, the tail is very different, gray instead of green, with broad white tips to the outer feathers. The bill is shorter and thicker. In habits it is more active, frequents more open thickets, and is apt to be seen higher in the undergrowth. The name "Ground Warbler" is thus inappropriate for this bird, although I have found the two species in close association both in winter and summer. Occasionally the White-winged Ground Warbler utters a low chattering. This is apparently the extent of its singing ability. Nothing is known of its nidification, but individuals that have been collected in early June were in breeding condition.

The only other species of warbler native to the West Indies is the BAHAMAN YELLOWTHROAT (*Geothlypis rostrata*), which is found only on the northwestern Bahama Islands. It closely resembles the familiar Common Yellowthroat of North America (*G. trichas*), but is larger with a noticeably longer and thicker bill. It is most abundant on the northernmost islands, where it frequents the dense shrubbery and bracken of the pine barrens. The song is quite variable and to my ear virtually indistinguishable from that of Yellowthroats of Pennsylvania and the southeastern United States, but is usually louder. The call-note is decidedly less harsh than that of *trichas*. In mid-March at High-Rock Settlement, Grand Bahama, the early morning singing of Bahaman Yellowthroats dominated all other bird song. The breeding season evidently commences about this time of year and extends well into June when a nest with two young was found on Eleuthera. This was cup-shaped and situated in a cavity on top of a tree stub between two and three feet above the ground in a temporarily dry mangrove swamp. Both male and female attended the young.

Although the distribution and habitat requirements of West Indian wood-warblers are well-known, no comprehensive life-history study of any of the species has as yet been undertaken in this region. The Whistling Warbler of St. Vincent and the Ground Warblers of Hispaniola offer particularly attractive inducements for such work. Much may be accomplished even in a limited period thanks to modern air transport. The main requirement is the zest to do so.

JAMES BOND

CHAPTER 12

MIGRANT WOOD WARBLERS IN THEIR CENTRAL AMERICAN WINTER HOMES

THE WOOD WARBLERS are too dependent upon heat and insect food to withstand the severe winters of the northern lands where so many of them find conditions favorable for breeding in the summer months. Although the majority of the tropical members of the family reside permanently in the regions where they nest, all of those which breed well beyond the tropics are more or less migratory. Some individuals of the hardier species, which include fruit or seeds in their diet and can endure cold, manage to pass at least part of the winter amid snow and ice, although still well to the south of their far northern breeding area. Among these are the Myrtle Warbler, Audubon's Warbler, and the Palm Warbler. Most, however, seek low latitudes where snow never falls, performing great migratory journeys, chiefly by

night, an arrangement which permits them to hunt food as soon as day breaks and their long flight ends. Some warblers cross wide stretches of the Caribbean Sea or the Gulf of México. Others follow the land route through México, or take advantage of the Antilles to shorten their flights across the water.

Perhaps if we knew enough about the ancestral history of the several species of warblers we should understand just why each kind chooses the wintering area it at present uses. But in the absence of a fossil record which might enable us to reconstruct this history, the warblers' choice of a winter home seems in some instances capricious almost to the point of absurdity. Could anything be more improbable than that a small bird which nests only in a restricted area in the southern peninsula of

269

Michigan should winter only in the Bahama Islands, as is true of Kirtland's Warbler? Why should the Blackpoll, Bay-breasted and Cerulean Warblers make the long journey to South America, to sojourn in Andean valleys or the Guiana forests, while so many other species, which nest in the same regions as these far travellers, find a congenial winter home much closer to their breeding area, in México, Central America, or the West Indies? The one generalization we can make about the migrations of the wood warblers is that species which breed in the mountains of western North America tend to winter in the highlands of México and northern Central America, whereas those which nest in the east or far north are far more erratic in their choice of a winter abode.

In the months of the northern winter, some species concentrate in a small area whereas others disperse over a vast area. Among the former is the Chestnut-sided Warbler, whose winter range extends only from southern Nicaragua to central Panamá, an area very much smaller than the far-flung breeding range of the species in the United States and Canada. With birds from such an extensive region funneling into the narrow lower end of the Central American isthmus, they are naturally rather crowded there; and in Costa Rica, the heart of this limited wintering range, the Chestnut-sided Warbler is, at lower altitudes, a very abundant winter visitor. In contrast to the Chestnut-sided Warbler, the Black-and-White Warbler spreads in winter over many lands, including Florida, the Greater Antilles, much of México, nearly all of Central America, and north-western South America; and since the species is then so scattered, it is rarely found in abundance in any district. Still more tolerant in its choice of a winter home is the hardy Myrtle Warbler. One December I met these adaptable little birds in sere fields in Maryland, amidst melting snow within sight of the skyscrapers of New York, and on a verdant banana plantation in Guatemala, far from winter's chill.

Just as the resident birds of the tropics have definite altitudinal preferences, so the winter visitors choose particular vertical zones. During the spring and fall migrations one may encounter a species at almost any elevation within its extended migration route; but in mid-winter, when each bird has settled in its southern home, the altitudinal preferences of the several species are clearly evident. Among the heat-loving species which settle down at low or moderate altitudes are the Yellow Warbler, Chestnut-sided Warbler, Magnolia Warbler, American Redstart, Mourning Warbler, Common Yellowthroat, Ovenbird, Kentucky Warbler, Yellow-breasted Chat, and others. On the other hand, a number of hardy warblers prefer the high mountains, where frost forms on the open fields each clear and windless night while the sun is in the southern hemisphere and a man can hardly find enough blankets to keep himself warm while he sleeps. Among these dwellers in the highlands are Townsend's Warbler, Audubon's Warbler, Hermit Warbler, and MacGillivray's Warbler. Other species, including the Black-throated Green Warbler, Blackburnian Warbler, and Tennessee Warbler, have their center of abundance at middle elevations, from two or three to six or seven thousand feet above sea level, although some individuals may be found higher or lower than this. It is significant that the Black-and-White Warbler and the Myrtle Warbler, which pass the winter in such widely separated regions, have also a wide vertical distribution; and I have seen them in mid-winter at altitudes ranging from sea level up to 8500 or 9000 feet in the mountains.

Within each altitudinal belt, the wintering warblers find a great variety of habitats, and each selects the vegetation most congenial to it. Both among the resident birds and the visitors, restriction to a particular type of vegetation is more definite in the species which live on or near the ground than in those which forage well up in the trees; and this is understandable when one recalls that the topmost boughs of a tree in the midst of heavy forest may receive almost as much light as the crown of a tree standing isolated in a clearing, whereas the birds of the forest undergrowth dwell in a sort of perpetual twilight which contrasts sharply with the bright sunshine near ground level in fields and pastures. The one warbler which I have found wintering regularly in the dim undergrowth of the lowland rain-forests is the Kentucky. Indeed, this is the only species, resident or migratory, which represents the family in this habitat, where it mingles with antbirds, manakins, anttanagers, tinamous, and other distinctly tropical birds. At higher levels in the rain-forests one finds Chestnut-sided Warblers, Tennessee Warblers, Golden-winged Warblers, Black-and-White Warblers and American Redstarts; but none of these foragers in the treetops is so closely restricted to the heavier woodland as the shade-loving Kentucky Warbler.

Avoiding the dark forests, the Yellow Warbler chooses for its winter quarters bushy pastures, hedgerows, or dooryard shrubbery, and in the Central American lowlands is as closely associated with humans as on its northern breeding grounds. The pruned trees which provide a light shade for the coffee plantations at middle altitudes are attractive to the Tennessee Warblers, which at mid-winter swarm through them in incredible numbers. Mourning Warblers and MacGillivray's Warblers prefer fields with low, dense vegetation, the former in the lowlands, the latter at high elevations. The Northern and Louisiana Waterthrushes haunt the watercourses in their winter as in their summer homes, but in the tropics they also forage over trimmed lawns or bare ground at a distance from water, often close about the dwellings of men, although they are shy and take flight as soon as a human appears. Species which breed in coniferous forests may also winter among conifers in the highlands and even at lower elevations in northern Central America; but when, as with the Black-throated Green Warbler and the Blackburnian Warbler, they pass south of Nicaragua, they must perforce adjust themselves to broad-leafed trees.

The several species of wintering warblers differ as much in their social habits as in their choice of altitudes and types of vegetation. Among the most social are the Townsend's Warblers that winter in the high mountains of northern Central America, where they form the nucleus of the mixed flocks of small birds, resident and migratory, that wander through the highland forests after the close of the breeding season. It is of interest that some birds which in the non-breeding season are intolerant of their own kind, as the Black-and-White Warbler, the Red-faced Warbler, and the Guatemalan race of the Slate-throated Redstart (*Myioborus miniatus*) (Plate 32), join these mixed flocks for companionship. But only one individual of each of these species is to be found in a flock, and it attempts to drive away an intruder of its own kind although it lives on the friendliest terms with birds of other kinds. Audubon's and Myrtle Warblers are also gregarious and at times keep close company with bigger birds of other families. In the Guatemalan highlands, I often met Audubon's Warblers hunting over the open pastures with resident Bluebirds; while on a savanna in southern Costa Rica Myrtle Warblers associated closely with Fork-tailed Flycatchers. Although one often finds countless Tennessee Warblers in the shade trees of a coffee plantation, they are crowded rather than truly gregarious and do not travel in definite flocks. But most of the wintering warblers, especially at lower elevations, are solitary, each individual going its own way and resenting rather than seeking the proximity of others of its kind.

Some kinds of warblers claim winter territories; and in the autumn, when the birds arrive, there may be disputes for the possession of a suitable area. At this time I have often heard two Black-and-White Warblers singing against each other, with frequent chases, this behavior sometimes continuing for days until at last boundaries were agreed upon. Once in October I watched two Yellow Warblers acting in the same fashion; and in a garden in the Guatemalan highlands, at this season, I found two newly arrived Wilson's (Pileolated) Warblers fighting earnestly on the ground, apparently for possession of the garden. As the time for the northward withdrawal approaches, these territorial rivalries seem to be forgotten and the birds draw together for their long and perilous journey.

In their winter abode, the migrant warblers choose on the whole the same type of food that they eat on their breeding grounds. They are still predominantly insectivorous, although they can seldom find just the same species of insects and spiders in Central or South America as in northern United States or Canada. Tennessee Warblers come in numbers to eat bananas and plantains at my feeding shelf and are the only members of the family that do so.

Among the peculiar vegetable foods which the warblers find in the tropics are the protein corpuscles from the hairy cushion at the base of the long petiole of the broad, palmate leaf of the cecropia tree. These little pearly bodies, no bigger than a mustard seed, are the staple food of the azteca ants which dwell in the thick, hollow stems of these lanky, rapidly growing trees of warm and humid regions. But if the ants overlook a corpuscle, it stands out prominently from the brown fur that covers the cushion and is eagerly sought by a number of migratory as well as resident birds. A daintier morsel for a small bird is nowhere to be found.

Sometimes I have had the good fortune

to discover the sleeping places of the visiting warblers. From November until February, a Yellow Warbler roosted nightly on the leaf-stalk of a hibiscus bush close beside my cabin by the Río Buena Vista. Later I found two Tennessee Warblers and a Black-and-White Warbler sleeping on slender twigs of a cashew tree in our garden. Both kinds of warblers sometimes roosted with one foot clutching the perch and the other drawn up into the fluffed-out plumage. This method of roosting seemed practical when the two Tennessee Warblers slept pressed together, as they sometimes did. All three kinds of warblers rested beneath broad leaves that formed a roof over their heads on rainy nights but were exposed at the sides. Their heads were turned back and buried in their plumage, and they were not easily aroused from their slumber.

Except in the territorial disputes already mentioned, the warblers rarely sing after their arrival in Central America in the autumn. However, on a Guatemalan coffee plantation I found a Yellow Warbler who sang most persistently for several days in October, although I could discover no rival. During the winter months the migratory warblers scarcely ever sing, although each freely repeats its call-note as it forages. As the time for their northward journey approaches and the males don their bright nuptial attire, they not infrequently sing, although of course far less than they will soon do on their breeding grounds. Sometimes this sporadic singing begins as early as February. Among the wintering warblers which I have heard singing gaily in Central America are the Yellow Warbler, the Chestnut-sided Warbler, the Black-throated Green Warbler, Townsend's Warbler, Common Yellowthroat, Wilson's Warbler, and the Waterthrushes. But I have more records of singing by the Mourning Warbler in Costa Rica than of any other. Doubtless more extended observations would show that most or all of the warblers sing occasionally in their winter abode.

Some of the migratory warblers are, as species, present in their winter range for well over half the year. The Yellow Warbler has been recorded in northern Central America from early August until the middle of May, so that it is absent from the region for less than three months out of the twelve. Although it arrives equally early in autumn, the Black-and-White Warbler withdraws earlier in spring, so that its period of absence from Central America is somewhat over three months. On a farm in the Guatemalan highlands in 1933, I recorded the last Wilson's Warbler of spring on May 22 and the first of the autumn on September 3, so that its period of absence from this single locality was three months and twelve days. On this same mountain in the same year, Townsend's Warbler was absent exactly four months, from May 2 to September 2. In southern Costa Rica where it winters in great numbers, the Chestnut-sided Warbler is absent for about five months, from mid- or late April to past the middle of September. At the other extreme, the Myrtle Warbler, more tolerant of cold than most members of its family, has a far briefer sojourn in the tropics, being rarely seen in Central America before November or even December and usually withdrawing before the first of April. Thus the period of its presence in Central America is only about half as long as that of the Yellow Warbler. All of these statements refer to species rather than to individuals. We lack observations of banded birds which might show how long any individual remains in its winter home.

In many parts of Central America, migrants from the north form, during the winter months, a large proportion of the total avian population; and in many districts the wood warblers are, in species and individuals, the family best represented among these visitors. The departure, chiefly from late March to early May, of this vast multitude of migratory birds leaves far more food for the breeding residents, most of which start to nest at about the time the temporary population begins to dwindle. This is especially true of the resident passerines, which are just the birds whose food must be shared with the host of visiting passerines, among which are the warblers. The withdrawal of so many mouths appears to be one of the factors which make May and June the period which the resident passerines find most favorable for rearing their young, because at this time food for them is most readily available.

ALEXANDER F. SKUTCH

Collared Redstart

CHAPTER 13

Buff-rumped Warbler

THE RESIDENT WOOD WARBLERS
OF CENTRAL AMERICA

As one stands in tropical lowlands with his eyes raised to some snow-capped peak, he embraces in a single glance the major climatic zones of the earth. About him is the Tropical Zone, with its characteristic vegetable and animal life. Above him on the flanks of the mountains this merges into the Subtropical and then the Temperate Zone, whose life is very different from that of the lowlands. Higher still, the trees give way to shrubs, alpine meadows, or the coarse grasses and low bushes of the páramo; and this corresponds to the Subarctic regions at high latitudes. Finally, the everlasting snowfields of the mountain summit represent the frozen Arctic or Antarctic wastes. The transition from zone to zone is usually gradual rather than abrupt. The altitude at which it occurs varies with latitude and exposure, yet is on the whole surprisingly uniform over the whole broad belt between the Tropics of Cancer and of Capricorn. Beyond the tropics, no mountain range, however high, can exhibit an equally wide range of climatic zones; for the simple reason that the mountain's base itself lies in the Temperate or the Arctic Zone, and warmer zones are excluded. These altitudinal variations in temperature and exposure, combined with the great differences in rainfall which often occur on opposite sides of a tropical mountain chain, account for the vast diversity of birds in a mountainous tropical country, which may support more species than are to be found in a far larger country that lies beyond the tropics.

In mountainous regions of the tropics, many families of birds have definite altitudinal preferences. Parrots, antbirds, tan-

PLATE 32

(*top row left to right*)

Vitelline Warbler (*Dendroica vitellina*) Swan Island
Olive-capped Warbler (*Dendroica pityophila*) Grand Bahama
Adelaide's Warbler (*Dendroica adelaidae*) St. Lucia

(*second row left to right*)

Plumbeous Warbler (*Dendroica plumbea*) Guadeloupe
(*above*) Slate-throated Redstart (*Myioborus miniatus connectens*)
   Guatemala, Northern South America to Bolivia
(*below*) Slate-throated Redstart (*Myioborus miniatus aurantiacus*)
   Costa Rica
Yellow Warbler (*Dendroica petechia petechia*) Barbados

(*third row left to right*)

Golden-browed Warbler (*Basileuterus belli*) Mexico
(*above*) Rufous-capped Warbler (*Basileuterus rufifrons*)
   Mexico
(*below*) Chestnut-capped Warbler (*Basileuterus delattrii*)
   Costa Rica, Colombia, Panama

John H. Dick

John H. Dick

agers, and honeycreepers are most abundant, in species and individuals, in the warm lowlands and become increasingly rare as one ascends the cool heights. Thrushes, jays, and wood warblers are more in evidence in the mountains than in the lowlands. The hummingbirds, so hardy and adaptable, are well represented by species and individuals at all elevations from the coastal plains up to the bleak páramos, with many of the most ornate kinds occurring in the altitudinal Temperate Zone. This vertical distribution of the bird families is to a certain extent paralleled by their latitudinal distribution. Thus antbirds and honeycreepers are scarcely known northward or southward of the tropics, while the parrot and tanager families are poorly represented there. But thrushes, jays, and wood warblers are abundant in northern regions.

The warblers which breed in Central America are, then, with a few exceptions birds of medium or high altitudes. They further differ from the warblers of the United States and Canada in that, as far as I know, they are all non-migratory, passing the whole year in the regions where they nest. Correlated with their sedentary life are certain striking differences in plumage and habits. Many of them remain in pairs throughout the year, an arrangement which birds of many kinds find satisfactory but which the highly migratory species can hardly achieve. Some, and possibly most, of the tropical warblers choose their mates soon after becoming independent of their parents, when only a few months old. Thus they pair in autumn rather than in spring, as with the migratory species. Moreover, in many species, including some of the most brightly colored, male and female are scarcely to be distinguished by their plumage, in this contrasting sharply with the migratory warblers, whose males, if gaily clad, usually have mates far duller than themselves. This brilliant adult plumage of both sexes is often acquired in the autumn, at about the time the birds mate, rather than in the late winter or spring, as with the migratory members of the family. And in these sedentary warblers of the tropics, seasonal changes in coloration, so pronounced in many migratory species, are slight or lacking.

These contrasts between the sedentary and migratory members of the same family are by no means peculiar to the wood warblers. In a number of families, especially among the more colorful songbirds, the migratory habit encourages striking sexual differences in plumage, or seasonal changes in coloration, or both together, along with the delayed acquisition of the adult attire, especially in the brighter males. Thus in the *Icteridae* or troupial family, the Bobolink, which travels farther than any other species, exhibits great sexual differences in plumage along with extensive annual changes in the more ornate male. In the Baltimore and Orchard Orioles, which perform shorter migrations, the male is far more colorful than the female but wears the same gay attire at all seasons. But in many of the non-migratory orioles of the tropics, male and female are equally brilliant in their yellow and black plumage, and they never go into eclipse. Similarly, the greatest traveller of all the tanagers, the Scarlet Tanager, is the only species of which the male loses all his bright color in the winter. The male Western Tanager, which does not migrate as far, exhibits seasonal changes in appearance which are much less pronounced; while the Summer Tanager, whose winter and summer homes are much closer together than in the case of the Scarlet Tanager, shows sexual but not seasonal differences in coloration. In a large number of the most gorgeous non-migratory tanagers of the tropics the sexes are difficult to distinguish, and they wear the same brilliant colors at all seasons.

One is led to ask whether these differences in plumage in the migratory and non-migratory members of the same family have led to corresponding differences in domestic arrangements. As is well known, in the migratory wood warblers of the United States and Canada, as in a number of other families of songbirds, the brighter male never sits in the nest to warm the eggs or young. It is often held that this is because his more vivid hues would betray it to predators. But this reason for abstention from incubation and brooding is lacking to those males of tropical species which are not significantly brighter than their mates. Furthermore, many of these tropical birds breed in covered nests which hide their bright hues from hostile eyes. Thus there appears to be no excuse for the male's failure to take an equal share in the domestic tasks. But does he actually help his mate to incubate and brood? This is one of the questions that occurred to me early in my work with the tropical birds.

Since my first visit to Central America was to the lowlands, where resident wood warblers are few, I made the acquaintance of only one non-migratory species and, novice that I was, confused even this with a northern bird. In grassy areas among the cacao and banana plantations of the Almirante Bay region of western Panamá lurked a warbler which in appearance and voice so closely resembled the familiar Common Yellowthroat of the North that I included it in my list of migratory birds and tried to learn the date of its departure for its breeding ground. But by the end of May, when most of the winter visitors had withdrawn, I noticed no diminution in its abundance and was led to investigate its status. It turned out to be, not the Common Yellowthroat, but the closely related OLIVE-CROWNED, or LUTESCENT YELLOWTHROAT (*Geothlypis semiflava*), which breeds from Honduras to western Ecuador. Years later I found a few of these tropical Yellowthroats living amid tall, coarse pasture grasses in a clearing among the heavy forests of the Cordillera Central of Costa Rica, 5500 feet above sea level. Their song, full, ringing, long-continued and varied, was in my opinion superior to that of the Common Yellowthroat and one of the finest performances I have heard from a wood warbler. From time to time a male would rise singing above the grass, sometimes ascending to a height of twenty or twenty-five feet before he dropped back to concealment in the herbage. Although in May I found parents feeding a fledgling, I never succeeded in finding the nest of this species.

It was not until my third long visit to the Central American lowlands that I found my first nest of a tropical warbler. This belonged to the GROUND-CHAT or GRAY-

CROWNED YELLOWTHROAT (*Chamaethlypis poliocephala*) (Plate 8), a species ranging from Texas to Panamá. Like the Olive-crowned Yellowthroat, it is a bird of open places rather than woodland. Here in the valley of El General in Costa Rica, I have met it only among grasses, bracken, and low bushes in areas too sterile for agriculture. This species is also an outstanding songster, with a sustained and richly varied refrain. Some of its calls are so melodious that one unfamiliar with the true song might mistake them for it. My first and only nest of this species was six inches above the ground in a clump of grass in a pasture in the Motagua Valley of Guatemala.

On my farm in the valley of El General in southern Costa Rica, 2500 feet above sea level, two kinds of warblers reside and breed. Both are species of *Basileuterus,* a large and varied genus practically confined to tropical America, chiefly at higher elevations, mostly in South America, and exhibiting a great variety of attractive color patterns, but on the whole less varied and brilliant than the largely migratory *Dendroica.* Of these two local warblers, the most common and familiar is the BUFF-RUMPED WARBLER (*B. fulvicauda*), which lives along the rushing mountain streams, flitting from boulder to boulder or hunting over the shores. Although in its mode of life it bears a certain resemblance to the water-thrushes, it usually moves over the ground by hopping rather than walking. Like so many other fluviatile birds, when standing or perching it constantly wags its broad tail up and down. Except for the dark terminal half, the tail is yellowish-buff like the rump and contrasts with the dull brownish-olive body (Plate 33). The male sings a jubilant crescendo, in ringing tones which rise above the sound of mountain streams whose roar would quench the notes of many a weaker warbler's song. On rare occasions his mate answers with a full, rich warble that contrasts sharply with his more assertive notes but is even more delightful to hear. These songs are delivered through most of the year, but most freely in the breeding season, which extends from late March to July or August.

Both sexes of the Buff-rumped Warbler share the work of building the domed, oven-shaped nest, which is usually placed on a steep bank, with its round doorway facing a rushing stream or a little-used road. The two eggs are incubated by the female alone, who from time to time receives an insect from her mate. He is sometimes so impatient to begin feeding the nestlings that he offers food to the unhatched eggs, and as soon as the young emerge from the shells he takes his full share in nourishing them, although he does not brood. Although I once found eggs in August, most sets are laid in April and May; and it is probable that only a single brood is reared each year. This warbler differs from the migratory members of its family in its small annual production of young (probably rarely more than two) and the leisurely pace of its reproductive activities. Nest-building takes a week or more; incubation normally lasts 16 or 17 days; and the young remain in the nest from 12 to 15 days. This is substantially longer than the incubation periods of 11 to 14 days and the nestling periods of 8 to 11 days which have been recorded for a variety of northern warblers. Many other resident birds of the tropics exhibit the same contrast with their migratory relatives. Because they are not exposed to the hazards of migration, they can maintain their numbers with a slower rate of reproduction; and because they enjoy a long breeding season, short incubation and nestling periods do not confer the same great advantage as at high latitudes.

The other wood warbler which breeds on my farm is the CHESTNUT-CAPPED WARBLER (*B. delattrii*), whose chestnut head is prettily marked with white superciliary stripes, while the back is olive-green and the under plumage largely bright yellow (Plate 32). Avoiding both the heavy forest and shady pastures, it dwells amidst high, dense second-growth, where it is difficult to study. The male's little song is pleasant but it lacks the commanding force of that of his buff-rumped neighbor, who is obliged to contend with the roar of mountain torrents. The domed nests are placed on the ground, sometimes on a bank but at other times in a nearly level area, and are so well concealed that in fifteen years I have found only five of them, and I have never succeeded in watching the birds as they build. The two or three white, cinnamon-speckled eggs are incubated by the female alone; but the male helps to feed the young, which venture into the open when twelve days old. So far as we know, all species of *Basileuterus* build domed nests; but we have far too little information about the mode of life of these attractive warblers of the tropical mountains, which present a standing challenge to the eager young ornithologist.

Higher in the mountains over which I look from my window live other species of *Basileuterus*. The first that the climber is likely to meet is the THREE-STRIPED WARBLER (*B. tristriatus*) (Plate 31), named for the white or buffy-gray stripes on its largely black head, one along the center of the forehead and crown and one above each eye. Its upperparts are generally plain greenish-olive, without wing bars, and its under plumage is dull yellow, washed with olive on the sides and flanks. In Costa Rica it dwells in the undergrowth of heavy forest from about 3000 to 6000 feet above sea level, while in neighboring parts of Panamá it has been recorded as high as 7500 feet. Although it is considered rare in Costa Rica, I found it rather abundant beneath the epiphyte-laden forests on the northern slope of the Cordillera Central, around 5000 feet; but it was so retiring that I learned little of its manner of life. These warblers seem to remain mated throughout the year, like other members of their genus; for in November I watched a pair in a motley crowd of other small birds that had gathered around a swarm of army ants and were picking up the fugitive insects, spiders, and other hapless creatures. This variable species ranges from Costa Rica to Venezuela and Bolivia. At about 4000 feet in the Pastaza Valley of Ecuador, I met individuals of another race, whose head stripes were whiter than those of the Costa Rican form. These Three-striped Warblers lived in thickets along the river, sometimes going about in large mixed flocks of small birds. In mid-October one pair were attending fledglings, and they were a noisy family. The male's song was sharp and rapid.

John H. Dick
'55

PLATE 33

(top row left to right)

Fan-tailed Warbler (*Euthlypis lachrymosa*) Nicaragua
Oriente Warbler (*Teretistris fornsi*) Cuba
White-browed Warbler (*Basileuterus leucoblepharus*) Brazil, Argentina
Paraguay

(second row)

Red-breasted Chat (*Granatellus Venustus*) Mexico
Collared Redstart (*Myioborus torquatus*) Costa Rica, Panama

(third row)

Arrow-headed Warbler (*Dendroica pharetra*) Jamaica
White-winged Ground Warbler (*Microligea montana*) Hispaniola
Buff-rumped Warbler (*Basileuterus fulvicauda*) Honduras,
    Costa Rica, Panama, Brazil, Peru, Ecuador

(fourth row)

Slate-and Gold (Fraser's) Warbler (*Basileuterus fraseri*) Ecuador, Peru
Whistling Warbler (*Catharopeza bishopi*) St. Vincent (Immature)

(fifth row)

Pink-headed Warbler (*Ergaticus versicolor*) Guatemala
Flame-throated Warbler (*Vermivora gutturalis*) Costa Rica
Semper's Warbler (*Leucopeza semperi*) St. Lucia

At higher altitudes one finds the BLACK-CHEEKED WARBLER (*Basileuterus melanogenys*) (Plate 31), which is confined to Costa Rica and western Panamá. Its crown and forehead are chestnut, framed in black. There is a white stripe above each eye, and the sides of the head are largely black. Otherwise it is olive on the upperparts and dull white below, tinged with yellow on the flanks. These pretty warblers are at home in the undergrowth of mossy mountain forests from about 5300 to 10,200 or more feet above sea level. In Panamá they have been recorded as low as 4500 feet, but in Costa Rica they seem to remain higher. In November I found them in pairs on the summit of the Tablazo Mountains, where they foraged in company with Gray-breasted or Highland Wood-wrens (*Henicorhina leucophrys*) and Chestnut-capped Brush-finches (*Atlapetes brunnei-nucha*). No one, as far as I can learn, has ever found the nest of either the Three-striped Warbler or the Black-cheeked Warbler.

Another noteworthy genus of tropical wood warblers is *Myioborus,* which in Central America begins to appear about 2000 feet above sea level, thence extends far up on the mountains. In this group the upper plumage is usually dark slaty or blackish, the lower plumage yellow, orange, or vermilion, with usually a chestnut patch on the crown and sometimes a black band across the chest. These warblers are usually called "redstarts," a name which implies the possession of a reddish tail, although their broad, dark tails are variegated with white, never with red or orange. Yet in their sprightly ways and mode of foraging on the wing they resemble their relative

the American Redstart, which affords a certain justification for a name which is etymologically inapplicable. These warblers are fine musicians, but the COLLARED REDSTART (*M. torquatus*) of the Costa Rican highlands easily excells the other Central American species in the fullness and mellowness of its song (Plate 33). Once, while I squatted beside a wren's nest in a clearing in the mountain forests, one of these pretty warblers came to stand on my hat, a manifestation of the fearlessness which has earned for this species the appellation *amigo del hombre*—friend of man.

Like *Basileuterus,* the species of *Myioborus* build oven-shaped nests, often in a niche in a bank or steep slope but sometimes amidst epiphytes on a fallen log. One male SLATE-THROATED REDSTART (*M. miniatus*) (Plate 32) helped his mate to build, but several other females built alone, as did a female Collared Redstart (Plate 33) whom I watched while she worked at her nest. In both of these species the two or three, white, brown-speckled eggs are incubated only by the female and hatch in 13, or more often 15 days. The males, however, take a share in feeding the nestlings, which leave the nest when from 12 to 14 days of age. When driven from their nests by man, female redstarts sometimes give distraction displays, fluttering over the ground as though unable to fly.

We have given attention chiefly to species of *Basileuterus* and *Myioborus* because these genera are widespread in South no less than Central America and may be considered the most characteristically tropical of the wood-warblers. Northern Central America and tropical Mexico are the home of other, less widely distributed types of warblers, including the Red-breasted Chats of the genus *Granatellus* (Plate 33), and the Red-faced Warbler *Cardellina rubrifrons* (Plate 30), which range to Guatemala; as well as the Painted Redstart *Setophaga picta* (Plate 29), Fan-tailed Warbler *Euthlypis lachrymosa* (Plate 33), and Olive Warbler *Peucedramus taeniatus* (Plate 9), which extend into northern Nicaragua. There are also breeding representatives of such widespread northern genera as *Dendroica* and *Vermivora*.

One of the most arresting and attractive of these resident warblers of northern Central America is the PINK-HEADED WARBLER (*Ergaticus versicolor*), a bird so different in coloration from all its relatives that when I first met it in the Guatemalan highlands it never occurred to me that I was in the presence of a wood warbler. Male and female are alike in appearance and both are clad in a warm red, which on the head seems so heavily encrusted with hoarfrost that it is faintly pink. But if viewed from behind rather than in front, the bird's head is red like the rest of its plumage—whence the specific name, *versicolor* (Plate 33). It is easy to imagine that this warbler has a frosted head, because at the altitudes where it dwells, chiefly from 7000 to 11,000 feet above sea level, nights and early mornings are always chilly, and during the winter months heavy frosts cover over the open fields at dawn. As with so many other tropical birds, pair bonds are preserved throughout the year and two individuals are nearly always found together.

This warbler also builds a domed nest on a bank or steep slope, often making the outer walls of pine needles, a material unavailable to the birds of southern Central America except where men have planted pine trees. Delicate capsule stalks of mosses form the lining in the bottom of the snug chamber. The only nest of which I watched the construction was built by the female alone. The set consists of from two to four eggs, hence is at times larger than any warbler's set that I have found in southern Central America. Only the female incubates, but she is sometimes fed by her mate. Fledglings have no trace of red on their dark plumage but soon begin to acquire the adult color. Hatched in April or May, by September they cannot with certainty be distinguished from their parents, and they seem already to have formed pairs. In the high mountains of México, north of the Isthmus of Tehuantepec, occurs a related species, the RED WARBLER (*Ergaticus ruber*), clad largely in rich red, with a silver-gray patch on the auricular region. Little seems to have been recorded about its nesting (Plate 31).

Only two species of the northern genus *Vermivora* are known to breed in Central America. Not quite typical, they were formerly placed in a separate genus, *Oreothlypis*, the mountain-warblers. The most widespread is the CRESCENT-CHESTED or HARTLAUB'S WARBLER (*V. superciliosa*) (Plate 31), which resides in the highlands from México to northern Nicaragua. In Guatemala it has been found from 4000 to 10,500 feet above sea level, but it is rare below 6000 feet. Its upper plumage is dark gray with a broad patch of olive-green on the back and shoulders. There is a conspicuous white stripe above each eye, below which the cheeks and sides of the neck are blackish. The throat and chest are bright yellow and the abdomen is gray. Some individuals of both sexes wear a broad, somewhat crescentic patch of chestnut on the breast, but on others which breed this bar is merely suggested by a tinge of chestnut on the yellow breast. These warblers generally forage high above the ground, both in the broad-leafed woodlands, whose dominant trees are often oaks, and among the pines and cypresses of the high mountains. When not nesting they roam through the treetops in small flocks, which in the autumn are joined by Townsend's Warblers, Hermit Warblers, and other migrants from the north.

In February the male Crescent-chested Warblers separate from the flocks and sing a dry, chaffy trill, rather like the buzzing of an insect. The nests which I found were well concealed on the steep, vegetation-covered sides of old ditches. They were open cups whose thick outer walls were composed almost wholly of green moss, while the lining consisted of fine fibrous and downy materials. Although they had no proper roofs, like the nests of *Myioborus, Basileuterus* and *Ergaticus,* each was well covered by large, fallen, dead leaves, beneath which the warbler had cleared a little niche for the reception of her structure. At the end of April, two of these nests held sets of three eggs, while the third had two. Of the eight eggs, seven were immaculate white, while the eighth bore a sprinkling of faint brownish dots on the thick end. The females alone incubated.

The southernmost representative of this genus, the FLAME-THROATED or IRAZÚ WARBLER (*Vermivora gutturalis*) (Plate 33), is one of the most colorful of all. It is an exceptionally beautiful bird in its slate-gray upper plumage with a broad, triangular patch of black on the back, bright orange or flame-scarlet throat and breast, and white or gray posterior underparts. Its bill is black and its legs are flesh color. Male and female are similar in appearance. This warbler is confined to the highland area of Costa Rica and western Panamá and rarely descends below 6000 feet. I found it the most abundant resident warbler in the massive oaks and other trees standing in the pastures on the great, sprawling mass of the Volcán Irazú, between 9000 and 10,000 feet above sea level. Restlessly active, it hunts well up in the trees, sometimes in company with wintering Black-throated Green Warblers, and it occasionally descends into lower growth, especially on the sides of deep ravines, where it is likely to meet wintering Wilson's Warblers. At the end of April, I watched a female Flame-throated Warbler building her nest on a narrow shelf on a nearly vertical bank beside a highway. Her site, five feet above the foot of the bank, was well hidden behind a hanging tuft of grass. The structure, still less than half finished, promised to be a deep cup composed of green moss, fine bits of grass and similar materials. Although only the female worked, her brighter mate accompanied her and drove away trespassing birds. I was unable to return and look for the finished nest, of which, as of the eggs, I can find no description. The serious study of tropical birds has barely begun.

ALEXANDER F. SKUTCH

CHECK-LIST OF THE RESIDENT WARBLERS OF CENTRAL AMERICA
(from Guatemala to the Panama Canal)

GENUS	SPECIES	PL. NO.	COMMON NAME
Vermivora	*gutturalis*	(33)	Flame-throated (Irazú) Warbler
Vermivora	*superciliosa*	(31)	Crescent-chested (Hartlaub's) Warbler
Parula	*pitiayumi*	(8)	Olive-backed Warbler
Peucedramus	*taeniatus*	(9)	Olive Warbler
Dendroica	*petechia*	(10)	Mangrove (Yellow) Warbler *
Dendroica	*graciae*	(9)	Grace's Warbler
Dendroica	*vitellina*	(32)	Vitelline Warbler
Geothlypis	*chiriquensis*		Chiriquí Yellowthroat
Geothlypis	*semiflava*		Olive-crowned (Lutescent) Yellowthroat
Chamaethlypis	*poliocephala*	(8)	Ground-chat
Granatellus	*sallaei*	(31)	Gray-throated Chat
Cardellina	*rubrifrons*	(29)	Red-faced Warbler
Setophaga	*picta*	(29)	Painted Redstart
Myioborus	*miniatus*	(32)	Slate-throated Redstart
Myioborus	*torquatus*	(33)	Collared Redstart
Euthlypis	*lachrymosa*	(33)	Fan-tailed Warbler
Ergaticus	*versicolor*	(33)	Pink-headed Warbler
Basileuterus	*tristriatus*	(31)	Three-striped Warbler
Basileuterus	*culicivorus*	(35)	Golden-crowned (Yellow-crowned) Warbler
Basileuterus	*melanogenys*	(31)	Black-cheeked Warbler
Basileuterus	*belli*	(33)	Golden-browed (Bell's) Warbler
Basileuterus	*rufifrons*	(32)	Rufous-capped Warbler
Basileuterus	*delattrii*	(32)	Chestnut-capped Warbler
Basileuterus	*fulvicauda*	(34)	Buff-rumped Warbler †

ALEXANDER F. SKUTCH

* Eisenmann considers the Mangrove Warbler to be a different species, *Dendroica erithachorides*. (See Chapter 14)
† Eisenmann and Blake, following Zimmer (Amer. Mus. Novit. 1949, No. 1428) consider the River Warbler and the Buff-rumped Warbler (*B. fulvicauda*) to be conspecific.

CHAPTER **14**

Golden-crowned Warbler

WOOD WARBLERS IN PANAMA

Pₐₙₐₘₐ, at the junction of North and South America, is notable for the variety of its birds. Warblers are represented by about forty species, the exact number depending on disputed questions of taxonomic judgment. Twenty-six species are migrants from the north. The rest are breeding birds, mostly confined to the highlands in the western and eastern parts of the country.

In considering bird distribution, it is well to recall that at Panama the continent of North America not only narrows to a width of thirty-one miles, but that it bends in a sinuous curve from west to east. Hence the Atlantic Ocean (Caribbean Sea) lies to the north and the Pacific Ocean to the south. Western Panama is the region adjacent to Central America (Costa Rica), and eastern Panama—Darien of the Conquista-

dores—borders on South America (Colombia). The Pacific outlet of the Canal is farther east than Florida and farther south than northern Colombia and Venezuela. Readers who wish to visualize this might well consult a map; it is apt to be confusing.

THE MIGRANT WARBLERS

For a number of warblers Panama is the southern limit of the winter range. Others continue into western South America. The narrowness of the Isthmus concentrates the migrant flyways. Yet the land bird migrants from the north are almost wholly species breeding east of the Rockies. This is strikingly true of the warblers. Very few exclusively western species regularly winter south of Nicaragua. Whether this is a matter of habitat preference we do not know. Mexico and north-

286

ern Central America have a greater extent of dry woodland; in Nicaragua pine trees (*Pinus*), favored by many warblers, reach their southern terminus. Both central Panama and southern Nicaragua are sites of ancient water gaps, now replaced by lowlands and large lakes that break the chain of mountains, which elsewhere in Central America sharply separates the Atlantic and Pacific slopes. These gaps do not seem to have affected the migratory pattern of the eastern warblers, many of which appear to reach their winter homes in Panama and South America by a land route through Mexico and Central America. Probably some species reach Panama by a different course—perhaps skipping over the Gulf of Mexico to the Yucatan Peninsula, then leaping over the Caribbean to the projecting "hump" of Honduras-Nicaragua, and then down to Panama, possibly with a third over-sea flight. It seems likely, especially with the more numerous species, that not all individuals of a species follow the same route. Actually we know very little of the details of migration in Middle America. There are very few resident bird students, and, with ornithology at the pioneer stage, their interest has been chiefly devoted to the local species.

The migration information for Panama, though far from adequate, is somewhat fuller than for most parts of continental Middle America. Many experienced bird-watchers have visited the Barro Colorado Island biological station in the Canal Zone and sent me their notes. From time to time Americans interested in birds have lived or been stationed in Panama. Among those who have been most helpful in supplying data on the migrant warblers are James E. Ambrose, Jr., Thomas A. Imhof, Dr. Robert T. Scholes, and above all Major (now Colonel) Francis O. Chapelle.

From September to April warblers are conspicuous in the avifauna of Panama. Both in spring and fall there are flight days when migrant land birds are especially numerous. The autumn migration of warblers is noticeable by mid-August (a few birds arrive early in the month), with the peak in late September and early October, and some still appearing in November. During the northern winter—which corresponds with the Panamanian dry season—numbers are reduced, but many remain. As the dry season progresses in January and February, many of the wintering warblers, especially on the Pacific slope, retire to more humid localities, such as the vicinity of rivers and other places with permanent water. A good number of the wintering warblers associate with the mixed bird bands that wander through the tropical forests and woodlands. These bands are composed of one or a few individuals of several species, of which the most vocal in Panama are generally the small arboreal antwrens of the antbird family (*Formicariidae*). The return migration is evident by early March, though it probably begins in February. During March and April warblers become more numerous; by the end of April most are gone, though stragglers can be found well into May.

BLACK-AND-WHITE WARBLER. Common migrant; rather less common in winter, as some go as far south as Ecuador. August 24–April 1.

PROTHONOTARY WARBLER. Common migrant and winter visitor. August 1–March 23. This species winters to Ecuador, and the return migration probably begins early. Major Chapelle, while at Taboga Island in Panama Bay, on February 5, 1955, witnessed at dusk a flight of over a hundred Prothonotary Warblers, which descended on the trees like an insect swarm, calling noisily and permitting close approach. By morning they were gone. In early March on the Canal Zone mainland they were more numerous than during the winter. The Prothonotary Warbler appears to migrate over large stretches of water. In Mexico it seems to have been recorded only from Yucatán Peninsula and Cozumel Island; it is next recorded in Honduras and from there southward.

WORM-EATING WARBLER. A winter visitor. Panama is at the southern end of the winter range. I know of only six records, extending from December 15–March 16.

GOLDEN-WINGED WARBLER. A migrant and winter visitor. September 19–April 16. This species appears to migrate chiefly on the Atlantic coast of Middle America, for it has not been recorded from El Salvador; yet in southern Central America and Panama it winters on both slopes. It reaches South America.

BLUE-WINGED WARBLER. This species is believed to winter chiefly in Mexico and Guatemala; but there are specimen records from Nicaragua, Costa Rica, Panama, and Colombia. There are also recent observations in the Canal Zone. Panama dates: December 30 (four seen), March 7 (specimen), March 27 (one seen). The hybrids between this species and the preceding have not been recorded in Panama. In the American Museum of Natural History are two specimens of the Brewster's Warbler type, taken respectively at Bonilla, Costa Rica, September 27, 1920 and Merida, Venezuela, April 8, 1895; this suggests that the hybrid winter range resembles that of the Golden-winged Warbler.

TENNESSEE WARBLER. A common migrant and winter visitor. September 25–April 12. Dr. J. W. Aldrich found this the most numerous warbler in early February on the Azuero Peninsula, Pacific coast of western Panama. Major Chapelle noted that in the Canal Zone they increased in early March and most left by the end of the month.

YELLOW WARBLER. The northern migratory populations, formerly regarded as a species (*Dendroica aestiva*) distinct from the West Indies group (*Dendroica petechia*), regularly migrate and winter in Panama. All of the subspecies of the *aestiva* group breeding north of the Mexican boundary have been recorded from Panama in winter or on migration. As the various subspecies cannot be definitely distinguished in the field, and even the identification of winter specimens is doubtful, the migration dates here given refer to the *aestiva* group as a whole. Most specimens have been identified as the eastern race, nominate *aestiva*, but Dr. Alexander Wetmore writes that the Newfound-

TOPOGRAPHY OF A WARBLER

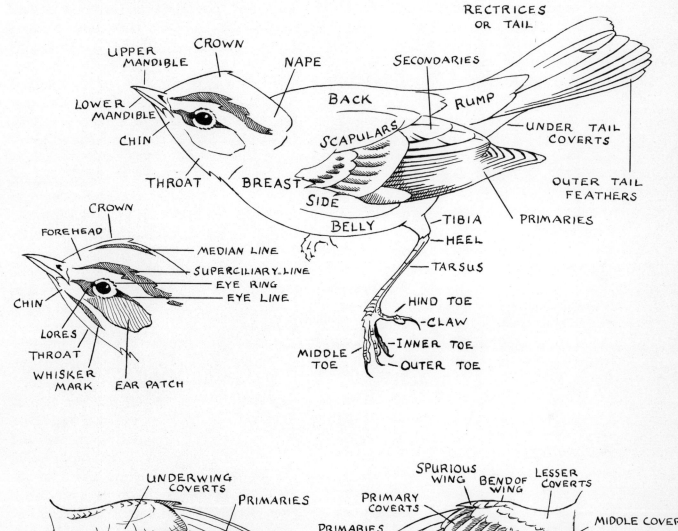

RECTRICES OR TAIL

SECONDARIES

UPPER MANDIBLE
CROWN
NAPE
BACK
RUMP
LOWER MANDIBLE
CHIN
SCAPULARS
UNDER TAIL COVERTS
THROAT
BREAST
SIDE
BELLY
OUTER TAIL FEATHERS
PRIMARIES
TIBIA
HEEL
TARSUS

CROWN
FOREHEAD
MEDIAN LINE
SUPERCILIARY LINE
EYE RING
EYE LINE
CHIN
LORES
THROAT
WHISKER MARK
EAR PATCH

HIND TOE
CLAW
INNER TOE
OUTER TOE
MIDDLE TOE

UNDERWING COVERTS
PRIMARIES
AUXILLARS
SECONDARIES

UNDERWING

SPURIOUS WING
BEND OF WING
LESSER COVERTS
PRIMARY COVERTS
PRIMARIES
MIDDLE COVERTS
SCAPULARS
GREATER COVERTS
TERTIARIES
REMIGES
SECONDARIES

UPPERWING

John H. Dick

land subspecies, *amnicola,* is also common. Panama dates run from August 13–May 12. From late August to May migrant Yellow Warblers are much commoner and more widely distributed than their resident relatives, the Mangrove Warblers, which some authors place in the same species. In Panama, separating the migrant birds from the resident population can generally be effected even in the field. A member of this complex with uniformly yellow or light olive-yellow underparts and lacking all rufous on the crown or throat is a migrant bird. Though spring males of *aestiva* in "high" plumage sometimes show a tinge of rufous on the forecrown, a bird in this plumage has most of the head (including the crown) bright yellow; Panama Mangrove Warblers never have yellow crowns.

MYRTLE WARBLER. Winter resident in small numbers. November 7–March 27. Panama is at the limit of the range, for though there is one record from northern Colombia, the most southerly specimen appears to have been taken in the Pearl Islands, Gulf of Panama on February 23, 1904.

MAGNOLIA WARBLER. Another species wintering regularly south to Panama, where it is uncommon. Records from the Canal Zone run from September 25–April 18.

BLACK-THROATED GREEN WARBLER. Panama is the southern limit of the regular winter range. In Veraguas, western Panama, Griscom found it common, but records are few from the Canal Zone. September 25–April 15.

CERULEAN WARBLER. Few Panama records; perhaps only a transient, for it winters from Venezuela and Colombia to Peru and Bolivia. Migration through Central America must be chiefly on the Caribbean slope, for records are lacking from El Salvador. However in Panama Cerulean Warblers occur on both slopes. There are specimens taken on islands in the Gulf of Panama on March 15 and 23. I saw an immature or female on August 27 on the Pacific slope of the Canal Zone, and a breeding plumage male on March 31 in the city of Panama. Other dates (sight observations of Chapelle and Scholes) are September 25 and November 4. The paucity of records may reflect the tendency of Cerulean Warblers to frequent the tops of trees.

BLACKBURNIAN WARBLER. Wintering chiefly in northwestern South America to Peru, this warbler may be no more than a transient in Panama, though it has been taken on November 17 in the Pearl Islands, and Skutch reports it "moderately abundant" in winter in the Costa Rican highlands and mountains. Perhaps the absence of winter records from the Canal Zone results merely from the absence of mountains in that area. Panama mainland dates run from September 22 to October 29 and from March 5 to April 28.

CHESTNUT-SIDED WARBLER. Despite reaching its southern winter limit in Panama, this species is common in the Canal Zone lowlands, generally associating with the wandering mixed bird bands. September 22–April 21.

BAY-BREASTED WARBLER. Though this species has been taken in Mexico and all Central American countries bordering on the Caribbean, the records are very few until one reaches Panama, where it commonly winters on both coasts, at least in central and eastern Panama to Colombia. The paucity of records farther north in Middle America, suggests either that on migration the Bay-breasted Warbler sticks to the coast where there have been few ornithologists, or that most of the population reaches Panama by several over-water flights, first stopping in the Yucatan Peninsula and then possibly pausing at the hump of Honduras-Nicaragua. Panama dates: September 18–April 27.

OVENBIRD. Panama is near the southern limit of the range in winter. Records available to me run to about a dozen, November 26–April 15. These dates, I feel sure, do not give an adequate idea of arrival and departure dates, for in Costa Rica Skutch has recorded Ovenbirds from early October to May.

NORTHERN WATERTHRUSH. This species, which winters to Peru, is a very common migrant and a common winter resident in Panama. September 18–May 4. In October 1953 Major Chapelle noted at Fort Clayton, Canal Zone, that five Northern Waterthrushes frequented the edges of certain concrete-lined drainage ditches until the water dried up during the dry season. The following year four ap-

peared on September 26. All three subspecies of Northern Waterthrush have been recorded.

LOUISIANA WATERTHRUSH. This waterthrush is much less common than the northern species; it arrives and leaves earlier. Panama and Colombia are at the end of the range. Because of the possibility of confusion with the pale race of the Northern Waterthrush (*notabilis*), I give only specimen dates: August 24–March 18. It is probable that this species remains somewhat later, as sight reports suggest.

KENTUCKY WARBLER. Though close to the southern limit of its range and easily overlooked in the undergrowth it favors, the Kentucky Warbler is a not uncommon winter resident, particularly in western Panama. September 8–April 8.

MOURNING WARBLER. A very common transient and common winter resident. September 24–May 7. A considerable influx of migrants, doubtless coming from Ecuador and Colombia, make this species numerous in late March and early April.

MACGILLIVRAY'S WARBLER. In Panama this species appears to be almost restricted in winter to the Pacific slope of the western province of Chiriquí. November 7–February 4. C. E. Hellmayr mentions having seen two taken at Colón, central Panama. Except for adult males, distinguishing MacGillivray's Warbler from the Mourning Warbler in the field in winter is exceedingly difficult. In fact even the identification of some winter specimens is doubtful, and R. M. de Schauensee in his list of Colombian birds has questioned the identification of two immature specimens long ago taken in that country.

COMMON YELLOWTHROAT. Panama seems to be just beyond the regular winter range, for I know of only one specimen—taken in the western province of Chiriquí and attributed to the northeastern race (*brachydactyla*). Casual occurrences may be expected, as the species has twice been taken in Colombia.

YELLOW-BREASTED CHAT. This species winters through Mexico and Central America, but the only Panama record is one taken on January 16, 1929, at Almirante on the Caribbean coast near Costa Rica. The specimen was allocated to the nominate eastern subspecies (*virens*).

HOODED WARBLER. The winter range of this species in tropical America is rather similar to that of the Chat, except that there are records from the West Indies and in Panama from as far east as the Canal Zone. Two recent sight reports of adult males are for September 24 and December 29. The only other record is an 1862 specimen, also from the Canal Zone.

WILSON'S or PILEOLATED WARBLER. This species winters regularly on the Pacific slope of western Panama, where Griscom found it fairly common; dates run

from September 10–April 30. Griscom also mentions it from the Canal Zone; the lack of other reports suggests that it is purely casual that far southeast. De Schauensee gives no Colombian records. This species probably occurs on the Caribbean coast of western Panama, for it has been taken just across the boundary at Cuabre, Costa Rica. Curiously enough, though a few Panama specimens have been attributed to the eastern and Pacific coast races (*pusilla* and *chryseola*), most specimens belong to the northwestern and Rocky Mountain subspecies (*pileolata*).

CANADA WARBLER. A common migrant in Panama—the last to pass through in numbers during the spring. Definite migration dates run from September 21–December 1 and from March 25–May 19. It winters chiefly in northwestern South America to Peru, but it is probable that some remain in Panama and sometimes farther north. In the American Museum of Natural History is a specimen from Cebaco Island, Panama, dated February 4, 1902, and one from Tegucigalpa, Honduras, dated December 11, 1934. Major Chapelle felt sure he repeatedly saw this species in December and January about Fort Clayton, Canal Zone, but failed to note definite dates after December 1 because he assumed it was a regular wintering bird.

AMERICAN REDSTART. A very common migrant and common winter resident. August 17–April 28. This is usually the first warbler to be noticed in August, though numbers increase in September. A return flight, presumably from Ecuador and Colombia, becomes apparent during March. Dr. Wetmore reports that both the northern and southern subspecies (*tricolor* and *ruticilla*) have been collected in Panama.

THE RESIDENT WARBLERS

In the central lowlands of Panama, about the Canal Zone, only three breeding warblers are known—the Mangrove, Chestnut-capped, and Buff-rumped Warblers. The other resident species are confined to the western and eastern parts of the country, most of them in the mountains.

FLAME-THROATED WARBLER (*Vermivora gutturalis*) (Plate 33). This beautiful species is restricted to the high mountains of Costa Rica and adjacent western Chiriquí, Panama. I have once seen it as low as about 5100 ft., in shrubbery on the sides of a wooded ravine in the Chiriquí Volcano region. Ordinarily it keeps above 6000 ft., as described by Skutch.

TROPICAL PARULA or OLIVE-BACKED WARBLER (*Parula pitiayumi*) (Plate 8). This species, with numerous subspecies, ranges as a breeder from southern Texas to Argentina. In Panama the known range is peculiarly interrupted, considering that it is not essentially a mountain species. The subspecies *speciosa*, which in Nicaragua and Costa Rica is found in the foothills of the Caribbean slope chiefly between 1000–3000 ft., is known in Panama only from the highlands of the Pacific slope between 2500–6000 ft. No Tropical Parula has been reported from the Caribbean slope of Panama (perhaps because of lack of ornithological explorations in the highlands), and the species is certainly absent from the lowlands of central Panama. In eastern Panama (Darien) a lowland race (*nana*) has been described. Recently Wetmore discovered an endemic subspecies in the lowlands of the isolated Coiba Island. Very likely the type of epiphytic material favored for nesting is absent or rare in most of the Panama lowlands. In the cloud forest of Chiriquí, especially about clearings, this species is common. In appearance and voice it strongly suggests the North American Parula. I noted the call as a sharp *tsip*, the song as an unmusical, sibilant, fricative trill, rising at the end: *tsip-tsip-tsip-tsip-tsip-ts-tsrrrrrrip*, sometimes *tsip-tsip-tsweeeerr*.

MANGROVE WARBLER (*Dendroica erithachorides*) (Plate 10). This bird (with various subspecies) breeds along both coasts from Mexico to northwestern South America and is recognized by the chestnut head in the adult male. Currently many taxonomists treat this group as conspecific with the northern migratory Yellow Warblers (*aestiva* group) and the West Indian Golden Warblers (*petechia* group), using the oldest name, *petechia*, as the specific designation. Aside from the disputed question of taxonomy, it is convenient for a student in Middle America to treat the sedentary Mangrove Warblers separately from the migratory Yellow Warblers. So reluctant are the resident birds to leave the coastal mangroves they inhabit, that differ-

John H. Dick

PLATE 34
SOUTH AMERICAN WARBLERS, GENUS *BASILEUTERUS* Pages 302–305

Yellow-green Warbler
(*signatus*)

Citrine Warbler
(*luteoviridis*)

Black-crested Warbler
(*nigrocristatus*)

Flavescent Warbler
(*flaveolus*)

Golden-bellied Warbler
(*chrysogaster*)

Gray-headed Warbler
(*griseiceps*)

Two-banded Warbler
(*bivittatus*)

Santa Marta Warbler
(*basilicus*)

Three-banded Warbler
(*trifasciatus*)

White-bellied Warbler
(*hypoleucus*)

Russet-crowned Warbler
(*coronatus*)

Golden-crowned Warbler
(*culicivorus*)

Russet-crowned
(*castaneiceps*)

Gray-throated
(*cinereicollis*)

ent subspecies (*erithachorides* and *aequatorialis*) are found on the Caribbean and Pacific coasts, though separated in central Panama by less than forty miles of well-watered country, where migrant Yellow Warblers are common nine months of the year. On the mainland I have occasionally found Mangrove Warblers in shrubbery away from mangroves, but never out of sight of such growth. On certain islands in the Gulf of Panama, where there is little competition from other resident birds, Mangrove Warblers are found not only in brackish areas but well into the wooded interior. Mangroves are abundant in Panama, yet this species is far from common. As A. J. van Rossem noted in El Salvador, there may be only a pair to a mile or more of apparently suitable habitat. In Panama City about a mile west of the ruined cathedral of Old Panama is a tiny mangrove islet attached to the mainland at low tide, which is inhabited by a pair. Unless the male be singing, the birds are very hard to find. The songs bear a distinct resemblance to those of the northern allies. I have noted a sibilant, whistled *sweet-sweeta, sowéechee-wéechew;* a more ringing *swee, swee, swee, chew, chéechoochéeoo;* and a *chee, chee, chee, wichoo-éecha.* I have seen this species fluttering twenty feet in the air picking insects off mangrove leaves in flight. On July 16, 1950 on this mangrove islet I found a recently vacated nest in a mangrove about six feet from the ground. It was a dense cup of fine grasses and plant fibres, with many small white feathers, probably dropped by shore birds that are common on the surrounding mud-flats. The outer diameter was 2½ in., outer

depth 3 in., inner depth 2½ in. Near by were two juveniles; one was fed by an adult male, the other by a bird with whitish underparts that I assumed to be the female, but which may have been an immature, perhaps of an earlier brood. A fifth individual with pale rufous tinge about the head and chest and dull whitish breast was also present. These birds called *chip* or *chit,* and a fast *chitchitchitchitchit.* Distinguishing Panama Mangrove Warblers from the more numerous migrant Yellow Warblers is usually not difficult. The chestnut-headed adult males are unmistakable. Juveniles are largely *grayish above* and *whitish below,* tinged with yellow only on rump, wings, tail, sides and under tail-coverts. This type of plumage seems to be retained for a considerable period, but in older birds olive appears on crown and back, and more yellow on the underparts, which continue mainly whitish. Immature males acquire a strong tinge of pale chestnut or rufous about the head, while still partly whitish below. Adult females with wholly yellow underparts are closest to the migrant Yellow Warblers, but such Mangrove females normally have their olive crowns tinged with rufous, and at least a slight rufous wash on the cheeks or throat. In specimens, the rounded wing of the Mangrove, with the ninth (outermost) primary decidedly shorter than the sixth (instead of as long or longer), is an additional distinguishing feature.

CHIRIQUÍ YELLOWTHROAT (*Geothlypis chiriquensis*). This apparently very rare bird is recorded only from the savannas in the mountains of western Panama at the base of the Chiriquí Volcano. It may be an isolated race of the South American Masked Yellowthroat (*G. aequinoctialis*). In appearance it resembles the migrant Common Yellowthroat (*G. trichas*), but has the underparts entirely yellow, and the adult male shows a broader black mask, and a gray mid-crown, the gray extending narrowly backwards above the mask.

OLIVE-CROWNED YELLOWTHROAT (*Geothlypis semiflava*). Along the Caribbean lowlands of Central America from Honduras to extreme western Panama (Bocas del Toro province), this species is common in suitable country. It reappears in the upper Cauca Valley of Colombia and on the Pacific slope of that country and Ecuador, though totally unknown from the Pacific slope of Panama. The wholly yellow underparts separate it from migrant Common Yellowthroats; adult males have the black mask extending further over the forecrown and without any whitish or grayish border. From the Chiriquí Yellowthroat (with which there is no overlap) adult males differ in having most of the crown olive, without any gray, and this also distinguishes it from the Gray-crowned Yellowthroat.

GRAY-CROWNED YELLOWTHROAT or GROUND-CHAT (*Chamaethlypis poliocephala*) (Plate 8). Ranging from the Rio Grande Valley of Texas to the Chiriquí highlands of western Panama, this species seems to be restricted to open areas of reduced rainfall or unfavorable soil. In behavior and appearance it closely resembles the Yellowthroats of the genus *Geothlypis*,

in which genus it was formerly placed and to which it should be restored. The main difference is the thicker bill with more curved culmen and the reduction in the male of the mask to a black area on the lores and just below the eyes. Adults of both sexes have gray caps. Brownish immatures, with buffy or whitish abdomens, might be confused with Common Yellowthroats; but the bill shape, greater extent of yellow on the cheeks, and darker lores should usually enable identification to be made.

SLATE-THROATED REDSTART (*Myioborus miniatus*) (Plate 32). The various races of this common highland species show a progressive change in color of underparts from red in Mexico to lemon yellow in South America. In Panama the western race (*acceptus*) of Chiriquí and Veraguas has the breast rich yellow; the race found in eastern Darien to Colombia and Ecuador (*pallidiventris*) is distinctly paler yellow. I have never seen this species below 3,000 ft. In the Chiriquí mountains it is very common, frequenting clearings and forest edge, flitting about the shrubbery and lower trees, with frequent spreading of the tail to expose the broad white tip.

COLLARED REDSTART (*Myioborus torquatus*) (Plate 33). This distinctive species has a range restricted to the mountains of Costa Rica and western Panama. Its yellow face and throat and black chest-band readily distinguish it from the Slate-throated Redstart. Although their ranges overlap, this species goes higher up the mountains, favors more densely forested areas, and is generally less common.

THREE-STRIPED WARBLER (*Basileuterus tristriatus*) (Plate 31). This is a montane species ranging from Costa Rica east to Colombia and Venezuela and south to Peru and Bolivia. In Panama the lowland breaks have resulted in three subspecies: *melanotis* of Chiriquí and Costa Rica, *chitrensis* farther east in Veraguas, and *tacarcunae* of Mt. Tacarcuna on the Colombian border. The latter is distinct in having the black of the cheeks very much reduced. Skutch has discussed the habits of this species.

GOLDEN-CROWNED WARBLER (*Basileuterus culicivorus*) (Plate 34). According to current taxonomic opinion, this species ranges (with many subspecies) from northeastern Mexico to northern Argentina. In Mexico and Central America it is found on both slopes, but in Panama it has been recorded only in the western part of the Pacific slope (Chiriquí and Veraguas) at elevations of 1500–7700 ft. It is unknown in the Darien highlands and the adjacent part of Colombia. The Golden-crowned Warbler rather resembles the Three-striped Warbler (which has an overlapping range), but the central crown stripe has a patch (sometimes hidden) of yellow or orange, the underparts, *including the throat,* are brighter yellow, and there is no black patch on the ear-coverts. In the Chiriquí Volcano region of Panama, this is a common species at the edge of clearings, fairly low in the trees and shrubbery. One finds them in small companies uttering

constantly sharp, dry, tittering calls *tsip-tsip-tsip-tsip*, which, as pointed out by A. J. van Rossem, give a castanet effect. At times a slower *tsup, tsup* is heard.

BLACK-CHEEKED WARBLER (*Basileuterus melanogenys*) (Plate 31). This is another species known only from the mountains of Costa Rica and Panama. Here again there are three Panama races, *eximius* in Chiriquí, *bensoni* in Veraguas, and *ignotus* of Mt. Pirri in southern Darien. In the one known specimen of the latter form, the black facial area is reduced to the lores, and dusky mottling on the cheeks, while the white areas are tinged with yellowish. These characters have caused some ornithologists to regard the Mount Pirri Warbler as a separate species. I can add little to what Skutch has written regarding this species. On July 10, 1949 on the highway leading to Cerro Punta near the Chiriquí Volcano, I encountered a pair at two places between 5500–6200 ft., carrying food to young—which gives some idea of the breeding season. At both localities the birds were in a thicket near a bamboo-choked ravine, bordered by mountain forest.

CHESTNUT-CAPPED WARBLER (*Basileuterus delattrii*) (Plate 32). This species, ranging from Guatemala to Colombia, is the only resident warbler common in the lowlands of Panama. It is a bird of second-growth thickets and open scrubby woodland, such as occur in much of the Pacific slope, but it has spread to the clearings of the Caribbean slope about the Canal Zone and up into the mountains at least to

4000 ft. It flits about nervously among the lower branches of trees and in shrubs, often with the tail jauntily uptilted. The usual call is a simple *chit,* and the song a dry but snappy *chit-cha-chup-cha-chuweép,* sometimes ending instead with *che-weécha,* and sometimes with two or three more introductory syllables. I have heard birds singing even in late August, though full-grown fledglings were being fed out of the nest by June 25.

BUFF-RUMPED WARBLER (*Basileuterus fulvicauda*) (Plate 33). Ranging from Honduras to Brazil and Peru, this species favors the edge of clear, rapid streams, in wooded country. Preferring a more hilly terrain, the Buff-rumped Warbler is not common in the tropical lowlands of central Panama. Near the waterfall on the scenic Madden Forest Preserve Road in the Canal Zone one may often hear its calls, *trit* or a harsher *chuck,* and at times its loud, ringing song, a gradually accelerating *chow, chow, chow chow chow-chow-chow.* Three subspecies are recorded from Panama, but their habitat and behavior seem not to differ from what Skutch has described in Costa Rica.

Two other Panama birds may be warblers, though traditionally included in the honeycreeper family (*Coerebidae*). The White-eared Conebill (*Conirostrum [Ateleodacnis] leucogenys*) belongs to a group which Ridgway placed among the warblers. Studies of the tongue structure by Zimmer and of the jaw musculature by Beecher support Ridgway's views. Objection to inclusion of the conebills in the *Parulidae* is based chiefly on the fact that color and pattern suggest the honeycreeper genus *Diglossa* and that the range is exclusively South American. Beecher has proposed also transferring to the warblers the well-known Bananaquit (*Coereba flaveola*). As this book follows the taxonomy of the A.O.U. Check-list Committee, which, so far, has not accepted Beecher's proposal to suppress the honeycreeper family, we limit the discussion to the *Parulidae* in the traditional sense.

EUGENE EISENMANN

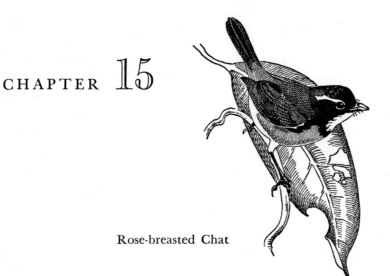

CHAPTER 15

Rose-breasted Chat

THE WARBLERS OF SOUTH AMERICA

INTRODUCTION

This chapter for the first time provides under one cover diagnostic descriptions of all currently recognized species of South American wood warblers. It is also the first time that English names have been supplied for each comprehensive species unit. The technical nomenclature conforms basically with that of C. E. Hellmayr's *"Catalogue of Birds of the Americas,"* Pt. 8, 1935, as modified by J. T. Zimmer, *"Studies of Peruvian Birds, No. 54"* (Amer. Mus. Novit. no. 1428, 1949). Two Venezuelan endemics are included that were discovered after Hellmayr's book. Most of the distributional data are summarized from these two works, with additions from many other recent sources, chiefly O. M. de O. Pinto, *"Catálogo das Aves do Brasil"* Pt. 2, 1944; W. H. Phelps and W. H. Phelps, Jr. *"Las Aves de Vene-*

zuela" Pt. 2, 1950; R. M. de Schauensee, *"The Birds of the Republic of Colombia,"* 1951; F. Haverschmidt, *"List of the Birds of Surinam,"* 1955. Migration dates are drawn chiefly from the de Schauensee and Haverschmidt works.

Those who would compare the number of warblers breeding in North America and South America respectively should be warned of two pitfalls: 1. The species concept here used as to South American species, following Hellmayr and Zimmer, is "broader" than that applied by the A.O.U. Check-list for North American warblers. Obviously allied populations replacing each other geographicaly without overlap are generally treated as subspecies of the same species, even though showing constant and striking differences in coloration not bridged over by intergradation or

298

individual variation. Were the same criteria applied to North American warblers, the number of full species would be reduced by about ten per cent. 2. Only such South American species are here included as have traditionally been regarded as wood warblers. There are several South American genera (*Conirostrum, Hemispingus,* and their allies), including many species, traditionally placed in the honeycreepers (*Coerebidae*) or tanagers (*Thraupidae*), though considered by Ridgway and others to be warblers (*Parulidae*). These small, slender-billed birds look more like "typical" warblers than does the Yellow-breasted Chat (*Icteria*). Many species of *Hemispingus* and its allies show colors and plumage patterns similar to the northern warblers. Whether reliable anatomical features will be found sharply to separate these closely allied "families" is doubtful. Characters which serve to distinguish the few North American tanagers from warblers definitely do not hold when we consider the multiform variety of the South American species currently called tanagers. Actually, there is no sharp line between warblers and tanagers if one considers South American birds. The line was drawn for North Americans long ago when the only tanagers they knew resembled the *Piranga* type with heavy bills. Modern students realize this, but there is an understandable reluctance to change classification.

EUGENE EISENMANN

[*Comment:* Just because the genera *Conirostrum* and *Hemispingus* "look like" warblers does not necessarily imply that they are. A Galapagos *Certhidea* "looks like" a warbler and was regarded by Ridgway as a warbler, but its palate structure has shown it to be one of the "Darwin Finches." Another point to consider is that if *Conirostrum* and *Hemispingus* are considered wood warblers, they would be the only genera of this North American family not represented in North and Middle America (from the West Indies and western Panama northward).

The two leading authorities in recent years on South American birds are the late Dr. Hellmayr and Dr. Zimmer, both of whom adopted conservative treatment in dealing with the admittedly heterogeneous honeycreepers and tanagers. In fact, Zimmer recently told me that he thought the tanagers sufficiently well characterized to be regarded as a distinct family. Conservative treatment in taxonomy is admirable, and if changes are made in our present classification, one must have sound reasons. (JAMES BOND)]

RESIDENT SPECIES *

OLIVE-BACKED WARBLER. *Parula pitiayumi.*
Bluish above, the back with a large olive-green patch; throat and breast tawny (male) or dingy yellow (female), becoming bright yellow on belly and flanks; under tail-coverts white; lores and cheeks black; two conspicuous white wing-bars; outer tail feathers with a white sub-terminal bar. (Plate 8)
Northern South America (east to the Acary Mts., British Guiana) and adjacent

* A species is considered resident if represented in South America at all seasons by one or more races. Endemic species—known *only* from South America—are marked with an asterisk.

islands south to Bolivia, s. Brazil, Uruguay and central-east Argentina (Buenos Aires). Ranges north to southern Texas. (*Other Names:* TROPICAL PARULA, Pitiayumi W.).

YELLOW WARBLER. *Dendroica petechia.* *Male:* Bright olive green above and golden yellow below, where more or less conspicuously streaked with bright chestnut; crown and sometimes entire head bright chestnut. *Female:* Similar to male, but somewhat duller and without chestnut markings (birds with brown heads —the *erithachorides* group—are often called Mangrove Warblers and formerly were considered a distinct species by many ornithologists). (*See Chapter 14*)

Colombia, Venezuela, and adjacent islands (including the Galapagos) south to Peru, chiefly in coastal mangrove swamps and near brackish estuaries. Breeds also in North America, in West Indies, and along coasts of Middle America. North American migrants (the *aestiva* group) winter extensively in the interior south to Peru and northern Brazil. (Plates 10, 32)

MASKED YELLOWTHROAT. *Geothlypis aequinoctialis. Male:* Olive green above, the underparts bright chrome yellow. Crown gray. Forehead and sides of head black, except in races of western Ecuador and Peru, which have mask much reduced. *Female:* Similar to male, but duller (less greenish) above and without a black mask. Crown and sides of head greenish, or faintly tinged with gray.

Trinidad; mainland, chiefly east of the Andes, south to northern Argentina (Cordoba, Buenos Aires). A subspecies or close ally in western Panama (Chiriquí).

OLIVE-CROWNED YELLOWTHROAT. *Geothlypis semiflava. Male:* Olive green above, the median underparts bright chrome yellow becoming strongly tinged with olive on the sides and flanks. Forehead, forepart of crown, and sides of head black. *Female:* Similar to male, but without black on head.

Lowlands of western Colombia (east to the upper Cauca Valley) and western Ecuador. Also Caribbean Honduras, Nicaragua, Costa Rica and western Panama.

* ROSE-BREASTED CHAT. *Granatellus pelzelni. Male:* Back, rump, and wing-coverts slate-blue, the flight feathers and tail black; forehead (sometimes entire crown), sides of head, and band below throat black; a white stripe above and behind the eye; throat, under wing-coverts, and flanks (sometimes) white; breast, belly, and under tail-coverts rosy red. *Female:* Slate-blue above, but duller than in male, and without black on head; underparts grayish or tinged with buff; a tawny stripe above and behind the eye.

Lowlands of southern Venezuela (Orinoco-Caura basin) and western British Guiana south to the Amazon Valley and northern Bolivia. (Plate 35)

SLATE-THROATED REDSTART. *Myioborus miniatus.* Head, throat, and upperparts dark slate, becoming black on inner tail feathers; crown-patch chestnut; breast, belly, and sides bright yellow, the first sometimes tinged with tawny buff; two outer tail feathers white, the third broadly white-tipped.

Mountains of Colombia, Venezuela, and

western British Guiana south to Bolivia and Peru. Ranges northward through Middle America to Mexico. (Plate 32)

* GOLDEN-FRONTED REDSTART. *Myioborus ornatus.* Fore part of head and underparts bright yellow or orange-yellow, the chin and area around eye sometimes white; hindneck black; back and wings clear slate or tinged with olive; tail black, the outer feathers white.

Colombian Andes and adjacent mountains of western Venezuela (Páramo de Tamá, Táchira). (Plate 35)

* SPECTACLED REDSTART. *Myioborus melanocephalus.* Upperparts essentially slate-gray, the crown contrasting black, or chestnut bordered behind with black; eye-ring, area bordering the forehead, and underparts bright yellow or orange-yellow; lores black, this usually extending below eyes to cheeks; tail black, the outer feathers white.

Humid mountain forests of southwestern Colombia (Nariño) and Ecuador south to Peru and western Bolivia (La Paz, Cochabamba). (Plate 35)

Myioborus ruficoronatus (Plate 35) regarded by Hellmayr as a separate species, has for some years been regarded as a subspecies of *M. melanocephalus; cf* de Schauensee and Zimmer. There is much variation within the species.

* WHITE-FRONTED REDSTART. *Myioborus albifrons.* Upperparts slate-colored, becoming black on the tail and sides of crown; underparts bright golden yellow; a black-spotted chestnut patch (forming an erectile crest) in center of crown; eye-ring, lores, and narrow band across base of forehead white; outer tail feathers white.

Humid mountain forests of western Venezuela in the states of Mérida, Trujillo, and Táchira. (Plate 34)

* SAFFRON-BREASTED REDSTART. *Myioborus cardonai.* Sides of head, back, rump, and wings dull brownish slate; crown and inner feathers of tail black, the outer tail feathers white; underparts bright orange-yellow.

Humid mountain forests of southeastern Venezuela (Cerro Guaiquinima, Bolívar). (Plate 35)

* WHITE-FACED REDSTART. *Myioborus albifacies.* Similar to Saffron-breasted Redstart, but entire face white instead of dark gray (slate).

Southwestern Venezuela in the Subtropical Zone of Cerros Paraque and Yavi (Territory Amazonas). (Plate 35)

* YELLOW-CROWNED REDSTART. *Myioborus flavivertex.* Center of crown and underparts bright yellow; forehead, sides of head, hindneck, and chin black; eye-ring and narrow band across base of forehead whitish; back and rump olive green; tail black, the outer feathers white.

Northern Colombia, in the Subtropical and Temperate Zones of the Santa Marta Mountains. (Plate 35)

* BROWN-CAPPED REDSTART. *Myioborus brunniceps.* Sides of head and upperparts dusky brownish or slate

colored, the underparts bright yellow; entire crown rich chestnut brown; eye-ring, supraloral streak, and narrow band across base of forehead white or yellow; tail dusky or black, the outer feathers white.

Subtropical forests of northern and southern Venezuela, western British Guiana (Mt. Twek-quay), Bolivia, and northwestern Argentina (south to La Rioja). (Plate 35)

* BLACK-CRESTED WARBLER. *Basileuterus nigrocristatus*. Olive green above, the underparts bright yellow shading to olive green on sides and flanks; forehead, crown, and lores black.

Humid mountain forests of Colombia (Central and Eastern Andes), western Venezuela, and northern Peru (upper Marañón Valley). (Plate 34)

* CITRINE WARBLER. *Basileuterus luteoviridis*. Olive green above; underparts usually bright yellow; sides and flanks olive green; tinge of olive on chest; lores dusky black, extending narrowly around eye to dusky or dark olive postocular area; superciliaries yellow or pale yellowish. Subspecies *richardsoni* (coast range west of Popayán, Colombia) has whitish superciliaries restricted to supraloral area, underparts dingy olive yellowish, fading to whitish on upper throat. Subspecies *euophrys* (southeastern Peru and Bolivia) has forehead and sides of crown black, and very conspicuous yellow superciliaries.

Temperate Zone forests of Colombia, northwestern Venezuela (Mérida, Táchira), Ecuador, Peru, and northwestern Bolivia. (Plate 34)

* YELLOW-GREEN WARBLER. *Basileuterus signatus*. Very similar to the more brightly colored races of Citrine Warbler (*B. luteoviridis*), but smaller, less conspicuous (yellow) superciliaries, and yellow eyelids. Feet yellowish flesh color, instead of brownish.

Mountains of Peru and northwest Bolivia, chiefly in Subtropical zone. (Plate 34)

* FLAVESCENT WARBLER. *Basileuterus flaveolus*. Bright olive green above; underparts rich golden yellow, shading to olive green on sides and flanks; superciliaries and eyelids bright yellow; a dusky line through eye; bill dark, feet pale yellowish.

Northeastern Colombia (Zulia Valley in Norte de Santander), northwestern Venezuela, central and eastern Brazil (chiefly south and east of the Amazon), south to eastern Bolivia and Paraguay, mainly in semi-arid woodland. (Plate 34)

* GRAY-HEADED WARBLER. *Basileuterus griseiceps*. Sides of head, crown, and hindneck slate gray, shading to olive green on back, rump, wings, and tail; a white streak above the lores; cheeks often speckled with white, chin white, the underparts otherwise bright yellow shading to olive green on sides and flanks. (Plate 34)

Subtropical Zone of northeastern Venezuela in the states of Sucre, Monagas, and Anzoátequi.

* WHITE-STRIPED WARBLER. *Basileuterus leucophrys*. Top of head and hindneck slate-gray; back, rump, wings, and tail brownish olive; sides of head and

underparts largely white, the flanks and under tail-coverts tinged with buff; a conspicuous slate-colored eye-streak extending from the bill to the auriculars, below broad white superciliary stripe.

Interior of Brazil, from Matto Grosso south to western São Paulo. (Plate 35)

* WHITE-BROWED WARBLER. *Basileuterus leucoblepharus*. Bright olive green above, becoming slate gray on the hindneck, sides of head, and crown; eyelids and supra-loral streak white; median underparts white, the sides and sometimes breast more or less heavily washed with gray; flanks olive green, brightening to yellow on the under tail-coverts.

Southeastern Brazil (north to Rio de Janeiro) and Paraguay south to northeastern Argentina (Santa Fé). (Plate 33)

* TWO-BANDED WARBLER. *Basileuterus bivittatus*. Sides of head and upperparts bright olive green; a concealed yellow-and-orange patch in center of crown, this bordered laterally by a conspicuous black stripe; eyelids, narrow streak above dusky lores, and underparts bright golden yellow shading to olive green on sides and flanks.

Southeastern Peru and Bolivia south to northwestern Argentina in the Provinces of Jujuy, Salta, and Tucumán. (Plate 34)

* GOLDEN-BELLIED WARBLER. *Basileuterus chrysogaster*. Very similar to the Two-banded Warbler (*bivittatus*) but much smaller, crown-patch less conspicuous, the black borders sometimes lacking, and region of eye olive green instead of dusky.

Lowlands and foothills of southwestern Colombia (Munchique region southward), western Ecuador (Chimbo northwards), and eastern Peru in the departments of Junín, Ayacucho, Cuzco, and Puno. (Plate 34)

* SANTA MARTA WARBLER. *Basileuterus basilicus*. Head essentially black or dusky, but conspicuously patterned with white (throat and posterior border of auriculars) and pale gray (superciliaries and median stripe of crown); back, rump, wings, and tail olive green, the underparts bright golden yellow shading to olive green on the sides and flanks.

Lower Temperate Zone of the Santa Marta Mountains, northeastern Colombia. (Plate 34)

THREE-STRIPED WARBLER. *Basileuterus tristriatus*. Sides of crown, lores, and auriculars black or dusky; median portion of crown, superciliaries, and throat whitish, buffy, or washed with pale yellow; back, rump, wings, and tail olive green; underparts variable, but essentially yellow or yellowish, this sometimes dingy or washed with buff; sides and flanks olive green.

Subtropical Zone of Colombia (except Darien and Santa Marta Mts.), northern and northwestern Venezuela, Ecuador, Peru, and Bolivia. Ranges northward to Costa Rica. (Plate 31)

* THREE-BANDED WARBLER. *Basileuterus trifasciatus*. Sides of head and broad crown-stripe grayish, the latter conspicuously bordered with black; a dis-

tinct black eye-stripe; back, rump, wings, and tail dull olive green, brightest on wings; throat pale gray, shading to bright yellow on the underparts; breast and flanks usually tinged with olive.

Mountains of southwestern Ecuador and northern Peru. (Plate 34)

* WHITE-BELLIED WARBLER. *Basileuterus hypoleucus.* Sides of crown black, the median crown-stripe grayish, heavily intermixed with orange; sides of head pale gray, but broken by a distinct black eye-stripe; back, rump, wings, and tail olive green; underparts white, the leg feathers and under tail-coverts pale yellow.

Interior of southern Brazil and western Paraguay. (Plate 34)

GOLDEN-CROWNED WARBLER. *Basileuterus culicivorus.* Similar to the White-bellied Warbler (*hypoleucus*), but entire underparts *bright yellow,* and back sometimes essentially gray with very little greenish wash.

Tropical and Subtropical Zones from Colombia, Venezuela, and western British Guiana south to eastern Bolivia and northern Argentina (Tucumán; Buenos Aires). Ranges northward through Middle America to Mexico. (Plate 34)

CHESTNUT-CAPPED WARBLER. *Basileuterus delattrii.* Crown and auriculars chestnut; superciliaries white and usually conspicuous; lores black; back, rump, wings, and tail olive green, the underparts bright golden yellow shading to olive green on the sides and flanks.

Lowlands and foothills of Colombia from the Santa Marta region and Magdalena Valley south to Tolima and Huila. Ranges northward through Middle America to Guatemala. (Plate 32)

* GRAY-THROATED WARBLER. *Basileuterus cinereicollis.* Head and hindneck essentially gray, shading to paler gray on the throat and chest; a conspicuous yellow crown-patch; eyelids and supra-loral streak white; back, rump, wings, and tail olive green; breast and posterior underparts bright yellow shading to olive green on the sides and flanks.

Tropical and Subtropical Zones of Colombia and northwestern Venezuela (Zulia; Táchira). (Plate 34)

* RUSSET-CROWNED WARBLER. *Basileuterus coronatus.* Much like the Gray-throated Warbler (*cinereicollis*) but larger, less greenish above, with a very conspicuous rufous or orange-rufous (not yellow) crown-patch bordered with black. In this species throat and sides of head are wholly gray, except for a black eye-streak. In the *castaneiceps* group (eastern and southwestern Ecuador to northwestern Peru) breast and belly are whitish (not yellow) shaded with gray. (Plate 34 lower left)

Subtropical Zone of Colombia and northwestern Venezuela south in the mountains to Peru and Bolivia.

* SLATE-AND-GOLD (FRASER'S) WARBLER *Basileuterus fraseri.* Sides of head and upperparts slate gray, the back washed with olive green; forehead and sides

of crown black, this bordering a bright yellow or ochraceous crown-patch; a white spot above the lores; underparts bright golden yellow.

Lowlands and foothills of southwestern Ecuador and northwestern Peru. (Plate 33)

RIVER WARBLER. *Basileuterus rivularis.* Top of head gray, becoming dull olive green on the back, rump, and wings; tail olive green or (in *fulvicauda* group) buffy yellow broadly tipped with olive green; superciliaries white or tawny, the latter sometimes diffusing over cheeks; underparts either tawny buff, palest along the median line, or essentially white.

Colombia east to Guianas and Brazil and south to Peru, Bolivia, Paraguay, and northern Argentina, chiefly in wooded lowlands and foothills. The *fulvicauda* group (sometimes called Buff-rumped Warbler) ranges from Colombia to Peru and western Brazil and north in Central America to Honduras, and is by some regarded as a separate species. (Plate 35)

NORTHERN MIGRANTS

1. BLACK-AND-WHITE WARBLER. *Mniotilta varia.* Colombia (Aug. 21–March 12), northwestern Venezuela, and Ecuador, wintering chiefly in mountain forests.
2. PROTHONOTARY WARBLER. *Protonotaria citrea.* Trinidad; lowlands of northern Colombia (August 26–April 5), western Venezuela (western and southern Zulia), and northwestern Ecuador; once Surinam (Jan. 22).
3. GOLDEN-WINGED WARBLER. *Vermivora chrysoptera.* Mountains (chiefly) of Colombia (Sept. 6–March 20) and northern Venezuela (south to Táchira).
4. BLUE-WINGED WARBLER. *Vermivora pinus.* Casual or accidental in northern Colombia (Chirúa, Santa Marta Mts., March 21).
5. TENNESSEE WARBLER. *Vermivora peregrina.* Colombia and northern Venezuela.
6. YELLOW WARBLER. *Dendroica petechia.* North American migrants (*aestiva* group) winter in Colombia (Aug. 26–May 1), Venezuela, the Guianas (Surinam, Aug. 23–May 12), northern Brazil and Peru.
7. MAGNOLIA WARBLER. *Dendroica magnolia.* Colombia, once (Soatá, Dec. 23, 1952).
8. CAPE MAY WARBLER. *Dendroica tigrina.* A single record (possibly erroneous) for the island of Tobago, near Trinidad.
9. BLACK-THROATED BLUE WARBLER. *Dendroica caerulescens.* Casual or accidental in northern Colombia (Las Nubes, Santa Marta, December 16).
10. MYRTLE WARBLER. *Dendroica coronata.* Casual or accidental in northern Colombia (Ciénaga, Magdalena, March 23).
11. BLACK-THROATED GREEN WARBLER. *Dendroica virens.* A single record for northern Colombia (Cincinnati, Santa Marta region, April 12).
12. CERULEAN WARBLER. *Dendroica cerulea.* Eastern Colombia (Nov. 21, Dec. 1, Jan. 24. March 4–21, possibly a transient) and mountains of northern Venezuela south to eastern Peru and northeastern Bolivia.

13. BLACKBURNIAN WARBLER. *Dendroica fusca*. Mountains of Colombia (Sept. 9–April 29) and Venezuela south to eastern Peru; accidental in Tobago.

14. BAY-BREASTED WARBLER. *Dendroica castanea*. Mountains (chiefly) of Colombia (Nov. 9–April 29) and northwestern Venezuela.

15. BLACKPOLL WARBLER. *Dendroica striata*. Colombia (Sept. 4–April 29), Venezuela, and western British Guiana south to Peru and the Amazon River; accidental in Tobago and Chile. *D. breviunguis* is correct name under the International Rules of Nomenclature.

16. OVENBIRD. *Seiurus aurocapillus*. Casual in northern Colombia (Bonda, Santa Marta region, October 4) and northwestern Venezuela (Paraguaná Peninsula, Falcón).

17. NORTHERN WATERTHRUSH. *Seiurus noveboracensis*. Colombia (September 8–April 30), Ecuador, Peru, Venezuela, British and Dutch Guiana (Oct. 11–May 12).

18. LOUISIANA WATERTHRUSH. *Seiurus motacilla*. Mountains of northern Colombia (Santa Marta region, Nov., Dec., Jan. 31) and northwestern Venezuela (Lara).

19. KENTUCKY WARBLER. *Oporornis formosus*. Northern Colombia (Santa Marta region, Oct. 7, Jan. 28) and northwestern Venezuela (Perijá, Zulia).

20. CONNECTICUT WARBLER. *Oporornis agilis*. Migrates through Colombia (Oct. 22, April 28) and Venezuela; winters in western Brazil south to central Matto Grosso.

21. MOURNING WARBLER. *Oporornis philadelphia*. Colombia (Oct. 13–April 30) eastern Ecuador, and northwestern Venezuela.*

22. COMMON YELLOWTHROAT. *Geothlypis trichas*. Casual in Colombia (Santa Marta Mts., April 21; Choco, June 16) and possibly Venezuela (Mérida); accidental in Tobago.

23. CANADA WARBLER. *Wilsonia canadensis*. Colombia (September 29–April 28), and mountains of western Venezuela south to eastern Peru (Urubamba Valley).

24. AMERICAN REDSTART. *Setophaga ruticilla*. Trinidad and northern South America (except Brazil and French Guiana), Colombia (Aug. 24–May 1), Surinam (Jan. 22, 30), south to Ecuador and Peru (Moyabamba Oct. 6, 1933).

EMMET R. BLAKE

As this book goes to press, the Chestnut-sided Warbler has been recorded from Colombia. (Oct. 23, 1954 and Nov. 11, 15, 1956)

* The Colombian records of MacGillivray's Warbler (*Oporornis tolmiei*) appear to be doubtful.

CHAPTER 16

THE WARBLERS IN ALASKA

ALASKA has a rich and varied avifauna. This richness, however, is due largely to the great numbers of species in the groups that may be generally classified as water birds. Less than half of the more than 400 species and subspecies of Alaskan birds are land forms. Among these last the family known as *Fringillidae*—which includes the grosbeaks, finches, sparrows and buntings—is easily the largest. It is followed by the family of Wood Warblers or *Parulidae,* but even here the 14 species and subspecies that have been recorded for Alaska are but a small segment of the 55 species in this family that are found in the United States. The reason, of course, is obvious, as these diminutive sprites have their center of abundance in a broad band that extends from east to west across the continent from the central United States to central Canada.

ORANGE-CROWNED WARBLER. Two races of this inconspicuous little warbler are found in Alaska—the Eastern, *Vermivora celata celata* (Say), which is found from Bristol Bay and the base of the Alaska Peninsula north to the timber line in the northern part of the Yukon Valley; and the Lutescent Orange-crowned, *Vermivora celata lutescens* (Ridgway), which is found in southeastern Alaska, about Yakutat Bay, Prince William Sound, on the Kenai Peninsula, and on Kodiak Island.

Although the eastern form has a wide range through the interior of the Territory, it is seldom found in large numbers. It has been found breeding at Ft. Yukon, at Eagle, in the Lower Yukon Valley, and in the Bristol Bay area at Lakes Clark and Iliamna. In addition to actual breeding records at these points there are many summer records which probably indicate breeding and

PLATE 35
SOUTH AMERICAN WARBLERS

(top group left to right)

Golden-fronted Redstart (*Myioborus ornatus ornatus*)
Golden-fronted Redstart (*Myioborus ornatus chrysops*)
Chestnut-crowned Redstart (*Myioborus ruficoronatus*)
Spectacled Redstart (*Myioborus melanocephalus*)

(second row)

White-faced Redstart (*Myioborus albifacies*)
Rose-breasted Chat (*Granatellus pelzelni*)
White-fronted Redstart (*Myioborus albifrons*)

(third row)

Saffron-breasted Redstart (*Myioborus cardonai*)
Yellow-crowned Redstart (*Myioborus flavivertex*)

(fourth row)

Brown-capped Redstart (*Myioborus brunniceps*)
River Warbler (*Basileuterus rivularis*)
White-striped Warbler (*Basileuterus leucophrys*)

John H. Dick

which extend throughout the valleys of the Kuskokwim and Yukon Rivers. It also probably breeds in the upper part of the Copper River drainage and has been recorded in summer in the lower part of the Kobuk Valley. A single straggler was collected at Point Barrow on June 5, 1928. It arrives on its breeding grounds during the early part of May and remains until early September.

The Lutescent Warbler is much more abundant within the limits of its range. In the Prince William Sound region it is the most common breeding warbler and both young and old birds have been found in a wide variety of localities. It is also a common breeder on the Kenai Peninsula and in the vicinity of Yakutat Bay, where nests have been found as early as June 2. Many nests with eggs or young have been reported from southeastern Alaska, including the many islands of the Alexander Archipelago. In this part of the Territory it is present from April 20 to September 24. The first specimen of this bird to be taken in Alaska was collected by a Russian naturalist, Wosnessensky by name, on July 4, 1842.

Both races (Plate 6) agree in lacking any distinctive coloration except for an orange crown patch on the heads of the males which is seldom visible under field conditions. These birds do, however, have a rather distinctive greenish-yellow coloration on their breasts and bellies that is not like any other bird found in Alaska. They are particularly hard to find after the breeding season when they become silent and when the thick leaves of the trees they frequent give them an almost abnormal protective coloration. All Alaskan nests that have been reported were placed on or very close to the ground, invariably in small clumps of shrubbery. They have been built of coarse grass tied together with strips of bark and sparingly decorated with plant down. Feathers, hair and fine grasses have been used for linings.

YELLOW WARBLER. This is the only other Alaskan warbler that is represented in the Territory by two geographic races—the Newfoundland Yellow Warbler, *Dendroica petechia amnicola* Batchelder, is found through the great wooded valleys of the interior north to the limit of trees; and the Alaska Yellow Warbler, *Dendroica petechia rubiginosa* (Pallas), which breeds from Unimak Island and Bristol Bay, along the coast and coastal islands south through the southeastern region.

The Newfoundland Yellow Warbler has been found commonly in the valley of the Kobuk River, where it arrives about June 9 and remains until the latter part of August. It has been noted to arrive at St. Michael (at the mouth of the Yukon River) and at Nulato, further up the valley, about the 10th of May. It appears to nest rather commonly in the valley of this great river, as nests have been found from its mouth northeastwardly to Circle and Eagle. It is probable that it also breeds in McKinley National Park, in the Copper River and Chestochina valleys, and in the general vicinity of Fairbanks. Stragglers have been taken on Nunivak Island, at Wainwright and Icy Cape on the Arctic Coast, and at Umiat in the lower part of the Colville River Valley.

The Alaska Yellow Warbler is quite widely distributed on the Alaska Peninsula, where it has been reported on numerous occasions by many observers. This area seems to be its center of abundance, for although reported with fair regularity in coastal areas from the peninsula to southeastern Alaska, it does not appear to be common in any particular part of this great region. It is occasionally found at the timber line in the Kenai Mountains, around Prince William Sound and at Yakutat Bay, but no one has reported it commonly from these areas. This also is true of the mainland and islands of southeastern Alaska, although some are usually present from the middle of May to the early part of September.

This brightly colored little warbler prefers willow and alder thickets, where it is surprisingly hard to see. In such locations birds may be heard singing continually but if they decide to stay out of sight an observer will wait a long time without catching a glimpse of the singer. Nests of the Yellow Warbler in Alaska, as elsewhere, are neat structures usually built in the forks of a small tree or bush generally within two or three feet of the ground. They are built of fine plant fibers such as dried grasses, inner bark and bits of plant down, sometimes including also hair and other soft, pliable material. These are woven into a tiny, compact cup so substantially built that a nest will often last for several seasons, even in the stormy climate of Alaska. For this reason old nests of these birds are among those that are most commonly found in the thickets after the leaves have been shed.

ALASKA MYRTLE WARBLER. As its name would indicate, the Alaska Myrtle Warbler is most common in the Territory from which it gets its name. It breeds south to northern British Columbia and possibly into Alberta, and east to northwestern and central Mackenzie. It is widely distributed during the breeding season in the great interior valleys of the Kobuk, Yukon and Kuskokwim Rivers and also in Mt. McKinley National Park. In the vicinity of Bethel on the lower Kuskokwim it has been recorded from May 8 to August 21, while on the lower Kobuk River it does not arrive until about May 22 but may remain until the last of August. In this great interior region the bird is found from areas not far from the coast of Bering Sea east to the valley of the Porcupine River. South of the Alaska range it appears to be a common summer resident only on the Kenai Peninsula and although it may breed in southeastern Alaska most of the records for that part of the Territory are during the period of migration.

As is the case with many other birds, the Myrtle Warbler occasionally straggles to the Arctic Coast. Two specimens have been taken at Point Barrow, one on June 4, 1930 and the other on May 7, 1943. One was taken at Wainwright on May 11, 1939 and two were obtained on Carbon Creek on May 22, 1942, while another was taken at Point Tangent on June 3, 1898.

Insofar as Alaska warblers are concerned this is one of the more common species, particularly in the great mainland interior where it is found north to the Brooks Range. As a bird of the coniferous areas it is relatively conspicuous for a warbler and is frequently seen catching flies in midair from the tops of perches in small trees or from dead branches, acting very much like a miniature flycatcher. It is a hardy bird, arriving rather early on its breeding grounds, staying somewhat later and wintering farther north than most of its relatives (northwest Oregon on the Pacific Coast and somewhat further south in the Rocky Mountain region).

Almost invariably nests are placed in coniferous trees, the majority of them being located between four and ten feet from the ground. They are made of fine, soft vegetable fibers and grasses woven into a compact cup and then lined with finer grasses, feathers and down material. Although Alaskan nests of this species do not seem quite as neat and compact as do those of the Yellow Warbler, they have many of the same characteristics.

MAGNOLIA WARBLER. As an Alaskan bird the status of the Magnolia Warbler is based upon a single immature specimen that was found dead (apparently from cold and exhaustion) on the sea ice about one mile offshore from Humphrey Point in the Arctic Ocean on October 1, 1913.

TOWNSEND'S WARBLER. This dainty little warbler is an uncommon summer resident of the coastal coniferous forest from the Kenai Peninsula south and east along the coast to Dixon's Entrance. Although in this region there are many records during the breeding season, no actual nests thus far have been recorded from Alaska. The nearest approach to a

breeding record is several birds of the year that were taken at Port Nellie Juan in Prince William Sound during the period from August 13–18, 1909. Other ornithologists have reported it during this season in the Kenai Mountains, along Lynn Canal, at Sitka, and on many of the islands south to the Canadian border. Few detailed migration data are available but it has been observed as early as April 27 at Craig and as late as September 14 at Taku.

This exquisite little warbler frequents coniferous trees and in Alaska, as elsewhere, it is not easy to see except during the breeding season. At that time the males frequently may be detected by their characteristic wheezy song. The species does not appear to be common anywhere in Alaska and its appearance seems to be somewhat erratic as it has been reported as fairly common in one season and entirely absent the following year.

BLACKPOLL WARBLER. The Blackpoll is one of the many eastern American birds that has spread throughout the Alaskan mainland, where it ranges north to the limit of trees and westward to Nulato, Bethel and Bristol Bay. Despite the wide territory over which this species is found there are few definite breeding records. Several observers have stated that birds were breeding in certain localities but the only known record of the collection of a set of eggs is from Fort Yukon on June 10, 1861. In collections throughout the country, however, there are many Alaskan specimens that were in breeding condition when collected. The general range during the summer seems to be from the Yukon boundary west and south to the lower part of the Yukon Valley, the Seward Peninsula, Bristol Bay and the Kenai Peninsula. It has been recorded as far north as the Kobuk River at Kotzebue Sound. There is only one record for southeastern Alaska, this being a bird taken on the Taku River on September 4, 1909. It has been recorded as arriving at Nulato as early as May 15 and has been noted at Fort Yukon as late as September 18.

This bird is comparatively inconspicuous when compared with the other more brightly colored warblers of Alaska, and accordingly is easily overlooked. It is most frequently seen in and about the willow and alder thickets that are interspersed with black spruce. In this habitat it is rather shy and retiring. The nest is likely to be in a small evergreen tree, placed fairly close to the ground, although in some parts of the Arctic region it is reported to nest directly on the ground under or near a coniferous tree. The nests are more loosely made than those of most other warblers and consist of a foundation of twigs, roots and dried grasses or sedges, lined with hair, feathers or or other soft material.

OVENBIRD. This common warbler of the eastern woodlands and city parks has been reported in Alaska on only two occasions. In their list of the birds of Alaska published in 1869, Dall and Bannister referred to a specimen collected on May 30, 1867 at a point 15 miles below the native village of Saccalolontan on the Yukon River. They added that it was found also at Fort Yukon but was not common.

Dr. E. W. Nelson, writing in 1887, cites this record, adding that it is known to breed from Fort Yukon for some distance down the river. Despite the fact that many competent ornithologists have worked in this region since the time of these early investigators no one else has reported seeing this bird. Nevertheless, Nelson also reported seeing a dried skin in an Eskimo hut near the mission at St. Michael. Many other typically eastern birds do reach Alaska, so this is a species that should be constantly watched for.

GRINNELL'S NORTHERN WATERTHRUSH. This warbler breeds throughout the wooded sections of Alaska from Kotzebue Sound and from the timber line on the Brooks Range south to Bristol Bay, the Kenai Peninsula and the Copper River Valley. It is considered a fairly common nesting species along the Kobuk River, where it has been noted to arrive in the spring about May 22. Eggs have been collected in the vicinity of Fort Yukon, and it also breeds at Mountain Village in the lower part of the Yukon Valley. It nests in the low mountain ranges between the deltas of the Yukon and Kuskokwim Rivers and has been reported on numerous occasions on the latter stream. Specimens have been taken during the breeding season at points along the shores of Bristol Bay and as far to the northeast as the Porcupine River. A specimen was taken at Demarcation Point on the Arctic Coast on May 17, 1914, while another straggler appeared at Nunivak Island on August 22, 1927. It remains in Alaska until the latter part of August, late departure dates being St. Michael at the mouth of the Yukon, on August 25 and Flat on the Kuskokwim, on August 22.

This brown-backed warbler with the conspicuous light stripes over its eyes and with yellowish underparts heavily streaked with black, is an inhabitant of stream edges throughout most of the mainland of Alaska. As elsewhere, during the nesting season, it is confined to the narrow strips of vegetation bordering the streams, where it moves about and under the debris-tangled logs and undergrowth almost in the manner of a mouse. When searching for it under a thick canopy of alders and willows its song rings startlingly loud and clear.

All nests found in Alaska have been placed on the ground beneath the roots of stumps or of trees, in a mossy bank, or under logs or overhanging branches. They have been made of grass, moss, rootlets and leaves, and frequently have been more or less roofed over with an entrance in one side. When the breeding season is over and the young are able to care for themselves, this waterthrush becomes even more of a skulker, hunting silently along the overhanging boughs and banks along rivers, creeks and lake shores.

MacGillivray's Warbler, which is widely distributed in the western United States and Canada, has been found in Alaska as a summer resident only in the southern part of the Alexander Archipelago and the adjoining mainland. Although it can hardly be called a common bird there are many records in June, July and August in the southern islands of this group and along the Stikine River. No actual nests have been found in Alaska but the dates of occurrence leave little doubt that it does breed to some extent. It is another species that offers unusual opportunities for study by resident Alaskan bird students, particularly in the brushy patches of evergreen blackberry, alder, willow or other brush that invariably springs up on cutover lands. In such tangles, and at the expense of plenty of time in the search, the bulky nests are almost sure to be found.

Northern Pileolated Warbler. This warbler is a widely distributed summer resident of Alaska from the Kobuk River and the south slope of the Brooks Range south to the Alaska Peninsula, the Shumagin Islands, the Kenai Peninsula, Prince William Sound, and through southeastern Alaska to Dixon's Entrance. Although never common in the Kobuk region it is seen regularly throughout the summer after the early part of June. It also breeds elsewhere along the shores of the Arctic Ocean at Kotzebue and Norton Sounds, as well as in the Yukon and Kuskokwim deltas and out on the Alaska Peninsula at least as far as Frosty Peak and False Pass. It is a common bird on Kodiak Island, where the Russian ornithologist Wosnessensky obtained the first Alaskan specimen in 1843. On this island it is easily the most abundant warbler, being found in the valleys and on the slopes of the mountains up to 1500 feet, the habitat having the heaviest population being that where there are interspersed areas of coarse grass and thickets of raspberry, alder and elder. It is equally numerous and widely distributed on the Kenai Peninsula and at many points around Prince William Sound. In the interior it is usually considered abundant in McKinley National Park and as far north as Circle and Eagle. It arrives in this region about the middle of May and remains until the early part of September.

The Pileolated Warbler is a common inhabitant of the willow and alder patches and other brushy areas where, in Alaska, it shows all of the ability at keeping out of sight that is inherent in many of these warblers that inhabit undergrowth. Nevertheless, because it is so energetic and excitable, it is more frequently seen than some of the others of its family that frequent the same type of habitat. It appears to be continually on the move, even doing much of its feeding on the wing as it flies from one place to another. All Alaskan nests found thus far have been built on or close to the ground, although one described from Admiralty Island was located in dense moss about five feet above the ground. This particular nest was built of moss and weathered leaves heavily lined with deer hair. On the other hand, several nests found in the Askinuk Mountains near Hooper Bay, were all sunken into the mossy sod or were built in the center of a large patch of grass. All were constructed of short, dried grass that was not interwoven, and with the lining entirely of fine thread-like grass shreds to which a mixture of dog hair was sometimes added. All of these ground nests were so fragile that it was difficult to retain their form when they were removed.

Although it is well distributed throughout the interior of Alaska in such regions, it never seems as abundant as in the coastal area. In the tundra country it lives close to Bering Sea and it is not unusual to find the last willow patch occupied by this bird, in company with Golden-crowned Sparrows and perhaps with Redpolls or Tree Sparrows.

NORTHERN PLAINS YELLOWTHROAT. This is another southern species which reaches Alaska only along the inland waterways as far north as the Taku River. Although no nests have yet been found in the Territory, there is no question that it does breed in the southeastern district as a female was collected on Chickamin River on July 21 that had already laid part of its set and which carried a perfectly formed egg that would have been laid within a day or two. Another specimen collected on June 23 was evidently incubating. Interestingly enough, all records from southeastern Alaska are from the mainland.

Despite its almost nation-wide distribution in the United States and Canada, the Yellowthroat must be considered a rare bird in Alaska. Possibly the reason is that its preferred habitat type of tules, cattails and bullrushes is not common anywhere in Alaska. Nevertheless, as timber is cut and brushy lands replace the virgin forests it may become more common in the wetter second-growth patches.

NORTHERN AMERICAN REDSTART. This is still another southerner that has been recorded twice in Alaska. The late Robert Ridgway, formerly Curator of Birds of the United States National Museum, took a male of this species on Gustavus Point at the entrance to Glacier Bay on June 12, 1899. A second specimen was taken on the lower Stikine River on June 9, 1946. In addition to these positive records of occurrence there is what seems to be an excellent sight record of a male of this striking little bird near the head of Savage River in Mt. McKinley National Park on July 25, 1926.

In addition to the Wood Warblers outlined above, Alaska has two other birds to which the name warbler is often applied. These are Kennicott's Arctic (Willow) Warbler *Phylloscopus borealis kennicotti* (Baird), and Northern Middendorff's Grasshopper Warbler *Locustella ochotensis ochotensis* (Middendorff). Both of these are Old World birds that are found in no other part of North America. They belong to the family *Sylviidae,* which includes our kinglets and gnatcatchers.

NOTES ON THE SONGS OF ALASKAN WARBLERS

ORANGE-CROWNED WARBLER Although it sings rather persistently, the song is not conspicuous, being a weak and rather colorlesss insect-like trill which drops in pitch and volume toward the end as though the bird were getting tired from its vocal exertions. In addition to the song, the Orange-crown has a scolding or alarm note that is a metallic *teek* or *pip,* and which, like the song, is not audible for any considerable distance.

YELLOW WARBLER We detect no recognizable differences in the songs of the two races found in Alaska nor from their more southern relatives, although as rendered by Alaskan birds, they seem to be somewhat shorter. As usually heard, the song consists of four or five notes on the same pitch, followed by two or three that are given rapidly with a rising inflection and the song then ends with a single note in the original pitch with a touch of the question mark. Roger Tory Peterson gives it very well as *"tsee-tsee-tsee-tsee-tseesi-weesee."*

ALASKA MYRTLE WARBLER Many observers have commented on the junco-like trill in the song of the Myrtle Warbler. This also is true of the Alaskan race, particularly when heard at a distance. At close range, it seems more musical and, unlike the junco, it always ends on a rising or falling note. There is much variation in the length of the songs of different birds and even in those of a single individual, but usually the syllables are uttered in a rather rapid monotone with either a slight rising or falling inflection. The notes may be recorded phonetically as *whee* or *weech,* and the song sometimes ends with a single *hew* which may be repeated two or three times. While foraging, these warblers keep up an insistent call of *chit, chit, chit,* etc.

TOWNSEND'S WARBLER As is true throughout its range, Townsend's Warbler may be detected during the breeding season by its characteristically wheezy song which seems to rise in a spiral. One of the best renditions I have heard is *weazy-weazy-weazy-weazy-tweea,* but I can see why Peterson records it as *dzeer dzeer dzeer tsee-tsee,* and why others have detected somewhat of a drawl in the opening notes.

BLACKPOLL WARBLER The song of the Blackpoll in Alaska is a high pitched, thin mechanical *zi-zi,* repeated some eight or ten times on one monotonous pitch. It is not audible at a distance. There is one peculiarity, namely, that the song seems to become louder and more emphatic in the middle and fades out toward the end.

GRINNELL'S NORTHERN WATER-THRUSH At Mountain Village on the lower Yukon, Henry C. Kyllingstad reports that the loud, clear and melodious song of this warbler is one of the most characteristic voices in the bird chorus. It has been rendered phonetically as *sweet sweet*

sweet chu-chu-wee-chu. The alarm note is a sharp, metallic *chip.*

MacGillivray's Warbler   No differences have been detected in the songs of the Alaskan representatives of this species. As elsewhere, there is a great variation in the songs of individual birds. A favorite word description that I frequently recognize is *sweeter-sweeter-sweeter, sugar-sugar.* Peterson also gives another version as *chiddle, chiddle, chiddle, turtle turtle.* A rather low pitched *chuck* or *chip* is used as an alarm note.

Northern Pileolated Warbler   The song of this warbler is hardly a notable effort, although it does serve to call attention to the bird when it might otherwise be overlooked. It is a rather monotonous song given on the same pitch but becoming louder and faster toward the end. I cannot improve on Peterson's rendition of *chi-chi-chi-chi-chit-chit-chit.* Other observers have used different "words" to describe it, but all agree in giving it about the same quality.

Northern Plains Yellowthroat   As a breeding bird, this warbler barely reaches southeastern Alaska, and I am unable to add anything to the well known and distinctive song of the species—*wichity-wichity-wichity-wichity-wich.* It is well known, however, that variations are more frequent among the western races than those of the East. This is something for the attention of bird observers in Alaska.

FREDERICK C. LINCOLN

CHAPTER 17

THE WARBLERS IN BRITISH COLUMBIA

Twenty-four species and subspecies of warblers are summer visitants to British Columbia. Each biotic division of the Province, from the rain forests of the Pacific littoral to the prairies of the Peace River country, from the arid valleys along the forty-ninth parallel to the boreal forests, provides a combination of plant and insect life suited to the particular needs of one or more species. Only the barren heights of permanent ice and snow are without a summer population of wood warblers.

In the geological sense British Columbia is a new country that only recently has become habitable for land birds. Looking backwards in time to the retreat of the great glaciers, perhaps ten thousand years ago, perhaps longer, one sees in imagination the gradual but persistent encroach-ment of vegetation with its attendant symbiotic insects; one imagines the gradual building of harmonious animal communities and the fluid ever-changing bird populations of these communities. I like to think that perhaps Audubon's Warbler, that hardy and adaptable adventurer, was the first warbler to come.

Now, as then, the face of the land is changing and fluidity of bird life, the advance of one species as conditions for it become favorable, the retreat of another when conditions become adverse, continues.

The various routes along which warblers first invaded and colonized acceptable territory is indicated by the complex pattern of migration that now is observable.

The political boundaries of British Columbia enclose 355,855 square miles of chiefly mountainous country through which great rivers have scoured wide valleys, some lying north and south, others east and west. These, together with low passes in the Rocky Mountains, are highways of migration. Thus in central and northern British Columbia certain bird species, including warblers, which in the south are known not at all or only as vagrant strays, have established summer colonies.

The study of migration routes and distribution of warblers is further complicated by the altitudinal zoning of biotic areas and the longtitudinal division of wet and dry climates, both of which exert profound influence. This complexity is given point when contrasted with the more simple facts of migration in the geologically older and more stable eastern North America.

In British Columbia the migrating waves of warblers, so familiar to bird students in eastern North America, are unknown. Nowhere is it possible to enjoy the sight of a dozen or more warbler species during a morning's walk. So also there seems to be a difference in behavior at this time. Whereas in the eastern woodlands, which once I knew well, warblers often showed a pleasing lack of concern at my presence, in British Columbia more often than not there is a shyness, an elusiveness, that defies close scrutiny of the subject.

The ORANGE-CROWNED WARBLER, as represented in British Columbia by three geographical races, is a summer visitant throughout the length and breadth of the Province and all follow a general south and north migration route. One brightly colored race, known to many as the Lutescent Warbler, inhabits that part of the mainland west of the coast mountain ranges as well as the islands off shore, including the Queen Charlotte group situated just south of the Alaska-British Columbia boundary. On the spring migration the usual time of arrival both at Vancouver Island and the mainland is mid-April; however, it has been seen at Victoria as early as March 26, while the earliest record for the Queen Charlotte Islands is May 1. In autumn the bulk of the population moves south during the first two weeks in September.

There are authenticated nesting records at Vancouver Island and on the mainland coast region.

The two other geographical races of the species occurring in British Columbia, the eastern and the Rocky Mountain Orange-crowned Warblers, which ornithology has designated as *Vermivora celata celata* and *Vermivora celata orestera*, are both common migrants through the interior and as the two are difficult to distinguish except when specimens are available for comparison they are treated here as one. The following selected dates of first arrival, from a locality in the south to one in the extreme northwest of the Province, indicate the time covered by the spring migration: Okanagan Landing, April 29; Quesnel, May 8; Atlin, May 14. In reverse order the dates for last migrants observed during the autumn migration are: Atlin, August 28; Quesnel, September 2; Okanagan Landing, October 4.

There are summer records representing

various localities through the length of the Province, based on specimens collected and females accompanied by young, but a nest with eggs or with young has yet to be reported.

The distribution of the TENNESSEE WARBLER is unlike that of all other warblers that inhabit British Columbia. The path of migration in both spring and autumn follows the eastern flank of the Rocky Mountains and from this route a limited population penetrates relatively short distances into these mountains where there is suitable nesting habitat along the foothills and where at higher levels in the coniferous forest aspens have succeeded lodge-pole pine after spot fires. The main migration, however, proceeds much farther north to enter the interior plateau by way of low mountain portals such as the Yellowhead Pass and others still father north. From this east and west route it fans out to populate aspen woodlands to the northern boundary of the Province. A smaller population proceeds south at least as far as Lac la Hache in the Cariboo Parklands Biotic Area. The following migration records illustrate this southern spring movement on the interior plateau from north to south: Nulki Lake, May 18; Quesnel, May 27; Horse Lake, May 26. The earliest spring record for Atlin near the British Columbia-Alaska boundary is May 26.

Near Vanderhoof on June 11, 1946, a nest made entirely of dry grass, and containing six eggs, was built in the entrance of a short tunnel at the base of a willow growing beside a faint deer trail through the aspen woods.

The distribution and migrations of the NASHVILLE WARBLER are quite different again. This species is but moderately common and for the most part restricted to the dry valleys in the southern section of the Province.

As with many other warblers, when newly established on their nesting territories, they are easily located. With this species the territories commonly encompass some shrubby glade on open hillside or at the forest edge. Generally the "singing tree" is one of moderate height, perhaps a second growth conifer with topmost branches high above the lesser growth. Thus in such a place near Creston for a week or so in early May rival males sang continually from the tops of the young larches. Later, after incubation was advanced, the periods of song lessened, then ceased, and both males and females seemed but furtive shadows in the greenery they matched so well.

On June 14, 1930, in a little aspen draw among thick woods of cedar, larch and cottonwoods near Vernon, I flushed a Nashville Warbler from its nest containing four eggs. The site, a foot from the ground in a wild raspberry bush where the nest was shielded by thick foliage, was unusual; indeed I know of no other instance of a Nashville nest built above the ground.

The migration routes are along the main valleys, north and south. The earliest dates of arrival are April 22 at Okanagan Landing and May 5 at Creston. The southern movement takes place from mid-August through early September, the latest date recorded being September 13 at Okanagan Landing.

The familiar, friendly YELLOW WARBLER occupies deciduous woodlands from Vancouver Island on the west to the Alberta boundary on the east and north to Alaska and the Yukon. At home in settled areas, here as elsewhere, it sometimes nests in orchard and garden shrubbery.

In the extreme south the dates for the first arrivals on the coast are little earlier than are those for the interior valleys where spring comes later. Thus the record from west to east is: Victoria, April 24; Vancouver, May 3; Okanagan Landing, May 2; Creston, May 4. The earliest date of arrival at Atlin in the far north is May 15. Latest dates for autumn migration are: Atlin, August 26; Okanagan Landing, September 4.

Prominent among those species which reach the boreal forests through passes in the Rocky Mountains is the MAGNOLIA WARBLER. We found it in groves of mountain birch along the Fraser River at Quesnel—about as far south as the species penetrates—and in aspens and in spruce stands farther north. The earliest date of arrival, May 31, comes from Tupper Creek in the Peace River Parklands. From farther west on the interior plateau the earliest dates are June 3 at Hazleton north of latitude 55°, and June 9 at Quesnel, latitude 53°. The latest recorded dates in autumn are August 30 at Nulki Lake, and September 5 at Hazleton. Undoubtedly the Magnolia Warbler nests throughout its summer range but there are no nesting data.

In British Columbia the summer home of the MYRTLE WARBLER is confined to the forests in the northern part of the Province.

Without a doubt the main channel of migration is through east-west portals of the Rocky Mountains but there are minor routes as well, one along the coast, the others through interior valleys. For example, at Lac la Hache in the Cariboo Parklands, a total of fifty were identified among Audubon's Warblers between April 30 and May 10, 1943. In the autumn migration the two species are difficult to distinguish, the bulk of the movement being composed of young in first-winter plumage. However there are specimen records of Myrtle Warblers from such widely separated places as Creston, September 5, 1952, and Vanderhoof, September 28, 1952.

Whether on migration or on its nesting ground AUDUBON'S WARBLER is one of the most abundant and most widely distributed land birds. Moreover it is the only warbler for which there is more than a single record of winter occurrence in British Columbia. So also it is the first warbler to arrive in spring and the last to depart in autumn, as the following migration data attest: Victoria, March 20; Departure Bay, Vancouver Island, March 22; Vancouver, March 29; Okanagan Landing, October 13; Vancouver, October 5.

When the new leaves of the aspens are no bigger than mouse ears, and the pungent scent of bursting cottonwood buds stirs the senses, we look for the first Audubon's Warblers on the shores of Okanagan Lake. Like so many alert northern travelers this warbler uses by choice the highways of shoreline and river-bank. Doubtless the choice of this water-route in spring is dictated in part by the presence of countless midges which hatch at this season and which the warblers, flying out over the water, capture in mid-air. So also in autumn they frequent the waterways and may be seen foraging for insects in cattail and bulrush marshes.

The most favored nesting habitat in the central interior is the lodge-pole pine and aspen type of forest cover, where the ground beneath carries grass and a light shrubbery, such as is characteristic of the Cariboo Parklands. Farther south a mixed association of Douglas fir and Ponderosa pine is most to their liking, although occasionally a pair will nest in orchard trees, or rather did so before the concentrated spraying practiced in recent years extirpated insect life in these places. During August the heavily-streaked young, southbound, usually represent a major item in the population of any woodland area; the adults have preceded them by some weeks, or so it is assumed, for in autumn the proportion of adults to young in this species as in all other warblers is in the ratio of one to fifty or thereabouts.

The BLACK-THROATED GRAY WARBLER is a summer visitant, never particularly common, to the forests of the mainland coast north at least to latitude 53°, to some of the coast islands, excluding Vancouver Island, and east along the Fraser and Pitt rivers as far as Lillooet. There are no interior records.

Earliest spring records are: Caulfield, April 28; Port Coquitlam, May 8; Chilliwack, May 10; Lillooet, May 7. Latest autumn records in the lower Fraser Valley are: Aldergrove, September 7; Chilliwack, September 7; Sumas Lake, September 24.

In the deep spruce and hemlock forests of the Queen Charlotte Islands, where moss-draped stumps and windfalls are partly hidden by a vigorous underbrush of salal, and in the open park-like stands of lesser spruce along the sea beach into which blown sand forever is encroaching, TOWNSEND'S WARBLER is one of the commoner summer land birds. It is a summer visitant also to other coniferous forests on the mainland coast, to the wide valley of the Columbia River which has a forest cover resembling that of the coast, and to subalpine forests of the interior north to the Yukon boundary. It does not nest, and is seen less often as a migrant, in the lower altitudes of interior valleys.

On the coast the first spring arrival of this species at Victoria was noted on April 16; the first on the Queen Charlotte Islands, at the northern coastal boundary of the Province, on May 1. The spring migration through the interior is somewhat later —Newgate, May 13; Armstrong, May 18; Atlin, May 18. The latest dates of the autumn migration as observed in the interior are Atlin, September 1; Kispiox Valley, September 15; Lac la Hache, September 12.

No record of a nest with eggs has been reported, but females accompanied by young have been seen on Queen Charlotte Islands, June 6, June 25, and on the Haines Road, near the northwest boundary of the Province, on July 27.

Another species which enters and leaves the Province through northern passes in the Rocky Mountains is the BLACKPOLL WARBLER. There are no records for localities south of Nulki Lake, situated six miles south of the 54th parallel of latitude, but in the forests of the north it is relatively common. The spring migration takes place in the latter half of May—Tupper Creek, May 18; Atlin, May 21. In autumn the bulk of the migrants pass through in late August—Atlin, August 27; Nulki Lake, August 27; Muncho Lake, August 27; Kispiox Valley, September 1.

The OVENBIRD is a common summer visitor in the Peace River area, which is the centre of its abundance in British Columbia, and has been recorded from various localities northwest of this region. There are no records from the central or southern parts of the Province.

The valley of the Columbia River, and the adjacent interior "wet belt," is the route by which the NORTHERN WATER-THRUSH enters the Province. In summer the species is distributed from Creston, close to the British Columbia-Idaho boundary, north through the Cariboo Parklands and far into the sub-alpine forest. Wherever found it inhabits thickets of dogwood, willow and alder along lake, river-bank or swampy ground. The earliest dates of arrival, north to south, are Quesnel, May 30; Nulki Lake, May 26. The latest recorded date is September 24, from Edgewood on the Upper Arrow Lake. Nests with eggs have not been reported. Parents feeding young were observed at Quesnel, July 8; Horse Lake, July 28 and Nulki Lake, July 16.

MacGILLIVRAY'S WARBLER is a moderately common summer visitor to all biotic areas of the Province which contain open stretches of shrubbery. This type of habitat may be small in extent and perhaps enclosed by tall forest trees; it may comprise waxberry and serviceberry thickets mixed with tall flowering plants of cow-parsnip and fireweed, such as margin the edge of some aspen woodlands, or, preferred perhaps above any other, an open brush-dotted hillside. Much habitat of this type has developed on logged-off mountain slopes near Creston. Here are ocean-spray spirea, ninebark and mock orange, which bloom profusely in their season, and here also about flowing springs a more dense cover of aspen, alder and dogwood has sprung up.

A nest containing four half-grown young on June 24, situated a foot above ground in a choke cherry bush, was made of dry grass and lined with horsehair.

Both spring and autumn migrations follow the valleys and lower mountain slopes. Earliest spring records are: Okanagan Landing, May 5; Tetana Lake, June 5; Telegraph Creek, June 1. The latest autumn records are Kispiox Valley, September 14; Okanagan Landing, September 10.

In British Columbia, as elsewhere, the YELLOWTHROAT dwells in riparian and lake-side thickets, more particularly those that margin marshes of cattail or bulrush. Its arrival in spring, usually during the first two weeks in May, is heralded neither by voice nor by display so that the presence of this shy marsh-dweller may at first escape detection. Soon, however, as the rhythm of the season beats faster, comes the urge to sing. The song, if song it can be called, is distinctive and unforgettable—an insistent and declamatory phrase that begs to be put into words. My own translation is *giddy-ap, giddy-ap, giddy-ap*. It is attuned, and contributes its small part to, the marsh orchestra of sora and coot, of marsh wren and grebes, of red-wing and yellow-headed blackbird that delights the discerning ear.

Spring migration dates for the interior from south to north are: Okanagan Landing, May 12; Lac la Hache, May 30; Quesnel, May 31. Latest dates of the autumn migration in reverse order are: Atlin, September 4; Lac la Hache, September 9; Okanagan Landing, September 27.

One of the several small land birds which reach the northern limit of distribution in the southern part of the Okanagan Valley is the YELLOW-BREASTED CHAT. As is usual with most land birds on the periphery of their range their numbers fluctuate from year to year. It would seem that following a year of more than normal nesting success in centres of abundance a surplus from this increase expands beyond normal boundaries to populate marginal territory. This seems to be so with the Chat, for in the Okanagan Valley it rarely is a common element of the summer bird population; less so in recent years since much of the riparian habitat of brush and deciduous trees has been reclaimed for agriculture.

A species with province-wide distribution is the PILEOLATED, or BLACK-CAPPED WARBLER. While for the most part its nesting habitat is restricted to mountain territory, nevertheless much of the migration, both spring and autumn, follows the lowland valleys.

Migration dates for coast and interior are about parallel in time, selected spring records being Cowichan Lake, Vancouver Island, May 9; Okanagan Landing, May 9; Quesnel, May 8; Telegraph Creek, May 29. Autumn records north to south are: Atlin, August 24; Kispiox Valley, September 11; Okanagan Landing, September 22. The late dates for some of the autumn records is notable and one for Departure Bay on November 26 probably indicates winter residence at that place.

A small population restricted to the most southerly part of coastal British Columbia is considered by ornithologists to represent a distinct subspecies designated as *Wilsonia pusilla chryseola*, the Golden Pileolated Warbler. Unlike the more widely distributed mountain-loving race *chryseola* nests at low elevations, sometimes close to the sea.

At least as far north as Hazelton the AMERICAN REDSTART is a summer visitor to the interior valleys, much more abundant in the central parts of the Province than elsewhere. For example, in the low-lying deciduous woodland south of Vanderhoof it is by far the commonest land bird.

There is little that is secretive, and there is much curiosity, in Redstart behavior. On migration or on its nesting territory comes a quick response to pygmy owl call or to the simulated distress signal used to excite birds by the practiced naturalist when attempting to census a bird community. Times without number in my experience a male Redstart has been the first to investigate the source of these disturbing sounds. The fluttering approach, like a gorgeous butterfly, the spread wings and tail revealing a pattern of scarlet and black, these are ever a stimulant and a reward to the naturalist.

An important migration route into the interior, probably the most important, is by the Columbia River valley.

Spring migration dates are: Creston, May 28; Quesnel, May 28; Nulki Lake, June 5. Latest autumn dates are Kispiox Valley, September 8; Shuswap Falls, September 22.

There are nesting records from Penticton near the British Columbia-Washington boundary to the Kispiox Valley north of latitude 55°.

Remaining for consideration are four species about which so little is known it has seemed advisable to put them in a separate category. These are the BLACK-AND-WHITE WARBLER, CONNECTICUT WARBLER, BAY-BREASTED WARBLER and PALM WARBLER. The presence of these four in northeastern British Columbia has been established by the collecting of two or more specimens of each—and that is the sum total of our knowledge. It may be that when the remote regions they inhabit are thoroughly explored all will prove to be more common and more widely distributed than present evidence indicates.

The Black-and-White and Connecticut Warblers have been reported as common in the aspen forests east of the Rocky Mountains in the Peace River District. The Bay-breasted Warbler is also included in the Peace River bird-list on the basis of two specimens collected there in the summer of 1938. There are other records of this species from Trutch and from Liard Crossing on the Alaska Highway. From this same region comes also a report of the Palm Warbler being common there in the summer of 1944. None of these four warblers has ever been reported from southern British Columbia. They belong to an eastern fauna whose western periphery penetrates the boreal forests of north-central British Columbia.

J. A. MUNRO

CHAPTER 18

WARBLERS IN THE PRAIRIE PROVINCES

THE Prairie Provinces of Canada, comprising Alberta, Saskatchewan, and Manitoba, cover an area of some 753,-500 square miles and extend from the 50th to the 60th parallel and from the eastern slope of the Rocky Mountains to the Ontario border. Greatly diverse ecological conditions present in this great area account for correspondingly notable differences in the distribution, species composition, and numbers of the warblers found there.

Along the southwestern border of Alberta the Rocky Mountains tower high above the relatively flat country in the remainder of the province. East of the Rockies, flat to rolling grasslands stretch across southern Alberta, southern Saskatchewan, and southwestern Manitoba. The vast remainder of the land is covered, with a few exceptions, by boreal forest.

The woodlands of the Prairie Provinces are not so rich in warbler life as are those of the southern half of eastern Canada. However, 32 warbler species, including accidentals, have been recorded within the boundaries of these provinces. Of these, 19 species are widely distributed in the boreal forests, breeding regularly in all three provinces.

The YELLOW WARBLER, while not the most numerous, probably has the broadest distribution of all. Its habitat requirements for moist-bottom tall shrubbery are met locally throughout the great expanse of Boreal Forest, in the Rocky Mountains, and even along streams in the semi-arid Grassland Formation.

Broad distribution patterns in the area perhaps may best be discussed under the following three headings: the Rocky Mountains, the Boreal Forests, and the Grassland Formation and Cypress Hills.

THE ROCKY MOUNTAINS. A part of the eastern slope of the Rocky Mountains lies within Alberta along the southwestern border of that province. The irregular terrain and great altitudinal variations in climate (the higher peaks reach 11,000 feet) make vegetation and bird distribution patterns intricate. The mountain slopes from tree line down to about 4000 feet are occupied by a sub-alpine forest in which spire-like Engelmann spruce and alpine fir are dominant, with lodgepole pine a fire subclimax. In the lower levels of this forest type, aspen and balsam poplar are frequent intrusives along rivers. Below the subalpine forest, beginning at about a 4500-foot elevation, is a Boreal Forest with white spruce, sometimes associated with black spruce, and with a fire subclimax of lodgepole pine and aspen. Willow, alder, and red-osier dogwood shrubbery occurs in river valleys. Where the mountains make contact with the plains an aspen belt is usually present.

The warblers of the Alberta Rockies are similar to those inhabiting contiguous southeastern British Columbia. The range of AUDUBON'S WARBLER, a familiar, widely distributed species in southern British Columbia, meets and apparently overlaps that of the more eastern and northern Myrtle Warbler in Banff and Jasper parks, Alberta. In Banff Park, according to Clarke and Cowan (1945), Audubon's occupies the subalpine forest and its area of intergradation with Boreal Forest; while the Myrtle is common only on the eastern fringes of that Park. In Jasper Park, however, Cowan (1955) found the Myrtle an abundant summer visitant throughout the forested areas with singing males of *both* species at Brazeau Lake. Ornithologists disagree as to whether or not Audubon's and Myrtle Warblers are two separate species or merely races of the same species. Careful study in such areas as Brazeau Lake, where the two seem to occupy common breeding areas, should shed additional light on their relationship.

TOWNSEND'S WARBLER, widely distributed in British Columbia, is on the eastern periphery of its range in the Alberta mountains where it is scarce and local. Its song, somewhat suggestive of that of its eastern relative, the Black-throated Green, is usually heard in the higher branches of coniferous trees. TENNESSEE WARBLERS are locally common in Boreal Forest valleys in Jasper and Banff Parks. ORANGE-CROWNS summer uncommonly in Jasper, frequenting poplars along streams, and are rather common in aspen on the east side of Banff Park. Yellows occur locally in willow and alder thickets along streams and wood margins and REDSTARTS are irregularly distributed, sometimes common in the Boreal Forest zone where aspen, poplar, and tall shrubs are mixed with conifers. Brush and tall shrubbery in both dry and moist places often have MACGILLIVRAY'S WARBLERS but in Jasper Park this warbler seems to be scarce. NORTHERN WATERTHRUSHES frequent willow and alder tangles along streams; and the bushy borders of ponds and streams often have YELLOWTHROATS. Shrubbery along streams and meadows attracts WILSON'S (Pileolated) Warblers which, in Jasper Park at least, inhabit also prostrate clumps of spruce and fir at timberline. In Jasper Park the BLACK-POLL is sometimes not uncommon as a migrant between May 21 and early June, and a few summer there; the BAY-BREAST has been observed on at least two occasions; the MAGNOLIA and CAPE MAY rarely in spring.

THE GRASSLAND FORMATION AND THE CYPRESS HILLS.

East of the Rockies the flat to decidedly rolling Grassland Formation extends across southern Alberta, southern Saskatchewan, and southwestern Manitoba. Characteristically the cover is grasses and small shrubs, some of the latter being xerophytic. The greater part of its surface is dry, treeless and therefore has no warbler population. Where rivers and streams cut across the land, however, the picture is entirely different. The flood plains of rivers often support profuse stands of willow and tall shrubbery, with poplars and other trees rising above the shrubs, often with a growth of rose bushes or other low shrubs flanking them. YELLOW WARBLERS favor the tall shrubbery and sing and forage also in the trees. Northern Plains YELLOWTHROATS (*G. t. campicola*) inhabit both the tall shrubbery and the outer zone of low bushes. Irrigation of considerable areas of the semi-arid plains, with tree plantations, as at Brooks and the Taber-Lethbridge regions of Alberta, have extended the ranges of these two warblers throughout such places.

Locally in southwestern Saskatchewan and southeastern Alberta, the valleys of the Frenchman and the Milk rivers contain jungle-dense shrubbery of willow and buckthorn. In these places the Long-tailed (Yellow-breasted) CHAT is sometimes common. Poplar and green ash rise above the shrubbery in many places and these trees are often used as singing perches. This is the only part of the Prairie Provinces where this warbler breeds commonly although a nest was discovered recently at Fort San in the Qu'Appelle Valley, Saskatchewan.

Isolated far out on the plains, on the southern end of the Saskatchewan-Alberta boundary, are the Cypress Hills, a 100-mile-long wooded plateau which rises some 1600 feet above the surrounding grassland. Its avifaunal affinities are with the Rocky Mountains to the west and their outliers to the south and southwest, not with the Boreal Forest to the north. Its higher parts are in marked contrast to the surrounding semi-arid treeless plains. Its flat top and upper north-facing slopes have extensive stands of lodgepole pine, white spruce, and aspen. Below the coniferous forest down to middle and lower levels is a broad belt of aspen. Willow shrubbery is often dense in damp depressions and on drier ground is mixed with serviceberry, cherry, hawthorn, and red-osier dogwood. Such shrubbery often follows streams from the Hills down onto the plains.

AUDUBON'S WARBLER is common but is confined in this area to the lodgepole pine and white spruce forests on top of the Hills, its easternmost breeding ground in Canada. The Rocky Mountain ORANGE-CROWNED WARBLER also is a common breeding species occupying the often-stunted, dense aspen patches on the plateau top and the upper slopes. Aspen woodland is inhabited also by the Gray OVENBIRD at both higher and lower elevations, this warbler using the lower stratum of such woods. MAC-GILLIVRAY's WARBLERS skulk about shrubbery and thickets in less dense woods, edges, and forest openings; and the incisive song of the YELLOW WARBLER is a common sound about moist willow thickets at all elevations. Locally and rarely, in dense deciduous shrubbery beside streams a pair of Long-tailed Chats may be found. Plains Yellowthroats are common in low and tall shrubbery around streams and in the rank vegetation of pond and marsh edges. A number of additional warblers occur in the Hills in migration.

THE BOREAL FOREST. The vast remainder of the land east of the Rockies and north of the Grassland Formation is covered by Boreal Forest. It contains the richest warbler populations in western Canada with many eastern species extending their breeding ranges across it, north of the Grassland Formation, for various distances into western North America. It is divisible into a number of Sections (Halliday, 1937) but only the broadest analysis is necessary here. Along the northern edge of the grasslands a relatively narrow belt of forest, the Aspen Grove Section, reaches in a semicircle from the foothills of the Rockies to southwestern Manitoba. In the western end of this zone aspen is the dominant tree and at the eastern end of the crescent, bur oak is an important forest component. Areas of grassland are characteristically scattered through the area, especially along its con-

tact with the prairies; and along rivers, where cottonwoods, Manitoba maple, ashes, and balsam poplar occur. Its western end is not rich in warblers.

Northward again, the Aspen Grove belt gives way to an extensive forest in which coniferous and deciduous trees are variously mixed. This is the Mixedwood Section of the Boreal Forest. It covers most of central and northern Alberta, central Saskatchewan, and central western Manitoba. In it white spruce, balsam fir, aspen, balsam poplar, and white birch are associated in various proportions. Jack pine predominates on sandy soils and there is black spruce and tamarack in bogs and other wet places. Alder and willow thickets follow streamsides and are found on the margins of lakes and ponds, bog and meadow edges, and in moister areas under forest as a sparse understory.

To the east, about the large Manitoba lakes, this Mixedwood Section gives way to the Manitoba Lowlands Section of Halliday (1937). The area is poorly drained. Black spruce and tamarack are important forest components, with jack pine on the higher ridges. The southern part particularly has associations of aspen and balsam poplar either in pure stands or mixed with white spruce, white birch, or balsam fir. On drier ground of the southern parts bur oak is a common intrusive. Elm, Manitoba maple, and green ash are distributed along rivers and lake shores. The extreme southwestern corner of Manitoba is covered by an extension of the Great Lakes-St. Lawrence Forest of Halliday (1937) with white cedar swamps, some red and white pine, good development of black spruce in bogs, various hardwoods especially along rivers, and considerable amounts of alder scrub.

The extensive forests north of the Mixedwood and Manitoba Lowlands sections are predominantly coniferous. The TENNESSEE, ORANGE-CROWNED, MYRTLE, PALM, WILSON'S, YELLOW, BLACKPOLL, and NORTHERN WATERTHRUSH extend their ranges northward into these forests, the Blackpoll actually reaching peak numbers along its northern periphery.

Southern and southern middle Manitoba (apart from the Grassland Formation) together with the Mixedwood Section of middle Saskatchewan and middle and northern Alberta has the richest warbler population of the Prairie Provinces. Breeding in this belt in all three provinces are the following species: BLACK-AND-WHITE, TENNESSEE, ORANGE-CROWNED, YELLOW, MAGNOLIA, CAPE MAY, MYRTLE, BLACK-throated GREEN, BAY-BREASTED, BLACKPOLL, PALM, CONNECTICUT, MOURNING, WILSON'S, and CANADA WARBLERS, and the OVENBIRD, NORTHERN WATERTHRUSH, YELLOWTHROAT, and REDSTART.

The Tennessee, Orange-crowned, Myrtle, Palm, and Wilson's warblers, and the Northern Waterthrush, while well-distributed in this belt, extend their ranges also well north of it. The Blackpoll reaches peak numbers much farther north as the edge of timber is approached. On the other hand, Yellowthroats are near the northern periphery of their range along the north edge of this belt (Wood Buffalo Park, Alberta; and Cormorant Lake, Manitoba). Yellow Warblers breed far to the north and south of this belt.

Three species, the NASHVILLE, BLACKBURNIAN, and CHESTNUT-SIDED warblers are rather common inhabitants of the Manitoba end of this belt but their numbers dwindle rapidly in eastern Saskatchewan and they fall out completely as breeders in Alberta.

In the forests of southern Manitoba and the Mixedwood Section of the other two provinces the MYRTLE WARBLER is common and well-distributed in most coniferous or mixed woodland, foraging at almost all forest levels but usually selecting higher branches for singing. BLACK-THROATED GREENS and MAGNOLIAS inhabit conifers of different ages, the former using various tree levels; the latter lower to medium heights and preferring more immature forest stages. Mature coniferous woods are favored by the locally distributed BAY-BREASTS and CAPE MAYS both of which are most often found in the higher strata. BLACKBURNIANS are common in the tops of both conifers and broadleafed trees in southern Manitoba but their range does not extend west of central Manitoba. TENNESSEES sing from the more open-canopied moist bottom coniferous or mixed woods, while ORANGE-CROWNS like the deciduous element of mixed woodland or pure stands of aspen. BLACK-AND-WHITES are common about the lower branches and trunks of deciduous or mixed forest. BLACKPOLLS, which farther north breed in stunted spruces, here find medium to large conifers to their liking. AMERICAN REDSTARTS are common in deciduous or mixed forests, thickets, and advanced second growth. OVENBIRDS occupy the forest floor and lower branches of drier, more mature deciduous woods and, less frequently, mixedwoods.

Willows, alders, and other tall shrubs are favored by others. The Yellow Warbler and Plains Yellowthroat select such places especially in the vicinity of water, the latter using also low shrubbery as well as the rank vegetation of marsh edges and the bushes of bogs. Wilson's Warbler also inhabits willow-alder shrubbery, its breeding range extending south to Nevis, Alberta; Nipawin, Saskatchewan; and Lake St. Martin, Manitoba; and northward to near tree limit in Mackenzie. Canada Warblers inhabit moist shrubbery along small woodland streams and sometimes the understory of moist woods. Northern Waterthrushes select wet thickets along streams and lakes.

MOURNING WARBLERS frequent bushy tangles of young second growth and thickets in forest openings. CONNECTICUT WARBLERS in most parts of Manitoba choose spruce and tamarack bogs, but occasionally use higher ground on which dense young saplings are springing up under scattered mature trees left standing by loggers. In central Alberta, where, as at Belvedere, it is locally rather common, it uses dry ridges and knolls in aspen and poplar country. Singing is often some 15 to 35 feet up in aspens or poplars in small areas with little underbrush but usually there is a shrubby hollow nearby.

PALM WARBLERS frequent spruce, tamarack, and alder bogs and similar wet places; and often in both Manitoba and Saskatchewan dry open Jack Pine country.

The NASHVILLE WARBLER in the Boreal Forest summers commonly in southern Manitoba north to The Pas and sporadically west to central Saskatchewan (southern Prince Albert National Park). The CHESTNUT-SIDE has a similar range, the westernmost definite breeding record being at Nipawin, in the central eastern part of Saskatchewan.

The PINE WARBLER is locally not uncommon in jack pine areas of southeastern Manitoba (Julius). Oddly enough a singing male was collected in far distant Alberta on June 5, 1924, south of Castor, and there is an observation of several pairs in the Athabasca district (Randall, 1933).

The GOLDEN-WINGED WARBLER has been reported in the migration season from Winnipeg, Portage-la-Prairie, Aweme, Ponemah Beach, Whitemouth, and Vivian, all in southern Manitoba. B. W. Cartwright (in litt.) stated that on July 22, 1932, he, T. M. Shortt, and others succeeded in finding three "family groups" at Vivian, three specimens of which were collected.

The BLACK-THROATED BLUE WARBLER has been reported in mid-June, 1920, at Indian Bay, southeastern Manitoba (Rowan, 1922), and at Emma Lake, central Saskatchewan, in late June and early July (Mowatt, 1947). Migrants have been reported from Treesbank, Manitoba; Percival, Saskatchewan; and at Edmonton and Beaverhill Lake, Alberta. The PARULA has been observed in summer a few times in the extension of Great Lakes-St. Lawrence Forest into extreme southeastern Manitoba.

Two species are of accidental occurrence in Manitoba: A female CERULEAN WARBLER was collected at Whitewater Lake, Manitoba, on June 24, 1924 (Harrold,

1925). A male HOODED WARBLER was found dead at Churchill, Manitoba, on June 10, 1952 (Sutton, 1952).

W. EARL GODFREY

References cited

Clarke, C.H.D., and Ian McT. Cowan. 1945. *Birds of Banff National Park, Alberta. Canadian Field-Nat.* 59(3): 83–103.

Cowan, Ian McTaggart. 1955. *Birds of Jasper National Park, Alberta, Canada.* Canadian Wildlife Service, *Wildlife Management Bull.,* Ser. 2, No. 8, pp. 1–67.

Halliday, W. E. D. 1937. *A Forest Classification for Canada.* Canada Forest Service Bull. No. 89, pp. 1–50, map 1.

Harrold, E. S. 1925. *Notes from Manitoba. The Auk* 42(1): 146–147.

Mowatt, F. M. 1947. *Notes on the Birds of Emma Lake, Saskatchewan, Canadian Field-Nat.* 61(3): 105–115.

Randall, T. E. 1933. *A List of the Breeding Birds of the Athabasca District, Alberta. Canadian Field-Nat.* 47(1): 1–6.

Rowan, William. 1922. *Some Bird Notes from Indian Bay, Man. The Auk* 39 (2): 224–232.

Sutton, R. W. 1952. *A Hooded Warbler from Churchill, Manitoba. Canadian Field-Nat.* 66 (6): 175.

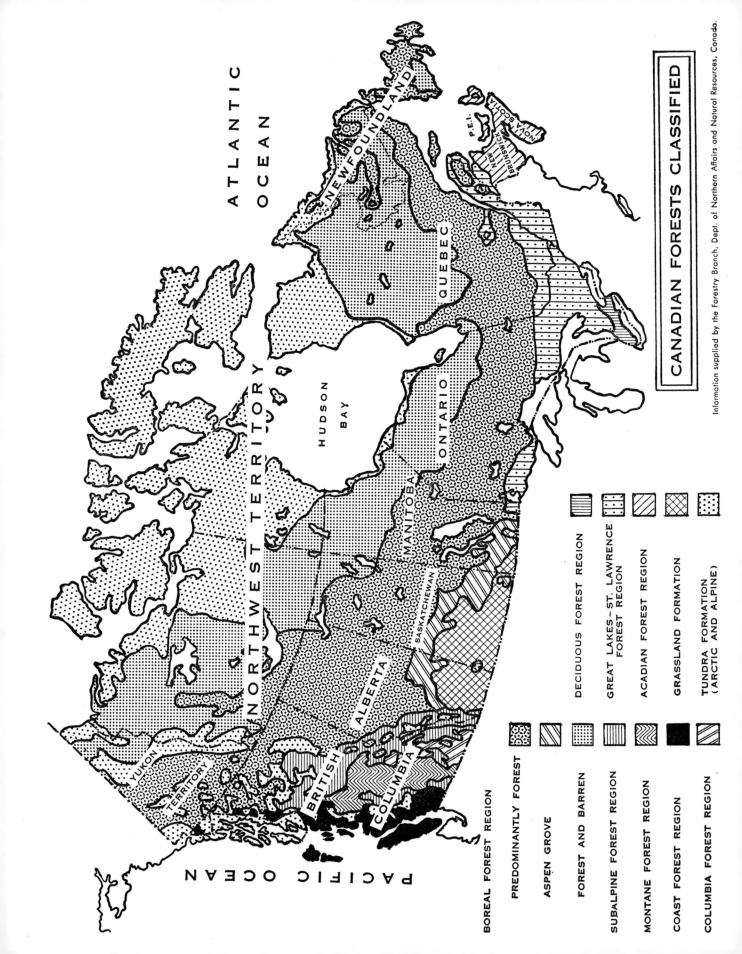

CANADIAN FORESTS CLASSIFIED

Information supplied by the Forestry Branch, Dept. of Northern Affairs and Natural Resources, Canada.

ATLANTIC OCEAN

PACIFIC OCEAN

HUDSON BAY

NEWFOUNDLAND

QUEBEC

ONTARIO

MANITOBA

SASKATCHEWAN

ALBERTA

BRITISH COLUMBIA

NORTHWEST TERRITORY

YUKON TERRITORY

P.E.I.

NEW BRUNSWICK

NOVA SCOTIA

BOREAL FOREST REGION

PREDOMINANTLY FOREST

ASPEN GROVE

FOREST AND BARREN

SUBALPINE FOREST REGION

MONTANE FOREST REGION

COAST FOREST REGION

COLUMBIA FOREST REGION

DECIDUOUS FOREST REGION

GREAT LAKES – ST. LAWRENCE FOREST REGION

ACADIAN FOREST REGION

GRASSLAND FORMATION

TUNDRA FORMATION (ARCTIC AND ALPINE)

CHAPTER 19

THE WARBLERS IN EASTERN CANADA

A HIGH SUMMER population of wood warblers characterizes the eastern half of the great belt of coniferous forest that extends across Canada from the Yukon to Newfoundland. Whereas a hundred acres of coniferous woodland of similar appearance in other regions usually has less than a hundred breeding pairs of all species taken together, the forest between Manitoba and eastern Quebec often has over two hundred pairs per hundred acres, two-thirds of them warblers.

Some idea of the significance of this area as a nursery and summer resort for about 20 species of warblers may be gained from the estimate that, on the basis of one pair of warblers per acre of forest, its 350 million acres may be inhabited by a like number of pairs of warblers. Small wonder, then, that these sibilant sprites are the most abun-

dant birds of the spruce-scented forests of the Canadian North Woods.

Halliday (1937) classified the eastern Canadian forest as comprising four Regions and these divisions are used in this chapter as convenient natural units bearing an ecological relationship to warbler distribution.

1). By far the largest and most important unit is the eastern *Boreal Forest,* which covers four-fifths of eastern Canada. It is the most northern forest and the characteristic tree is the White Spruce, but other conifers—Black Spruce, Balsam Fir, Tamarack, and Jack Pine—extend widely and characterize certain parts of it. It interdigitates with arctic tundra to the north and with two transition, coniferous-deciduous forests to the south: the Great Lakes-St. Lawrence Forest inland and the Acadian Forest in the Maritimes.

2). Only in extreme southern Ontario does the true *Deciduous Forest* have a foothold in eastern Canada. This relatively small region does however provide suitable habitat for representatives of half a dozen species of warblers not found elsewhere in Canada. Along secluded pools in swampy woodland, Prothonotary Warblers flash momentarily in flight through the dappled sunlight; high above them, Cerulean Warblers forage and sing in the broad canopy of the tall hardwoods and occasionally, at levels between these two extremes, Blue-winged Warblers may now be found. In one or two well-drained woodlots of mature beech, oak, and pine, Hooded Warblers have established themselves in the understory. Yellow-breasted Chats frequent overgrown raspberry and grapevine tangles, and it is the Louisiana Waterthrush rather than the Northern Waterthrush that is the summer resident along the streams flowing into Lake Erie.

3). Several warbler species reach their greatest numerical density in the long, irregular, west-east ribbon formed by the *Great Lakes-St. Lawrence Forest*. It has Hemlock, White Pine and Red Pine as coniferous dominants, with an interspersion of such northern hardwoods as Sugar Maple, Red Maple, Yellow Birch, and Beech. Always ecotonal, the deterioration of this Forest through lumbering, fire, and clearing has made it even more of a hybrid zone between the Boreal Forest to the north and the Deciduous Forest to the south. It thus contains a great variety of habitats and niches suitable to many kinds of warblers.

In remnant stands of mature pine, hemlock, and maple, Black-throated Blue and Black-throated Green Warblers are prominent, the Blues selecting sites with a somewhat higher proportion of deciduous trees than the Greens. Pine Warblers are also found in this habitat along the southwestern fringes. American Redstarts and Ovenbirds favor mature woodlots but also mingle with Black-and-White, Magnolia, and Myrtle Warblers in second-growth stands of poplar, Balsam Fir, White Birch and White Spruce.

The Canada Warbler, with its sharp, incisive song, is one of the common warblers in all but the southern portions of this Forest. It is most often found at medium-low level in small, sun-touched semi-openings in fairly dense mixed forest. In the same areas, Blackburnian Warblers occupy the tops of Hemlocks and the larger White Spruces and Jack Pines.

Nashville Warblers extend southward to the central part of this Forest where, in contrast to the sphagnum bogs they take to in the Boreal Forest, they usually take up territory in rather well-drained, open-canopy woodland in which aspen is prominent. Golden-winged Warblers are now penetrating this aspen habitat in south-central Ontario. Prairie Warblers have a few colonies in Ontario in differing habitats—close to the Great Lakes they choose pine and Ground Juniper in dune country; farther east, they pick sunny hillsides with a brushy covering of sumach.

Mourning and Chestnut-sided Warblers often occur close together in clearings and roadside edges; if the clearings are really large, Yellow Warblers may also be present. At the water's edge, Yellowthroats inhabit the willow and alder swales, and Northern Waterthrushes vie with gurgling streams and rapids to make their voices heard.

4). The *Acadian Forest,* having much the same mixture of coniferous and northern hardwood trees, is so closely related to the Great Lakes-St. Lawrence Forest that it is not differentiated in more recent forest classifications. Jack Pine is unimportant here, but large stands of Red Spruce, especially on slopes, were Halliday's basis for setting this subregion apart. It is, it is true, a maritime region, with higher precipitation and higher mean temperatures. This is well reflected in the abundance of the lichen *Usnea,* Old Man's Beard, which in turn supplies the special niche requirements of the Parula Warbler which consequently has its center of abundance in this forest region.

But this is a secondary characteristic of the region, one based on humidity rather than the forest itself. Floristic distinctions seldom correlate well with bird distribution because it is the "life form" of plants which seems to determine their suitability for birds. Thus, the Red Spruce is not so unlike White Spruce as to constitute a unique habitat. At least, our rather rudimentary understanding of the ecological relations of warblers makes it difficult to draw other conclusions at present. As one might expect, Red Spruce, where it still occurs in large stands, links this region to the Boreal Forest, and the Acadian Forest, even more than the Great Lakes-St. Lawrence Forest, is a patchwork of post-climax boreal stands and pre-climax stands of mixed forest. Having been extensively and drastically altered by man, the region is another hybrid zone with much the same combination of warbler species listed under the Great Lakes-St. Lawrence Forest except for the preponderance of Parulas and the near absence of Pine Warblers.

Moving north again, we return to the eastern Boreal Forest. It shows a high degree of uniformity in the species composition of its trees and its warbler populations. There are indications, however, that violent numerical fluctuations occur in the bird populations from time to time. The most striking and best documented of these show a direct relationship with outbreaks of the spruce budworm—a lepidopteran insect which in the larval stage attacks the foliage of balsam fir, white spruce, and black spruce in that order of intensity. Bay-breasted, Cape May, and Tennessee Warblers seem to be those most directly affected by these outbreaks. These birds (and others) wax abundant during the several years the insects infest a forest area—to the extent that the total bird population may reach a density of 300 or even 400 pairs per 100 acres—and then nearly or quite disappear from it when the insects subside after devastating the woodlands. Magnolia and Blackburnian Warblers, and the kinglets, seem to benefit most from the decline of the dominant trio, since they become more numerous when the others dwindle. Far from exercising control over the insects they prey upon, these warblers actually appear to be controlled by the numbers of their prey.

We owe our knowledge of this dynamic drama to the work of Kendeigh (1947) in

Ontario, and of Stewart and Aldrich (1952) in northern Maine. It remains to be demonstrated whether there is actually a population build-up resulting from the increased food supply, or merely a concentration of birds (with resulting local production of young) at the expense of surrounding territory. Stewart and Aldrich (1951) found that removal of breeding birds resulted in immediate repopulation by what appeared to be a floating population as large as, or at times twice as large as, the original territorial population. Here is one of the most intriguing problems in modern field ornithology.

The center of abundance for the full complement of typical boreal forest warblers lies south of latitude fifty, and between Lake Nipigon, Ontario, and the interior of the Gaspé Peninsula in eastern Quebec. As one moves north or east from the eastern end of this axis, there is a falling out of species and the Blackpoll Warbler gradually assumes dominance. The warbler fauna of Newfoundland illustrates this thinning out of populations. There the Blackpoll and Wilson's (Pileolated) Warblers are the commonest species; the Black-throated Green, Mourning, Magnolia, Myrtle, Yellow Palm, and Tennessee Warblers occur in diminishing order; and the Parula, Cape May, Blackburnian, Bay-breasted, and Canada Warblers are rare or completely absent.

In Quebec, Myrtle and Wilson's Warblers extend well to the north and accompany the Blackpoll, though in greatly reduced numbers, almost to the edge of timber in Ungava and adjacent Newfoundland and Labrador.

In Ontario, there is the same diminution of species with northward progression, but the distribution of species is somewhat different. The Blackpoll nests only in the far north, close to the tree-line and Hudson Bay; two others, the Palm and Orange-crowned Warblers, begin to appear south of James Bay and extend north to Blackpoll country. West of the western end of the axis, Palm Warblers do occur locally in dense spruce and Jack Pine forest and, over the border in Manitoba, Orange-crowns become rather common to the west and north. The Connecticut Warbler, common along the western part of the axis but absent in the east, is a frequenter of spruce bog margins in Ontario but westward, in Manitoba, it is more likely to be found in well-drained poplar woodland.

As has been repeatedly inferred, an awareness of both the general ecological relationships and the particular niche requirements of the North Woods warblers is a prerequisite to an understanding of their local distribution patterns. Our present knowledge of these factors has been gained mostly about the periphery of their centre of abundance—in Maine, New Brunswick, and Ontario. Although what we have learned represents merely a beginning in this important descriptive work, it nevertheless seems generally applicable throughout the summer range of these species.

The following account of Boreal Forest habitats' groupings draws heavily on the work of Kendeigh (1947), Stewart and Aldrich (1952), Cruickshank (1956), and the compilations of Bent (1953) and Palmer (1949).

BOREAL FOREST HABITATS

a) On good sites the mature woodland of the Boreal Forest is a Closed Canopy Forest of spruces and Balsam Fir or Jack Pine with scant understory and a low ground cover of mosses and leafy liverworts, Goldthread (*Coptis*), Wood Sorrel (*Oxalis*), and Corn Lily (*Clintonia*). Five warblers are typical inhabitants: Cape May, Bay-breasted, Myrtle, Black-throated Green, and Blackburnian. Tall trees, rather than dense stands as such, seem important, since all five species also occupy woodland edges or more open stands; other warblers, however, occur only sparingly in the closed forest.

Each of the five species has its own niche within this forest, minor vertical differences in song perch, feeding, and nest placement permitting them to occupy the same area without undue conflict.

The denseness of the Closed Canopy Forest forces all five species to select song perches at or near the tops of the taller spires. However, whereas Cape May and Blackburnian Warblers seldom sing from anywhere but the terminal clump or the five or six feet below it, the Bay-breasted, Black-throated Green and Myrtle Warblers commonly sing at lower levels when small openings in the forest permit it.

Blackburnian Warblers feed very high—in fact, they never seem to come down. On the other hand, Cape Mays and, more rarely, Bay-breasted Warblers, will descend to about the 20-foot level to forage; Myrtle and Black-throated Green Warblers will feed at almost any height but show a preference for sunny outer branches.

Blackburnian and Cape May Warblers nest high up, in the thick terminal growth of foliage, but the Bay-breasted Warblers nest at an average of only 15 feet above ground; Black-throated Green and Myrtle nests are usually a little higher—around the 20-foot mark.

Black-throated Green and Blackburnian Warblers actually reach peak numbers south of the Boreal Forest, in hemlock and pine habitat. In Ontario, the Bay-breasted Warbler is normally much more numerous than the Cape May even in Closed Canopy Forest. The dense spruce-fir and Jack Pine forests about Lake Nipigon and along the northeast shore of Lake Superior form local centers of abundance.

b) The main body of the Boreal Forest may be classified as *Open Forest with Herbaceous Ground Cover* (ferns, Dwarf Cornel or Bunchberry (*Cornus*), etc.). Although scarce or absent peripherally, the Tennessee Warbler must be considered the dominant warbler here. With the open growth, there is not the necessity for selecting spire tops as song perches and although the Tennessee does some treetop singing, it also sings at intermediate levels and even down at feeding level—often in adjacent alders close to the ground. The nest is on the ground, as in all northern *Vermivora*, usually in wet moss at the base of a small shrub. Bay-breasted Warblers may be common in such woodland, especially in the east, and Myrtle and Nashville Warblers also occur in some numbers.

c) In *Open Forest with Dense Understory of Coniferous Reproduction* or at woodland edges with similar reproduction, the Magnolia Warbler is a dominant bird in the southern part of the Boreal Forest. This bird sings and feeds between 10 and 45 feet up, and nests about five (1–35) feet up. It is interesting to note that Saunders (1936) considered it a treetop bird in beech-hemlock woods in western New York, one of the many examples of habitat and behavior variation in different parts of a species' range.

In this woodland type, Bay-breasted, Nashville and Blackburnian Warblers may also be common, the first two extending farther north than the Magnolia.

d) In *Cut-over, Burnt,* and *Blow-down* areas within the forest, where raspberries, fireweed and Mountain Maple grow rank among fallen tree trunks, the Mourning Warbler is at home, singing its pleasant "turtling" song about 20 (1–60) feet up from some deciduous shrub or a higher dead tree nearby. Its nest is placed on or near the ground and the bird becomes as evasive as a mouse if pressed too closely.

e) In *Subalpine* and *Subarctic* areas, the Blackpoll Warbler is the characteristic warbler. It seems equally at home in the low spruce of timberline on all our northeastern mountains, the wind-lashed, fog-shrouded coastal islands of the Maritime Provinces; the vast monotonous expanse of northern Black Spruce forest, and the patchy tundra-coniferous forest ecotone of the subarctic. In these habitats, beset by almost constant winds, it nests 2–10 feet from the ground close to the trunk of a low spruce, where it sits closely. On quiet days it sings from the very tops of the trees.

f) *Black Spruce Bog* with sphagnum moss and patches of heath shrubbery is a habitat shared by three warblers in the western part of the Region—Nashville Warblers in the southern and central areas, Connecticut Warblers in the central area, and Palm Warblers to the north. Eastward, the Palm Warbler becomes dominant. It seems partial to the small "coves" at the edge of the bog, where it places its nest in a sphagnum hummock.

g) In *Alder Bog,* and in the alder-willow thickets which fringe most of the northern lakes and streams, the Wilson's Warbler and Northern Waterthrush are the common species, with the Wilson's extending farther north. In the southern third of the region, Yellow and Magnolia Warblers, Yellowthroats, Canada Warblers, and American Redstarts also occur.

ROLAND C. CLEMENT AND
W. W. H. GUNN

References cited

Bent, Arthur Cleveland. 1953. *Life Histories of North American Wood Warblers. U.S. Nat. Mus., Bull.,* 203.

Cruickshank, A. 1956. "Nesting heights of some woodland warblers in Maine," *Wilson Bull.,* 68:157.

Halliday, W. E. D. 1937. *A Forest Classification for Canada.* Dept. of Mines and Resources, Ottawa Forest Service Bull. 89.

Kendeigh, S. Charles. 1947. *Bird Population Studies in the Coniferous Forest Biome During a Spruce Budworm Outbreak.* Biol. Bull. No. 1, Div. Research, Dept. Lands and Forests, Ontario, Canada.

Palmer, Ralph S. 1949. *Maine Birds.* Bull. Mus. Comp. Zool., Vol. 102, Cambridge, Mass.

Saunders, Aretas A. 1936. *Ecology of the Birds of the Quaker Run Valley, Allegany State Park, New York.* N.Y.S. Mus. Hdbk. 16, Albany.

Stewart, Robert E. and John W. Aldrich. 1951. "Removal and repopulation of breeding birds in a spruce-fir forest community." *Auk,* 68:471–482.

Stewart, Robert E. and John W. Aldrich. 1952. "Ecological studies of breeding bird populations in northern Maine," *Ecology,* 33:226–238.

NOTES ON THE CONTRIBUTORS

DR. ALBERT ELLIS ALLIN was born at Hampton, Ontario. Following studies in Biology and Medicine at the University of Toronto, he received his M.D. degree in 1932. He is a Specialist in Bacteriology and Pathology and is now Director of the Regional Laboratory of the Ontario Department of Health and District Pathologist at Fort William, Ontario. He has written some 100 papers on medical and natural history topics. He is particularly familiar with the fauna and flora of the rugged north shore of Lake Superior both in his native Ontario and also in the adjacent northeast angle of Minnesota.

Dr. Allin is active in the Federation of Ontario Naturalists and in the Minnesota Ornithologists' Union.

EMMET REID BLAKE was born at Abbeville, S.C. Nov. 29, 1908. He was graduated from Presbyterian College, South Carolina, in 1928. He received his Master's Degree at the University of Pittsburgh in 1933. Since then, he has been a Technical Assistant on National Geographic Society expeditions to Brazil and Venezuela and has led a Mandel-Field Museum expedition up the Orinoco River. He has been on many expeditions as ornithologist for the Field Museum, the Carnegie Museum and the Chicago Natural History Museum, where he is presently Curator of Birds. He is a Fellow of the A.O.U. and is the author of the definitive handbook, *Birds of Mexico* (1953), and numerous popular and technical papers. His specialty is Tropical American birds.

JAMES BOND was born in Philadelphia (January 4, 1900) and was educated both in this country and in England. Following graduation from Cambridge University in 1922, he became associated with the Academy of Natural Sciences of Philadelphia. In 1925 he went on an expedition to Brazil with R. M. deSchauensee.

In 1926 Bond initiated an ornithological survey of the West Indies, and up to the present time has visited and explored nearly one hundred islands in that region. His first book, *Birds of the West Indies*, was published by the Academy in 1936. This was followed in 1947 by the *Field Guide to Birds of the West Indies* (Macmillan). More technical publications include the "Check-List of Birds of the West Indies", the last edition published in 1956. In 1946 he was elected a Fellow of the A.O.U. In 1954 he received the Brewster Medal for his West Indian work.

DONALD J. BORROR was born in Columbus, Ohio, August 24, 1907. He was educated at Otterbein College where he was graduated in 1928. At Ohio State University he received his Master's Degree and his Ph.D. He has since held various positions there and is now Associate Professor of Zoology and Entomology. In addition, Dr. Borror has achieved a reputation at the Audubon Nature Camp of Maine where he is instructor in insect study, dragonflies and damselflies being his specialty. He is the author of many scientific publications and has collaborated with

W. W. H. Gunn on the first all-warbler record. Other recordings have been made of insect songs.

MAURICE BROUN writes of himself: "I have had a passion for birds ever since my 13th birthday, though the first 21 years of my life were spent in the brick and concrete wildernesses of New York and Boston.

"My career with birds began in 1927, under Edward Howe Forbush. For two years it was my great good fortune to be associated with him, and to help with the preparation of his *Birds of Massachusetts*. After this experience, which widened my horizons enormously and enabled me to meet many of the ornithologists of that day, I spent three years developing the Pleasant Valley Sanctuary in Lenox, Massachusetts. Then followed three years of research and bird-banding at the Austin Ornithological Research Station, on Cape Cod. Later I spent nine memorable summers directing the nature activities at Long Trail Lodge, home of the Green Mountain Club, near Rutland, Vt. But in recent years most of my time and energies have been concentrated at Hawk Mountain Sanctuary in Pennsylvania. The story of my adventures in conservation and bird-watching is related in my book, *Hawks Aloft*. I also had a three-year hitch in the Navy, during which time I spent many happy hours watching birds in the South Pacific."

ROLAND C. CLEMENT was born at Fall River, Mass., Nov. 22, 1912. He received his education at Massachusetts State College, Brown University and Cornell. He has been Executive Secretary of the Audubon Society of Rhode Island since 1950. He has been bird-bander, museum editor, and field biologist. During World War II he spent two years in Ungava-Labrador as army weatherman and did natural history work on the side. Since the war he has made five spring-time trips to the Gaspé Peninsula of Quebec to study its bird life. He has an M.S. degree in wildlife conservation from Cornell. He is married and has three children.

HOWARD L. COGSWELL reports: "My interest in birds was first developed in my boyhood on a Pennsylvania farm and during my high school years at Montrose, Pa. After beginning college in another science major, I shifted to a Zoology-Botany combination in order to prepare myself for work with living things, which always held more appeal for me than equations and chemicals. My college work was twice interrupted, however, particularly by a period of 11 years (1936–47) during which I married and worked in non-biological pursuits to support a family. After a period of service in the Navy in World War II a return to college was possible, and I graduated from Whittier College, California in 1948, then went

on for graduate study in Ornithology and Ecology at the University of California, Berkeley, where I received an M.A. in 1951, and hope to receive my Ph.D. in 1957. While now in a position to teach various aspects of Zoology and Ecology, which I do in my capacity as Assistant Professor at Mills College, bird study continues to be a regularly pursued hobby as well as being one of the subjects I teach."

ALLAN D. CRUICKSHANK was born in the Virgin Islands but grew up around New York City, where he obtained a B.S. degree from New York University. For more than 20 years he has been photographer, lecturer and ornithology instructor for the National Audubon Society. He is an elective member of the A.O.U. and past President of the Linnaean Society. He is the author of *Birds Around New York City* written for the American Museum of Natural History where he formerly worked. Other publications include *Wings In the Wilderness, Cruickshank's Pocket Guide to Birds, Summer Birds of Lincoln County, Maine* and his recently completed *Hunting With the Camera*. He is editor of the Christmas Bird Count for *Audubon Field Notes*. His bird photographs have appeared in over 100 books. He makes his home in Florida with his wife Helen.

JOHN HENRY DICK writes: "Since childhood I have been interested in birds. At my family's home on Long Island, I always had various species of Bantams, pigeons, ducks, etc., graduating in my teens to pheasants, fancy ducks, and quail.

"Started drawing birds at the age of eight. My only formal art education was two years at the Yale Art School 1939-1940. Served three years in the Army Air Corps of which one was overseas in the Pacific.

"Since World War II have been living at Meggett, S.C. spending most of my time painting. Travel quite a bit with bird study as the major motive. I have seen every North American Warbler (North of the Rio Grande) with one exception, the Mexican Ground-chat. My greatest personal triumph in the field was the opportunity to take Ludlow Griscom to a singing Male Bachman's Warbler, forty miles from my home: this rarest and most elusive of our small birds was one of the very few North American species which Mr. Griscom had never seen.

"Other published works of mine include plates in South Carolina Bird Life (Sprunt & Chamberlain) and Florida Bird Life (Sprunt)." Dick was born May 12, 1919. He took a month's safari in Kenya, in 1956, in order to study African birds.

EUGENE EISENMANN was born in Panama; now resides in New York. B.S. and LL.B. (both York, and Federation of New York State Bird Clubs. Elective Member, A.O.U. Life Member, Cooper and

Harvard). Former President, Linnaean Society of New Wilson Ornithological Societies. Author, *"The Species of Middle American Birds"* (1955), *"Annotated List of Birds of Barro Colorado Island, Panama Canal Zone"* (Smithsonian Misc. Coll., 1952), and numerous articles and papers on birds. For many years has spent vacations from active law practice studying birds in Panama, supplementing field work with research on neotropical birds at the American Museum of Natural History. *"The Species of Middle American Birds"* is the first complete list of all species known to occur from Mexico to Panama inclusive, with English as well as technical names for each species, and an outline of range. He had been active in the effort to achieve a Pan-American uniformity in the English names used for birds of widespread distribution, in the hope of facilitating recognition and simplifying the task of the ornithologist. Mr. Eisenmann has recently been appointed Research Associate, Department of Birds at the American Museum of Natural History.

W. EARL GODFREY is Curator of Ornithology at the National Museum of Canada. Born in Wolfville, Nova Scotia, he acquired there an early enthusiasm for birds. He has studied birds on scientific expeditions to various parts of Canada and has done field work also in central and eastern United States. From 1942 to 1946 he was Research Associate and Assistant Ornithologist at the Cleveland Museum of Natural History, Ohio. A Fellow of the American Ornithologists' Union, his published papers are both technical and popular, the former dealing mainly with the taxonomy and distribution of North American birds.

LUDLOW GRISCOM was born in New York City, June 17, 1890. He graduated from Columbia University in 1912 and received his Master's Degree at Cornell University in 1915. In 1926 he married Edith Sloan; they have three children. He started his teaching career at Cornell as a Biology Instructor. From there he went to the American Museum of Natural History as Assistant Curator of Ornithology; then to the Museum of Comparative Zoology at Harvard University, where since 1948 he has remained as Research Ornithologist. He has recently retired as Chairman of the Board of the National Audubon Society after serving on the board for 12 years. In 1956 he was elected President of the A.O.U. at Denver, Colorado, but was forced to resign for health reasons (1957). He is the author of many books and 500 papers on ornithology among which are *Birds of the N. Y. City Region*, 1923 and *Modern Bird Study*, 1945. His papers have dealt chiefly with Central American birds. Warblers have been his hobby ever since

he was a young man. In 1956 he received the Audubon Conservation Medal.

WILLIAM W. H. GUNN was born in Toronto, March 18, 1913; son of William Hamilton Gunn and Phyllis Moffat Gunn. Married in 1938 to Anne Frances Wright; they have two children.

After an early schooling abroad, and at Upper Canada College, he graduated from the University of Toronto in Commerce and Finance in 1934. He then engaged in business until 1941, when he enlisted as a private in the Royal Canadian Ordnance Corps. In 1945-46, he participated as ordnance observer in Exercise Musk-ox, which took place in the Northwest Territories. Among other duties, he assisted in the preparation of the wildlife report emanating from that Exercise. He was retired from the army in 1946 as a lieutenant-colonel.

Reaching the conclusion that his real interest lay in natural history, he then undertook graduate studies in zoology at the University of Toronto. His Ph.D. degree was granted in 1951.

Dr. Gunn has played an important role in exploring the relationships between weather and bird migration. He helped to organize co-operative studies of migration across the eastern part of the continent and is a co-author of a number of scientific articles dealing with bird migration and the weather.

While carrying on graduate studies at the University of Toronto, he spent his summers doing biological research for the Ontario Department of Lands and Forests. In the summer of 1949, he served as wildlife observer for the Canadian Wildlife Service on the joint Canadian-United States arctic weather station resupply mission in the little-known regions of the High Arctic.

In May, 1950, Dr. Gunn was appointed biologist on the staff of the Division of Research, Ontario Department of Lands and Forests.

He has been a member of the conservation committee of the Wilson Ornithological Club. In 1951, he was elected a member of the A.O.U.

Since 1952, he has served on the staff of the Federation of Ontario Naturalists and at present holds the position of Field Secretary. Much of his time is devoted to accumulating a library of sound recordings of birds, with warblers as a specialty. Three records have been published by the Federation of Ontario Naturalists. In 1957 he collaborated with Donald J. Borror on the first full length all-warbler record.

KARL W. HALLER was born in Wheeling, W. Va. October 12, 1916. Attended Bethany College, and received a BS degree in biology in 1939. An MS degree in zoology was received from West Virginia University in 1941.

He was instructor in biology at Washington and Jefferson College, Washington, Pa., 1948–49.

World War II service with the Air Force began in 1942 and ended in late 1946, with a year's duty in England and two in France. Re-entered military service in July 1949 and has continued there to the present.

Member of the Carnegie Museum—Cornell University ornithological group to Oklahoma in 1937. Member and photographer of the Carnegie Museum group to the Hudson Bay region of Canada in 1941.

Member of Brooks Bird Club, Royal Australasian Ornithologists' Union, and life member: British Ornithologists' Union, Wilson Ornithological Society, Cooper Ornithological Society, American Society of Mammalogists and the American Rifle Association.

FREDERICK CHARLES LINCOLN was born in Denver, Colorado, May 5, 1892. He received his education at the Denver Technical High School and the University of Denver. He started his career at the Denver Museum of Natural History where he became Curator of Ornithology from 1913 to 1920. At that time, he joined the U.S. Biological Survey and worked his way up to Senior Biologist. He is now Principal Biologist and Assistant to the Director, of the Bureau of Sport Fisheries and Wildlife. He is a Life Fellow of the A.O.U. and served as Treasurer and Business Manager, 1944–1948; was President of the Baird Ornithological Club from 1938–1941 and of the Washington Biologists Field Club, 1937–1940. He served in World War I and at the outbreak of World War II was Captain, Sig. Res. Office of the Chief Signal Officer. He holds the honorary degree of Doctor of Science from the University of Colorado, the Gold Medal and Distinguished Service Award from the United States Department of the Interior. He has done extensive field work in most of the States of the Union and in a dozen foreign countries, both for the Denver Museum of Natural History and the United States Fish and Wildlife Service. His technical and popular papers on ornithology and conservation number in the hundreds and include several books.

GALE MONSON was born August 1, 1912, at Munich, North Dakota. Reared on a wheat farm in the Red River Valley of the North. Graduated from North Dakota State College at Fargo in 1934. Went to Arizona that summer and has been there and in New Mexico ever since, with time out for U. S. Army service that took him to India, Burma, and Western China. Has been employed by the U.S. Fish and Wildlife Service since 1940; is presently refuge manager in charge of the Imperial National Wildlife Refuge, and the Kofa & Cabeza Prieta Game Ranges, stationed at Yuma, Arizona. Married Sally Myer of Tucson, Arizona in 1941, and has 5 children.

JAMES ALEXANDER MUNRO. Born at Kildonan, Manitoba. on November 8, 1884. Attended public schools in Toronto, Ontario. Moved to British Columbia in 1911 and adopted ornithology as a profession. For the next nine years was employed by various institutions and individuals to collect birds and mammals for scientific study. In 1920 joined the staff of the newly established Canadian government service which administered the Migratory Birds Convention Act. His duties were largely concerned with the study of the distribution and life histories of migratory birds in western Canada and the preparation of scientific papers on the subject. Since retirement from the Canadian Wildlife Service in 1949 these studies have been continued in British Columbia and the western United States.

An associate of the A.O.U. since 1912, he was elected Member in 1926, and Fellow in 1939. Member of the Cooper Ornithological Society and Charter Member of the Pacific Northwest Bird and Mammal Society and the Society of Systematic Zoology.

HARRY C. OBERHOLSER was born June 25, 1870, at Brooklyn, N.Y. He married Mary Forrest Smith of Washington, D.C., June 30, 1914.

Educated at George Washington University, Washington, D.C., where he received degrees of B.A. and M.S. in 1914, and Ph.D. in 1916.

Served as ornithologist in the U.S. Biological Survey, later Fish and Wildlife Service, in Washington, D.C., almost continuously from 1895 to 1942. There began and organized the federal bird banding work.

Author of about 800 publications, mostly on Birds. Describer of about 100 new or renamed genera; also about 560 new species and subspecies of birds from many parts of the world.

Member of scientific societies in five continents— North America, South America, Europe, Asia, and Australia.

ROGER TORY PETERSON's field guides have become the bird-watcher's bibles not only in America but in Europe. His famous paintings and prints adorn many bird books; and he has lectured before distinguished audiences throughout this continent and abroad for the National Audubon Society and others.

He was born in Jamestown, N.Y., where he attended the public schools. From the age of eleven the outdoor world formed the hub about which his life revolved. His art career began at the Art Students' League in New York City. Later he attended the National Academy of Design.

While teaching art and science in Boston he created his first *Field Guide to the Birds*. First published in 1934, it was regarded as revolutionary and has since sold over 400,000 copies. In that same year he joined the staff of the National Audubon Society. He continued to paint and to photograph birds. His *Field Guide to Western Birds* was published in 1941. In 1954 the *Field Guide to the Birds of Britain and Europe* was published in London. It was soon translated into Dutch, German, French, Swedish and Spanish. Peterson is editor of the Houghton-Mifflin Field Guide Series. He is also author of *Birds Over America,* featuring his own photography, and *Wildlife in Color.* His most recent book is *Wild America,* written in collaboration with James Fisher. He is a fellow and member of the council of the A.O.U. and honorary vice-president of the New Jersey Audubon Society, Massachusetts Audubon Society, Audubon Society of the District of Columbia, and Rhode Island Audubon Society, and a Director of the National Audubon Society. He is art director of the National Wildlife Federation and holds a degree of Doctor of Sciences from Franklin and Marshall College. He is a recipient of the prized Brewster Medal of the A.O.U.

As an author, artist, scientist and lecturer, Roger Tory Peterson has probably interested more people in bird life than any other man living.

HERBERT RAVENEL SASS has lived in the Carolina low country all his life, mostly in Charleston, where he now resides with his wife and children. He graduated from Charleston College in 1905 and subsequently worked at the Charleston Museum and on the staff of the *News and Courier.* In 1910 he became city editor and later assistant editor of that paper. In 1924 he decided to quit newspaper work and devote his entire time to free-lance writing. For many years his novels, historical articles and nature writings have appeared in leading American magazines. He is the author of a dozen books. Of all his works, perhaps his best known are his nature essays. His lifelong interest in nature, especially ornithology, has never flagged. He is a member of the St. Cecilia Society and the St. George's Society and is also a member of Phi Beta Kappa and Kappa Alpha fraternities.

ALEXANDER F. SKUTCH was born in Baltimore, Maryland, in 1904. He attended private schools in that city and in 1921 entered Johns Hopkins University. In the summer of 1926 he visited the island of Jamaica with a botanical expedition from Johns Hopkins, and after his companions returned to the north he stayed on a banana plantation to study the anatomy of the banana leaf, upon which he wrote his doctoral dissertation. After receiving the degree of Ph.D. from Hopkins in 1928, he was granted fellowships which permitted him to make long visits to the Caribbean lowlands of Panama and Honduras in 1929 and 1930.

After filling a temporary appointment as instructor in botany at Hopkins, he spent the year 1933 in the high mountains of Guatemala, engaged in ornithological and botanical studies, and the following year he travelled widely in the highlands of Guatemala as botanical collector for the Arnold Arboretum of Harvard University. He then went to Barro Colorado Island for four months of intensive bird study. In 1940 he travelled in Peru, Ecuador and Colombia as botanist of a party sent out by the United States Department of Agriculture to search for wild rubber trees and report on the possibility of developing rubber plantations. For a month the exploring party voyaged on the upper Amazon and its tributaries in a Peruvian gunboat.

After his return from this expedition, Skutch bought a farm newly carved from the great forests in the valley of El General in southern Costa Rica, a region so hemmed in by high mountains that it was then readily accessible only by air. Since 1941 he has dwelt on this farm, observing the birds and writing. In 1946 and 1952 he received fellowships from the Guggenheim Foundation which enabled him to visit the United States for study.

His published writings include *Life Histories of Central American Birds* (Cooper Ornithological Society, Berkeley, California, Vol. I, 1954; Vol. II, in press), a philosophical book and many papers on botany, ornithology, conservation, and the "ethical approach" to nature. He is a Fellow of the A.O.U. and was awarded this society's Brewster Medal for his accounts of tropical American birds. In 1950 he married Pamela Joan Lankester of Cartago, Costa Rica.

ALEXANDER SPRUNT, JR., was born in Rock Hill, South Carolina (1898), his family moving to Charleston, S.C., when he was 2 years old. He has lived there ever since. He attended Davidson College (N.C.) 1914-1918, enlisting in the U.S. Navy just before the close of his senior year. Returning to college after the 1st World War, he engaged in nature writing and in 1924 joined the staff of the Charleston Museum in the Department of Ornithology, becoming Curator in 1926. In the fall of 1934, he was asked to undertake a field research project for the National Audubon Society and in January of 1935, he became a member of the staff of that organization.

For several years he was Supervisor of the southern sanctuaries of the Society, then became the first leader of the now famous Audubon Wildlife Tours, which he has conducted in Florida, South Carolina, Virginia and Texas. He was among the first lecturers of the Audubon Screen Tours, a series of lectures now current in 200 cities of the United States, Canada and the West Indies. He had charge of bird instruction at the Audubon Camp of Texas during the years of its existence.

Writing has occupied much of his time; aside from many items of scientific interest in technical journals, he has contributed to several popular journals.

His major results have been *South Carolina Bird-life* (Univ. So. Car. Press, 1949); the revision of *Florida Birdlife* (Coward-McCann, 1954); *Album of Southern Birds* (Univ. Texas Press, 1953); *North American Birds of Prey* (Harper's, 1955).

He joined the American Ornithologists' Union as an Associate in 1923, was elected Member in 1936, and Fellow in 1950.

He has done field work in ornithology in every one of the 48 states, plus parts of Mexico and the West Indies. The majority of such work has been accomplished in the Southeast and Gulf Coast region.

In 1954 he was awarded the honorary degree of Doctor of Science by his alma mater, Davidson College, North Carolina. He is married and has two children.

HENRY M. STEVENSON was born in Birmingham, Alabama, February 25, 1914. He received his A.B. at Birmingham—Southern College, his Master's at the University of Alabama and his Ph.D. at Cornell (1943). Since then he has taught at the University of Mississippi, Memphis State College, Emory and Henry College and Florida State University, where he now holds the rank of Associate Professor. He is married and has four children.

JOSSELYN VAN TYNE, one of the deans of American ornithology, received his A.B. at Harvard and his Ph.D. at the University of Michigan. Until his untimely death, Jan. 30, 1957, he was Curator of Birds at the Museum of Zoology, University of Michigan. Under his influence, this University became a center of ornithological education. Professor Van Tyne was Past President of the A.O.U. and did extensive field work on birds in Panama, British Honduras, Guatemala, Yucatan, the Bahamas, Indo China and various parts of the United States. His final expedition took him to Northern Baffin Island. His articles and papers were widely published. Under his editorship the *Wilson Bulletin* was considered by many to be the best ornithological journal in the U.S. Generous of his time and unselfish in his friendships he will be greatly missed.

LAWRENCE H. WALKINSHAW, D.D.S. was born February 25, 1904 near Battle Creek, Michigan; went one year to Olivet College, graduated from the University of Michigan in Dentistry in 1929. He considers himself an amateur ornithologist. "I became interested in birds when 10 or 11 years old and have studied them ever since. Have made trips to Alaska, Cuba, Mexico and the far west of United States as well as into Northwest Canada in bird study."

A frequent contributor to the *Wilson Bulletin*, Dr. Walkinshaw's papers on the birds of the Michigan area are noteworthy. His book on the Sandhill Crane is outstanding. He is a fellow of the A.O.U.

FRANCIS MARION WESTON was born in Charleston, South Carolina, December 5, 1887, the eldest of four children. He graduated from the College of Charleston, June 28, 1907 having majored in Engineering. For some 42 years he served as draftsman under U.S. Civil Service, as follows: Charleston Navy Yard, 5¼ years; Bureau of Lighthouses, Washington, D.C., 2 years; Naval Air Station, Pensacola, Florida, 35¼ years. He has been married twice and has 2 children and 2 grandchildren. He is a Fellow of the A.O.U. Active in the Florida Audubon Society, Alabama Ornithological Society, and the Charleston (S.C.) Natural History Society. Extra-curricular interests: Ornithology, continuously since November, 1905, starting under the inspiration and guidance of Herbert Ravenel Sass. Has written distributional notes for ornithological journals as well as contributing to *Bird-Lore Magazine* as the "reporter" at Pensacola to its Season Department, 1924-1948; "voluntary collaborator" with U.S. Fish & Wildlife Service, sending in spring and fall migration reports every year from 1908 to the present (said to be one of the longest unbroken series of reports).

APPENDIX A

The Wood Warbler Family, Including Subspecies Recognized in the United States and Canada (1957 A.O.U. Checklist)

GENUS	SPECIES	SUBSPECIES	PL. NO.	COMMON NAME
Mniotilta	*varia*		(2)	Black-and-White w.
Protonotaria	*citrea*		(1)	Prothonotary w.
Limnothlypis	*swainsonii*		(3)	Swainson's w.
Helmitheros	*vermivoros*		(2)	Worm-eating w.
Vermivora	*chrysoptera*		(4)	Golden-winged w.
Vermivora	*pinus*		(4)	Blue-winged w.
Vermivora	*bachmanii*		(3)	Bachman's w.
Vermivora	*peregrina*		(6)	Tennessee w.
Vermivora	*celata* (4) *	*celata*	(6)	Eastern Orange-crowned w.
		orestera		Rocky Mountain Orange-crowned w.
		lutescens	(6)	Lutescent Orange-crowned w.
		sordida		Dusky Orange-crowned w.
Vermivora	*ruficapilla* (2)	*ruficapilla*	(6)	Eastern Nashville w.
		ridgwayi		Western Nashville (Caleveras) w.
Vermivora	*virginiae*		(5)	Virginia's w.
Vermivora	*crissalis*		(5)	Colima w.
Vermivora	*luciae*		(5)	Lucy's w.
Vermivora	*gutturalis*		(33)	Flame-throated (Irazu) w.
Vermivora	*superciliosa* (3)		(31)	Crescent-chested (Hartlaub's) w.
Parula	*americana*		(7)	Northern Parula w.
Parula	*pitiayumi* (13)		(8)	Olive-backed (Sennett's) w.
Parula	*graysoni*		(8)	Socorro w.
Peucedramus	*taeniatus* (4)	*arizonae*	(9)	Northern Olive w.
Dendroica	*petechia* (33)	*aestiva*	(10)	Eastern Yellow w.
		amnicola		Newfoundland Yellow w.
		rubiginosa	(10)	Alaska Yellow w.
		morcomi		Rocky Mountain Yellow w.
		sonorana		Sonora Yellow w.
		gundlachi		Cuban Yellow (Golden) w.
		castaneiceps	(10)	Mangrove w.
		brewsteri		California Yellow w.
Dendroica	*magnolia*		(11)	Magnolia w.

* Numbers after certain species refer to the total number of subspecies or races listed by Hellmayr (*Catalogue of Birds of the Americas,* etc., Field Mus. of Nat. Hist., Chicago, 1935, Part VIII), with subsequent additions by others.

GENUS	SPECIES	SUBSPECIES	PL. NO.	COMMON NAME
Dendroica	*tigrina*		(12)	Cape May w.
Dendroica	*caerulescens* (2)	*caerulescens*	(13)	Northern Black-throated Blue w.
		cairnsi		Cairns' w.
Dendroica	*coronata* (2)	*coronata*	(14)	Eastern Myrtle w.
		hooveri		Alaska Myrtle w.
Dendroica	*auduboni* (2)	*auduboni*	(14)	Pacific Audubon's w.
		memorabilis	(14)	Black-fronted (Rocky Mountain) w.
Dendroica	*nigrescens*		(15)	Black-throated Gray w.
Dendroica	*townsendi*		(16)	Townsend's w.
Dendroica	*virens* (2)	*virens*	(18)	Black-throated Green w.
		waynei		Wayne's w.
Dendroica	*chrysoparia*		(15)	Golden-cheeked w.
Dendroica	*occidentalis*		(16)	Hermit w.
Dendroica	*cerulea*		(17)	Cerulean w.
Dendroica	*fusca*		(17)	Blackburnian w.
Dendroica	*dominica* (4)	*dominica*	(7)	Eastern Yellow-throated w.
		albilora		Sycamore w.
		stoddardi		Stoddard's w.
Dendroica	*graciae* (2)	*graciae*	(9)	Northern Grace's w.
Dendroica	*adelaidae* (3)		(32)	Adelaide's w.
Dendroica	*pensylvanica*		(20)	Chestnut-sided w.
Dendroica	*castanea*		(19)	Bay-breasted w.
Dendroica	*striata*		(19)	Blackpoll w.
Dendroica	*pinus* (4)	*pinus*	(18)	Northern Pine w.
		florida		Florida Pine w.
Dendroica	*kirtlandii*		(21)	Kirtland's w.
Dendroica	*pityophila*		(32)	Olive-capped w.
Dendroica	*discolor* (2)	*discolor*	(21)	Northern Prairie w.
		paludicola		Florida Prairie w.
Dendroica	*vitellina* (3)		(32)	Vitelline w.
Dendroica	*palmarum* (2)	*palmarum*	(22)	Western Palm w.
		hypochrysea	(22)	Yellow Palm w.
Dendroica	*plumbea* (2)		(32)	Plumbeous w.
Dendroica	*pharetra*		(33)	Arrow-headed (Streaked) w.
Catharopeza	*bishopi*		(33)	Whistling (Bishop's) w.
Leucopeza	*semperi*		(33)	Semper's w.
Teretistris	*fernandinae*		(31)	Yellow-headed (Fernandina's) w.
	fornsi		(33)	Oriente (Forn's) w.
Microligea	*palustris* (2)		(31)	Green-tailed Ground w.
Microligea	*montana*		(33)	White-winged Ground w.
Seiurus	*aurocapillus* (3)	*aurocapillus*	(23)	Eastern Ovenbird
		furvior		Newfoundland Ovenbird
		cinereus		Gray Ovenbird
Seiurus	*noveboracensis* (3)	*noveboracensis*	(23)	Northern (Small-billed) Waterthrush
		notabilis		Grinnell's Waterthrush
		limnaeus		British Columbia (Northern) Waterthrush
Seiurus	*motacilla*		(23)	Louisiana Waterthrush

GENUS	SPECIES	SUBSPECIES	PL. NO.	COMMON NAME
Oporornis	*formosus*		(24)	Kentucky w.
Oporornis	*agilis*		(25)	Connecticut w.
Oporornis	*philadelphia*		(25)	Mourning w.
Oporornis	*tolmiei* (2)	*tolmiei*	(25)	Northern MacGillivray's w.
		monticola		Southern MacGillivray's w.
Geothlypis	*trichas* (14)	*trichas*	(26)	Maryland Yellowthroat
		brachidactyla		Northern Yellowthroat
		typhicola		Athens Yellowthroat
		ignota		Florida Yellowthroat
		campicola		Northern Plains Yellowthroat
		occidentalis		Western Yellowthroat
		insperata		Brownsville Yellowthroat
		chryseola		Golden (Sonoran) Yellowthroat
		arizela		Pacific Yellowthroat
		sinuosa		Salt Marsh Yellowthroat
		scirpicola		Tule Yellowthroat
		modesta		San Blas Yellowthroat
Geothlypis	*beldingi* (2)	*beldingi*	(26)	Belding's (Peninsular) Yellowthroat
		goldmani		Goldman's Peninsular Yellowthroat
Geothlypis	*rostrata* (3)			Bahaman Yellowthroat
Geothlypis	*flavovelata*		(31)	Yellow-crowned Yellowthroat
Geothlypis	*chapalensis*			Chapala Yellowthroat
Geothlypis	*chiriquensis*			Chiriqui Yellowthroat
Geothlypis	*semiflava* (2)			Olive-crowned (Lutescent) Yellow-throat
Geothlypis	*speciosa*		(31)	Blackpolled Yellowthroat
Geothlypis	*nelsoni* (2)			Hooded Yellowthroat
Geothlypis	*aequinoctialis* (5)			Masked Yellowthroat
Chamaethlypis	*poliocephala* (4)		(8)	Ground-chat
Icteria	*virens* (2)	*virens*	(27)	Eastern Yellow-breasted Chat
		auricollis		Western Yellow-breasted (Long-tailed) Chat
Granatellus	*venustus* (2)		(33)	Red-breasted Chat
Granatellus	*sallaei* (2)		(31)	Gray-throated Chat
Granatellus	*pelzelni* (2)		(35)	Rose-breasted Chat
Wilsonia	*citrina*		(24)	Hooded w.
Wilsonia	*pusilla* (3)	*pusilla*	(28)	Wilson's w.
		pileolata		Northern Pileolated w.
		chryseola	(28)	Golden Pileolated w.
Wilsonia	*canadensis*		(28)	Canada w.
Cardellina	*rubrifrons* (2)		(29)	Red-faced w.
Setophaga	*ruticilla*	*ruticilla*	(30)	Southern American Redstart
		tricolora		Northern American Redstart
Setophaga	*picta* (2)	*picta*	(29)	Northern Painted Redstart
Myioborus	*miniatus* (9)		(32)	Slate-throated Redstart
Myioborus	*torquatus*		(33)	Collared Redstart
Myioborus	*ornatus* (2)		(35)	Golden-fronted (Yellow-crowned) Redstart

GENUS	SPECIES	SUBSPECIES	PL. NO.	COMMON NAME
Myioborus . . .	*melanocephalus* (4)		(35)	Spectacled Redstart
Myioborus . . .	*albifrons*		(35)	White-fronted Redstart
Myioborus . . .	*ruficoronatus* (race of *melanocephalus*) . . .		(35)	Chestnut-crowned Redstart
Myioborus . . .	*cardonai*		(35)	Saffron-breasted Redstart
Myioborus . . .	*albifacies*		(35)	White-faced Redstart
Myioborus . . .	*flavivertex*		(35)	Yellow-crowned Redstart
Myioborus . . .	*brunniceps* (3)		(35)	Brown-capped Redstart
Euthlypis . . .	*lachrymosa* (3)		(33)	Fan-tailed w.
Ergaticus . . .	*ruber* (2)		(31)	Red w.
Ergaticus . . .	*versicolor*		(33)	Pink-headed w.
Basileuterus * . .	*belli* (2)		(32)	Golden-browed (Bell's) w.
Basileuterus . . .	*rufifrons* (5)		(32)	Rufous-capped w.
Basileuterus . . .	*tristriatus* (10)		(31)	Three-striped w.
Basileuterus . . .	*melanogenys* (4)		(31)	Black-cheeked w.
Basileuterus . . .	*delattrii* (2)		(32)	Chestnut-capped w.
Basileuterus . . .	*fulvicauda* (5) (race of *rivularis*)		(33)	Buff-rumped w.
Basileuterus . . .	*nigrocristatus* (3)		(34)	Black-crested w.
Basileuterus . . .	*luteoviridis* (3)		(34)	Citrine w.
Basileuterus . . .	*richardsoni* (race of *luteoviridis*)			Richardson's w.
Basileuterus . . .	*signatus* (2)		(34)	Yellow-green (Short-winged) w.
Basileuterus . . .	*flaveolus*		(34)	Flavescent (Baird's) w.
Basileuterus . . .	*griseiceps*		(34)	Gray-headed w.
Basileuterus . . .	*leucophrys*		(35)	White-striped w.
Basileuterus . . .	*leucoblepharus*		(33)	White-browed w.
Basileuterus . . .	*bivittatus* (2)		(34)	Two-banded w.
Basileuterus . . .	*chrysogaster* (2)		(34)	Golden-bellied w.
Basileuterus . . .	*basilicus*		(34)	Santa Marta w.
Basileuterus . . .	*trifasciatus* (2)		(34)	Three-banded w.
Basileuterus . . .	*hypoleucus*		(34)	White-bellied w.
Basileuterus . . .	*culicivorus* (9)		(34)	Golden-crowned (Lichtenstein) w.
Basileuterus . . .	*cinereicollis* (2)		(34)	Gray-throated w.
Basileuterus . . .	*coronatus* (4)		(34)	Russet-crowned w.
Basileuterus . . .	*castaneiceps* (3) (race of *coronatus*)			
Basileuterus . . .	*fraseri* (2)		(33)	Fraser's (Slate and Gold) w.
Basileuterus . . .	*rivularis* (3)		(35)	River w.

* Authorities differ on the number of species of Basileuterus. Blake recognizes 22, following Zimmer (Amer. Mus. Novit., 1949, no. 1428, pp. 53–57) and merges *B. fulvicauda* with *rivularis*, *B. richardsoni* with *leuteoviridis*, and *B. castaneiceps* with *coronatus*. De Schauensee's authoritative check-list of the birds of Colombia concurs in this. The same authorities consider *Myioborus ruficoronatus* as a race of *M. melanocephalus*. Today's tendency is toward lumping rather than splitting. And so the 117 species of warblers listed in this Appendix become 113.

APPENDIX B

Suggested Re-classification of the Warbler Genera

1. *Mniotilta* (Vieillot, 1816). It is strikingly distinct in color pattern, creeping habits and the important structural fact that the middle toe with claw is longer than the tarsus, and that the hind toe is longer than the inner toe. Rictal bristles weak, wing-tip long and pointed; bill very slender, compressed culmen slightly decurved. Monotypic, based on *varia* Linnaeus (1766).

2. *Helmitheros* (Rafinesque, 1819). Swamp or terrestrial warblers with strong feet, generally brown or dull coloration, with a long, slender bill, rictal bristles obsolete, long wing-tip, and short tail. Includes *Limnothlypis* (Stone, 1914), Swainson's Warbler, stated by Baird to be a "good subgenus" on trivial differences in the bill. Based on *Motacilla Vermivora* (Gmelin, 1789).

3. *Protonotaria* (Baird, 1858). A swamp warbler, nesting in holes in trees. Bill long, not acute or compressed, the culmen slightly curved; bristles apparent. Coloration with lots of brilliant yellow with white spots in tail but no wing bars. Undertail coverts greatly elongated, reaching base of tail. Monotypic, type *citrea* (Boddaert, 1783).

4. *Vermivora* (Swainson, 1827). Small, slender-billed, mostly arboreal warblers, usually highly migratory, with long wing-tip, but the resident tropical species with shorter wing-tip. Rictal bristles obsolete to conspicuous. Bill very acute, culmen usually straight, very rarely decurved; tarsus short, toes slender. Color exceedingly variable, usually bright and variegated, to very dull and drab. Type species *pinus* (Linnaeus, 1766). Includes *Oreothlypis* (Ridgway), *Parula* (Bonaparte), *Dendroica* (Gray), *Peucedramus* (Henshaw) and *Catharopeza* (Sclater).

DISCUSSION. As can readily be inferred from the analysis of generic characters, this vast genus clearly inosculates in every alleged generic character.

In the rictal bristles we pass from obsolete in *Vermivora* to obvious in *Parula* and *Dendroica*. In color *Oreothlypis superciliosa* bridges *Vermivora–Parula*. The bill varies from slender (*Vermivora*) (*Parula*) to stouter (*Dendroica*); subulate in *Peucedramus*, decurved in *Vermivora bachmanii*, to as long as head (*Dendroica dominica*). Years ago van Rossem disposed of *Oreothlypis*; Baird included the Olive Warbler in *Dendroica*; Bond has remarked on how poor a genus *Parula* was, and both Bond and Ridgway suggested that *Catharopeza bishopi* of St. Vincent was an aberrant *Dendroica*.

5. *Leucopeza* (Sclater, 1876). Of very dull coloration. Wing concave and greatly rounded; rictal bristles obsolete; bill long and pointed; supposedly terrestrial with long tarsus and claw. This very rare bird is little known, including its nest and song. Monotypic, type *semperi* (Sclater) of St. Lucia, Lesser Antilles.

6. *Seiurus* (Swainson, 1827). Terrestrial, with powerful, ringing songs. Rictal bristles obsolete. Wing long and pointed; tail even or slightly emarginate; coloration with no bright yellow, and streaked beneath. Undertail coverts elongated. Three species, the type *aurocapillus* (Linnaeus).

7. *Teretistris* (Cabanis, 1855). Small, generally terrestrial warblers, never arboreal; rictal bristles obsolete; wing rounded with a very short wing-tip; culmen strongly curved; song and call notes very peculiar. Confined to Cuba; two clearly representative species at opposite ends of the island. Type *fernandinae* (Lembeye) at western end and *fornsi* (Gundlach) at eastern.

8. *Microligea* (Cory, 1884). Small, mostly terrestrial warblers of plain coloration and peculiar rasping song and call notes. Rictal bristles obsolete; wing rounded with very short wing-tip; bill more or

less as in *Dendroica,* relatively stout, the culmen not strongly curved; tail as long as wing, graduated and decidedly rounded. Confined to Hispaniola. Type species *palustris* (Cory) in the lowlands and *montana* (Chapman) in the highlands; of very distinct coloration.

9. *Oporornis* (Baird, 1858). Smal or medium-sized terrestrial warblers with loud ringing songs. Rictal bristles obsolete. Wing long and pointed; tail strongly rounded; undertail coverts greatly elongated in the Connecticut and Kentucky Warblers. Coloration green and yellow, with no streaks below. Four species, the type *agilis* (Wilson). The Mourning and MacGillivray's Warbler do *not* have elongated undertail coverts and approach *Geothlypis* in other respects, where they were referred by all authors prior to Ridgway.

10. *Geothlypis* (Cabanis, 1847). Small, terrestrial swamp-loving warblers with attractive warbling songs. Rictal bristles obsolete; wing rounded; the wing-tip very short; tail of variable length, always rounded. Coloration chiefly green and yellow, males with some black around the head. At least ten species, mostly in tropical Central or South America, best developed in Mexico. Type species *trichas* (Linnaeus).

11. *Chamaethlypis* (Ridgway, 1887). Very close to *Geothlypis* in appearance, coloration and song, but tail longer than wing, strongly graduated; bill stout, the culmen strongly curved. Tarsus notably long and feet stout. Only one Middle American species, the type *poliocephala* (Baird).

12. *Granatellus* (Bonaparte, 1850). Medium sized warblers with stout bill, culmen strongly decurved, the tail very long and strongly rounded. Tarsus shorter, the toes not so stout. Coloration very different, mostly slate gray and brilliant red. Type *venustus* (Bonaparte). Three or four species in southern Mexico, one reappearing in Amazonian Brazil.

13. *Icteria* (Vieillot, 1807). Very large warblers, with green and yellow coloration and with a unique ventriloquial song of caws, chucks, toots and whistles. Bill short, stout, with culmen strongly decurved. Tail very long; tarsus short and toes stout. Monotypic, the type *virens* (Linnaeus).

14. *Cardellina* (DuBus, 1850). Medium sized arboreal "flycatching" warblers, with bill short and stout, *as deep as wide,* tit-like, the culmen decidedly curved; wing long and pointed, the tail quite long, rounded. Monotypic, the type *rubrifrons* (Giraud). Coloration gray, white and red. Mexican.

15. *Ergaticus* (Baird, 1865). Small "flycatching," highly arboreal warblers in high mountain conifer forests. Bill short, stout, as deep as wide, markedly tit-like, the culmen only moderately decurved, the rictal bristles only moderately developed. Plumage *bright red throughout.* Wings rounded with a shorter wing-tip, tail quite long and rounded. Two species, the type *ruber* (Swainson).

16. *Wilsonia* (Bonaparte, 1838). Small or medium-sized "flycatching" warblers, variously arboreal or terrestrial with rictal bristles better developed than the last, the bill broader than deep at nostrils, the lateral aspect warbler-like; wings and tail long. Three migratory North American species, the type *mitrata* (Gmelin).

17. *Setophaga* (Swainson, 1827). Small to very large "flycatching" warblers, with a short, very flat and broad triangular bill (as in *Muscicapa*), with still longer rictal bristles equalling length of culmen; wings long and pointed, except in tropical forms; tail long, very rounded or even fan-shaped, often fully spread in flight when hunting. Includes the tropical *Myioborus* (Baird, 1865), who regarded it as a good subgenus with a shorter wing-tip. Includes perhaps nine high montane or Andean forms, as well as the two Redstarts, the type *ruticilla* (Linnaeus).

18. *Basileuterus* (Cabanis, 1847). Similar to *Wilsonia,* but wing shorter and more rounded; bill longer, stouter and more depressed, the rictal bristles well developed, the culmen longer than the hind toe with claw. Includes at least 22 species ranging widely over Central and South America. Like *Vermivora* and *Dendroica,* of very variable color and structural details so that any diagnosis is exceedingly difficult. Includes *Euthlypis* (Cabanis), a gigantic Warbler of tropical Mexico and Central America, closely allied to *B. fraseri,* and regarded by Ridgway and Hellmayr as a very poor genus. Also includes *Myiothlypis* (Bonaparte), regarded by Hellmayr and Zimmer as a poor genus, *Idiotes* (Baird) and *Phaeothlypis* (Todd).

LUDLOW GRISCOM

APPENDIX C

Gulf Migration Routes of 38 Eastern Warblers *

RECORDS of birds on the Gulf and early median dates in Mississippi and Louisiana are signs of a trans-Gulf migration of the BLACK-AND-WHITE WARBLER. Comparative frequencies, however, show the migration on both sides of the Gulf to be just as important. The absence of the PROTHONOTARY WARBLER in eastern Mexico and its scarcity in the southern Florida Peninsula leave no room for doubt that it migrates chiefly across the Gulf, as has long been claimed. The sequence of arrival dates and records over the Gulf complete the evidence. Present evidence favors the same view for SWAINSON'S WARBLER, although it is so rare at some places on the northern Gulf coast that the significance of quantitative data is open to question. The trans-Gulf and circum-Gulf highways are utilized about equally by the WORM-EATING WARBLER; but the GOLDEN-WINGED and BLUE-WINGED WARBLERS evidently cross from Central America to Texas and Louisiana in greatest numbers. Early spring records of BACHMAN'S WARBLER in Louisiana and Mississippi suggest a direct flight from Cuba, but data are too scarce to be conclusive. Most TENNESSEE WARBLERS fly directly from their winter home to (or beyond) the shoreline stretching from Texas to Alabama, but a smaller migration passes through eastern Mexico. It does not appear geographically probable that many ORANGE-CROWNED WARBLERS would cross the Gulf of Mexico in spring, nor is there direct evidence that they do so. Most NASHVILLE WARBLERS reach the Texas coast from eastern Mexico, but a few apparently take a short cut from Yucatan to points as far east as Louisiana. Although the major migration of PARULA WARBLERS passes through the Florida Peninsula, many individuals cross from Yucatan (and Cuba?) to the northern Gulf as far west as Galveston Bay. The principal migration routes of the YELLOW WARBLER extend up the

* From *The Wilson Bulletin*, 69 pp. 65, 73 (March 1957).

Mexican-Texas coast and across the western Gulf. The statement that it is "less numerous in spring" than in fall in Florida (Howell, 1932) is extremely conservative, as it is decidedly rare in the Peninsula at that season. The case of the MAGNOLIA WARBLER is similar, but it is even scarcer in Florida. Notwithstanding the fact that the CAPE MAY WARBLER is a regular transient in peninsular Florida, it appears that a fairly important part of its spring flight carries northwestward across southern Florida and the eastern Gulf to northwestern Florida, coastal Alabama, and inland localities. This helps to explain the presence of a few on the open Gulf (Lowery and Newman, 1954). The migration of the BLACK-THROATED BLUE WARBLER is much more nearly confined to the Florida Peninsula, very few venturing across the Gulf. Conclusive evidence on the commonly-wintering MYRTLE WARBLER is difficult to obtain, but its quantitative distribution in spring and records on the Gulf denote trans-Gulf flights with an occasional straggler near the middle of May. The BLACK-THROATED GREEN WARBLER may be the only eastern member of its genus to migrate chiefly through eastern Mexico, but a few also cross the Gulf in spring. CERULEAN and BLACKBURNIAN WARBLERS precipitate on the Texas and Louisiana coasts, only small numbers occurring in eastern Mexico; their median dates are also earlier on the northern Gulf coast. Early arrivals on the northern Gulf and a record 60 miles off the Louisiana coast (Bullis and Lincoln, 1952) signify a trans-Gulf passage for the YELLOWTHROATED WARBLER, but it is possible that migrations through Mexico and the Florida Peninsula are equally heavy. The trans-Gulf migration of CHESTNUT-SIDED and BAY-BREASTED WARBLERS brings the largest numbers to that part of the coast lying between southern Texas and extreme western Florida. The spring migration of the BLACKPOLL and PRAIRIE WARBLERS is very similar to that described for the Cape May, except that many more precipitate on the southern Atlantic coast. Trans-Gulf migration for the rare KIRTLAND'S WARBLER is geographically most unlikely. With the probable exception of a small per cent of its total population, the PALM WARBLER appears not to cross the Gulf in spring. The OVENBIRD migrates on a broad front, but perhaps the most important flight crosses the Gulf (some northwestward?) to the stretch of coast from Galveston Bay to Pensacola, Florida. Essentially the same statement applies to the NORTHERN WATERTHRUSH, but the LOUISIANA WATERTHRUSH converges (appropriately enough) mainly on the Louisiana coast. The northern and western Gulf receives the greatest numbers of KENTUCKY WARBLERS in spring, eastern Mexico and the Florida Peninsula apparently having but few. The CONNECTICUT WARBLER is so rare that a dogmatic statement of its main migration route would be foolhardy, but there is no evidence that it concentrates on any major part of the southeastern United States. MOURNING WARBLERS pass northward mainly along the Mexico-Texas coast and the record of "many" 30 miles off the Louisiana coast on the early date of April 2 (Frazar, 1881) is very surprising, to say the least. The YELLOWTHROAT is a permanent resident along the Gulf coast, and the only definite clue to its migration route is the fact that numbers have been seen on the open Gulf on four occasions. It is possible that its migration on the sides of the Gulf is equal in volume. Most YELLOW-BREASTED CHATS move into the eastern United States through Mexico and Texas, but the likelihood that a few make the Gulf transit in spring should not be overlooked. The HOODED WARBLER is a striking example of a trans-Gulf migrant, despite the fact that only two offshore records are known. Many WILSON'S and CANADA WARBLERS travel up the Mexico-Texas coast in spring, but there is evidence that some fly directly from Central America to Louisiana. The heaviest movements of AMERICAN REDSTARTS are up the Florida Peninsula and across the central and western Gulf, with eight records on the Gulf.

HENRY M. STEVENSON

INDEX TO THE WARBLERS*

* Main reference is listed first; color plates last, in parentheses.

* Main reference is listed first; color plates last, in parentheses.

* Main reference is listed first; color plates last, in parentheses.

* Main reference is listed first; color plates last, in parentheses.